Single Side-Band

THEORY and PRACTICE

Single Side-Band

THEORY and PRACTICE

by Harry D. Hooton, W6TYH

EDITORS AND ENGINEERS, LTD.

NEW AUGUSTA, INDIANA 46268

Preface

The greatest problem in radiocommunications today is the serious lack of channel space in the radio-frequency spectrum. Virtually all the useful channels are already occupied by existing communications and broadcasting services; thus, the increasing need for additional space literally demands a more wide-spread use of multiplexing and single-sideband techniques. The NTSC color-television and recently approved FM stereo-multiplex systems are good examples of modern multiplexing techniques. Single-sideband systems, although long used by commercial telephone companies, are rapidly replacing AM systems in commercial, military, and amateur communications.

The design, construction, installation, and maintenance of multiplex and single-sideband systems require highly skilled personnel, for which the demand has already surpassed the supply. It is apparent, then, that this field offers great opportunities to those who are technically qualified.

Single Sideband: Theory and Practice was written to serve as a modern, one-source reference text on the subject. Emphasis has been placed on basic principles and circuitry, rather than on mathematics. Wherever possible, specific commercial equipment is used to illustrate how basic theory has been combined with good engineering practice. Such equipment has been carefully selected to be representative of that in current use. A careful study of the circuit descriptions and schematics will provide you with much valuable knowledge of single-sideband technology.

In the sections describing single-sideband generators and exciters, the number of construction projects has been kept to a minimum, since they require special facilities and are difficult to build. However, many amateurs with whom I discussed the book, both on the air and in person, showed much interest in the construction of linear RF power amplifiers—particularly those in the 600- to 1,000-watt class which can be driven by one of the popular "100-watt" commercial single-sideband transmitters. Accordingly, the chapters on the design, construction, and adjustment of linear amplifiers contain much detailed information. All linear power amplifiers shown and described have been thoroughly tested on the air. Moreover, they can be duplicated by any technically qualified person.

My sincere appreciation goes to the many engineers, both professional and amateur, who so generously contributed their time, ideas, and encouragement during the preliminary preparation of the manuscript. In particular, I wish to thank the following persons and organizations for supplying the essential technical data and photographs, without which this book could not have been written.

Bennett Cook
Stancor, Inc.

William I. Orr, W6SAI
Eimac Division of
Varian Associates

Jo Emmett Jennings, W6EI
Jennings Radio Mfg. Co.

W. J. D. Bradford
Collins Radio Co.

Paul Barton
Jennings Radio Mfg. Co.

E. T. Herbig, Jr.
E. F. Johnson Co.

Frank I. Lester, W2AMJ
Hammarlund Mfg. Co., Inc.

Karl Hassel
Central Electronics

HARRY D. HOOTON, W6TYH

To Elsie

Contents

Chapter 1

The Origin of
Single Sideband

A widespread belief exists that single-sideband techniques are of recent origin. Actually, the basic principles have been recognized and used in various commercial applications for over thirty years. The main reason for the delay in the large-scale development of single-sideband equipment was the lack of compact and economical high-precision components. The availability of the surplus FT-241-A precision low-frequency crystals (from which inexpensive lattice filters can be constructed), and the development of the phasing method of generating the sideband signal, now make possible the economical, wide-scale use of single-sideband equipment. Constant research and development of both single-sideband circuitry and components have resulted in extremely compact and highly efficient communications systems which would not otherwise have been possible. It is reasonable to expect that future developments, particularly in solid-state electronics, will bring forth even more compact communications equipment with a higher efficiency than the units available today.

CARRIER-SYSTEM TELEPHONY

The first, and still largest, use of single-sideband techniques is in connection with carrier-system voice transmission over long-distance telephone lines. The principal reason for the development and subsequent use of single-sideband techniques was economy. In the carrier system, the audible voice frequencies between 300 and 3,000 cycles are used to modulate an RF carrier, which is usually in the region of 20 to 50 kc. In the modulation process, additional radio frequencies are created and appear in the composite signal as sidebands. In a very simple telephone carrier system (Figs. 1-1, 1-2), the RF carrier and its sidebands are fed into a telephone line or coaxial cable and carried to a distant point. At the receiving end of

11

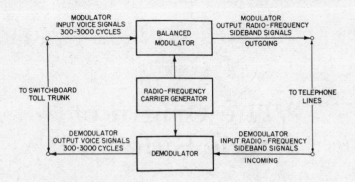

Fig. 1-1. Block diagram of simplified telephony carrier system.

the line, the composite RF signal is then demodulated and applied to the local telephone circuits as audio.

In actual practice, the modern carrier system of telephony is much more complex than would appear from the previous description. The system is similar to ordinary radio broadcasting except that the frequencies are much lower and are transmitted over telephone lines instead of through space. Neglecting any consideration of single-sideband techniques, it is apparent that, by careful selection of carrier frequencies spaced at regular intervals throughout the bandpass spectrum of the telephone system, a number of simultaneous long-distance telephone conversations can take place on *one line* without interference from each other. The number of conversations which can be transmitted over a single line is limited only by the channel space required for each conversation, the over-all bandpass of the

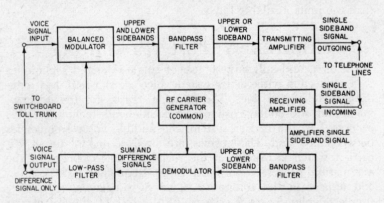

Fig. 1-2. Block diagram of essential components in modern telephony carrier system.

system, and the ability of the receiving equipment to select any one voice channel and reject the others. Present techniques make it possible to provide a frequency band nearly 8 mc wide, so that two coaxial cables can contain either 1,800 telephone channels, or 600 telephone channels plus a 4.2-mc television channel, in each direction.

For many years the range of telephony was severely limited by the loss of energy along the wires. However, after the invention of the vacuum tube in 1906, coupled with subsequent research and development, the telephone repeater or amplifier was developed. Through the use of repeater amplifiers, telephone service between New York and San Francisco was inaugurated in 1915. Today there are hundreds of thousands of repeaters in use, making possible long-distance telephony to all parts of the world.

In the early days of carrier-system development, it was discovered that transmission of the carrier component overloaded the repeater amplifiers, and also caused undesirable cross modulation. Up to then, the exact nature of amplitude modulation was not thoroughly understood. However, during the early period of telephone-circuit development it was mathematically demonstrated that along with the carrier, two sidebands existed which contained identical information and were, in fact, mirror images of each other. It was also found that the carrier itself contained no useful information, but was used merely as a reference signal for recovery of the sideband intelligence. Needless to say, these conclusions were the subject of much debate at the time; and until a few years ago, it was customary to omit any reference to sideband theory in standard communications manuals. In spite of the controversy, however, subsequent work by engineers and scientists has proved these theories to be true. As a result, a comprehensive body of literature on the theory, techniques, and components of single-sideband telephony has accumulated over the years. While these papers are of considerable interest from the historical point of view, in most instances they are highly mathematical and deal with extremely complex telephone equipment which cannot readily be duplicated outside a laboratory.

Except for having much lower frequencies, the early single-sideband signals transmitted over telephone lines were substantially the same as the signals transmitted today by amateur and military single-sideband transmitters. In modern single-sideband telephone circuits these transmission frequencies may be in hundreds of megacycles, although the original carrier and sidebands are generally below 100 kilocycles. It is common practice today to employ single-sideband techniques to multiplex a large number of voice channels over a band of radio frequencies in the microwave region. The sideband signal is generated, at a very low power level, in the low-frequency portion of the RF spectrum. It is then heterodyned, through a number of translator stages, to the transmission frequency. Here the signal is amplified to the desired power level in a system of linear amplifiers. It is then transmitted by a coaxial-cable system, or radiated through space by a highly directive radio antenna.

Chapter 2

The Derivation of Single-Sideband Signals

The single-sideband signal essentially is a modified AM signal from which certain components have been removed. In communications equipment designed for voice transmission, one sideband and the carrier are generally removed. However, before we can intelligently discuss single-sideband theory and practice, it will be necessary to thoroughly understand the formation of the ordinary AM signal from which the sideband signal is derived.

AMPLITUDE MODULATION

When the output of a CW transmitter is made to vary in amplitude at a single audio-frequency rate, a steady tone will be heard in a receiver tuned to the transmitter frequency. The frequency of the received audio tone will be the same as that of the original audio tone used to modulate the radio-frequency output of the transmitter. If, instead of a single tone, the modulation consists of a number of tones or audio frequencies such as those of speech or music, then the transmitter output will vary in unison with these frequencies, and the sound reproduced at the receiver will correspond to the original voice or music. This process is known as *amplitude modulation*.

The analysis of any modulation process becomes extremely complex when several modulation tones or frequencies are present. The accepted procedure in modulation analysis is to use only one or two tones as the modulating signal. Thus, when a single audio tone is used, the frequency components which appear at the transmitter output are the *carrier, a lower side frequency,* and an *upper side frequency.* However, with a complex modulating signal such as speech or music, two bands of frequencies will appear at the output along with the carrier. These two bands are called the *lower sideband* and the *upper sideband.* Unlike the lower and upper side frequencies, these

15

lower and upper sidebands consist of many frequencies instead of only one. However, at this time our discussion will be limited to the side frequencies. The more complex sidebands will be covered later.

Mixing

Amplitude modulation is essentially a form of *mixing*, or *combining*, two or more signals in a suitable nonlinear device. When a single audio tone is transmitted by means of amplitude modulation, the tone signal is mixed with a radio-frequency carrier to produce a composite signal consisting of the original carrier and *two* side-frequency signals.

The mixing action can be understood more clearly by the use of numerical figures in a typical example. Fig. 2-1 is a plot of the transmitter output-frequency spectrum, showing the relative

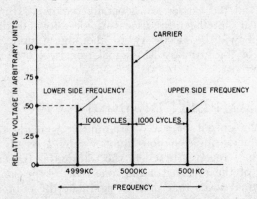

Fig. 2-1. Frequency-spectrum plot of AM transmitter.

characteristics of the carrier and the two side-frequency signals. The vertical scale indicates relative voltage (amplitude) in arbitrary units, and the horizontal scale indicates frequency in kilocycles. The 5,000-kc carrier is modulated by a pure sine-wave tone of 1,000 cycles (1 kc).

At 100% modulation, two side frequencies will be formed as shown in Fig. 2-1. One will be located at 4,999 kc, which is equal to the carrier frequency minus the modulation frequency (5,000 − 1 = 4,999); the other will appear at 5,001 kc, which is equal to the carrier frequency plus the modulation frequency (5,000+1=5,001). The 4,999-kc signal is known as the *difference frequency*, or *lower side frequency;* and the 5,001-kc signal is the *sum frequency*, or *upper side frequency.* Note that the 4,999- and 5,001-kc signals are *not* referred to as "sidebands" since the modulation is a single-frequency audio tone only. At 100% modu-

16

lation, the amplitude of each side frequency will be exactly half the carrier amplitude.

If a highly selective receiver (one with an over-all bandpass of about 500 cycles) is tuned to 4,999 kc, the lower side frequency will appear as a steady unmodulated "carrier" and no tone will be heard. If the signal is removed from the last IF stage of the receiver and displayed on an oscilloscope screen, it will have the same waveshape as any other 4,999-kc sine-wave RF signal. When the selective receiver is tuned to 5,001 kc, the upper side frequency will also appear as a steady carrier with no audible tone. In order for the 1,000-cycle audio tone to be heard in the speaker, or the modulation-waveform patterns to be displayed on the oscilloscope, the receiver must have sufficient bandpass to recognize at least the carrier and one of the side frequencies.

The side frequencies appear only when the 1,000-cycle tone modulation is applied at the transmitter. When the modulation is removed, the signals at 4,999 and 5,001 kc will disappear. If the amplitude of the 1,000-cycle modulation signal is varied from zero to maximum (100% modulation), the amplitude of the side frequencies will also vary from zero to a maximum value. It is apparent then that the two side frequencies are created by the amplitude-modulation process.

When a receiver with a 0.5-kc bandpass is tuned to the 5,000-kc carrier, no modulation will be heard and no change in the amplitude of the carrier will be observed when the modulation is either applied, varied, or removed at the transmitter. Since no change occurs in the carrier with modulation, we can reasonably conclude that the intelligence-bearing components of the signal are contained in the side frequencies, with none in the carrier.

POWER DISTRIBUTION IN THE AM SIGNAL

As shown in Fig. 2-1, when a carrier is modulated 100% by a pure sine-wave tone, the voltage value at either side frequency will be exactly half the carrier voltage. In a circuit where the resistance remains constant, the power will be proportional to the square of the applied voltage. In our earlier example, the power in each side frequency will thus be equal to $(0.5)^2$ times the carrier power. Assuming the carrier output is 1,000 watts, then the power in each side frequency will be 1000 $(0.5)^2$, or 250 watts. Since two side frequencies are present, the total side-frequency power is 500 watts.

Fig. 2-2 shows the usual *modulation-envelope* presentation of an AM signal as it might be displayed on an oscilloscope screen.

17

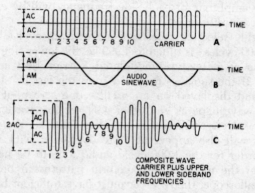

Fig. 2-2. 100% amplitude-modulated RF carrier.

This drawing is included in practically all communications texts and is usually labeled "carrier with 100% amplitude modulation." This type of display has caused considerable confusion since it seems to contradict previous statements that the carrier amplitude remains unchanged during modulation. What you are actually viewing here is the *composite wave,* which consists of the two side frequencies and the carrier being modulated by one cycle of audio frequency.

In Fig. 2-3, the carrier voltage is indicated by the long vector having a value of one voltage unit. The two short vectors, each

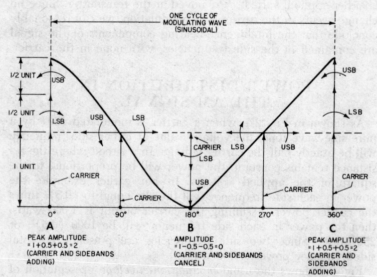

Fig. 2-3. Vector diagram of a 100% modulated carrier.

one-half unit in length, indicate the lower and upper side frequencies. Since the lower side frequency is 4,999 kc, it will contain fewer RF cycles than the 5,000-kc carrier. Assuming the carrier vector to be standing still, the lower-frequency vector will appear to rotate clockwise. The upper side-frequency vector will then appear to rotate counterclockwise, since the 5,001-kc frequency contains slightly more radio frequency cycles than the 5,000-kc carrier.

At the instant shown in Fig. 2-3, the three vector voltages will add up to 2 volts $(1+0.5+0.5=2)$. One half of a modulation cycle $(1/2,000$ of a second) later, the side-frequency vectors will have rotated one half-turn each and the three voltages will then add up to zero $(1-0.5-0.5=0)$. It is therefore evident that during the time required for one half-cycle of modulation, the voltage value of the composite signal will vary from a maximum of twice the carrier voltage, to zero. Since the power in a resistive circuit is proportional to the square of the applied voltage, the maximum, or *peak,* power of the 1,000-watt transmitter will be equal to $1,000 (2)^2$, or 4,000 watts. Half of a modulation cycle later, the signal voltage and power output will be zero. From this it is then apparent that a transmitter rated at 1,000 watts must have a peak modulation capability of 4,000 watts if 100% modulation without distortion is to be realized.

FORMATION OF THE SIDEBANDS

Up to this point the term *sideband* has been avoided, since we have been working with single-tone modulation. Strictly speaking, single-tone modulation produces side frequencies, whereas multitone, or complex, modulation is required to produce sidebands. This distinction between side frequencies and sidebands is important because you will later be working with "two-tone" test signals as well as other modulation waveforms.

The sidebands exhibit certain characteristics which are not apparent from our study of the simpler side frequencies. It was mentioned previously that the two sidebands are mirror images of each other—or, to use a common expression, they lie "back to back" on either side of the carrier. It is important to keep in mind, when discussing the sidebands, that we are referring to the amplitude of the output wave plotted against frequency. The very term sideband denotes that it occupies a portion of the spectrum. As you know, sidebands or side frequencies exist only during the process of modulation. The unmodulated carrier contains no sidebands and, surprisingly, occupies no channel or spectrum space.

19

In order to illustrate the formation of sidebands, let's again refer to our hypothetical 5,000-kc, 1,000-watt transmitter; but instead of a single tone, the modulation signal will consist of four sine-wave tones at frequencies of 1,000, 2,000, 3,000 and 4,000 cycles. For the purpose of discussion, these tones will be considered to be of equal amplitude, and any effects of interaction on each other will be ignored.

Fig. 2-4 illustrates the double-sideband spectrum formed when a 5000-kc carrier is 100% modulated by a four-tone audio signal. The sideband-frequency components which appear at 4,-999, 4,998, 4,997, and 4,996 kc correspond to the 1,000-, 2,000-, 3,-000- and 4,000-cycle tones. The group of frequencies between the carrier (5,000 kc) and 4,996 kc is known as the *lower sideband*.

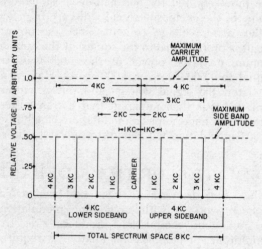

Fig. 2-4 Sideband formation of a four-tone,
modulated sine-wave signal.

Note that the lowest frequency (1,000 cycles) produces a sideband component only 1 kc lower than the carrier frequency, whereas the highest frequency (4,000 cycles) produces a sideband component 4 kc lower than the carrier frequency. The complete lower sideband is composed of *difference-frequency* signals, produced by subtracting the frequency of the audio components from the frequency of the carrier. Thus, the highest audio frequency will produce the lowest lower-sideband frequencies, and the lowest audio frequency will produce the highest lower-sideband frequency.

The upper sideband is exactly like the lower except that the audio frequencies add to (instead of subtract from) the carrier

20

frequency, to produce a series of "sum-frequency" sideband components. Fig. 2-4 shows the 1,000-cycle tone mixed with the 5,000-kc carrier, producing an *upper sideband* of 5,001 kc. The 2,000-, 3,000-, and 4,000-cycle frequencies produce upper-sideband components at 5,002, 5,003 and 5,004 kc, respectively. In the upper-sideband spectrum, the lowest audio frequency will produce the lowest frequency upper-sideband component, and the highest audio frequency will produce the highest-frequency sideband component. Compared with the lower-sideband components, precisely opposite frequency conditions prevail in the two upper sidebands. This is why the upper and lower sidebands are often called "mirror images" of each other.

Each upper (as well as lower) sideband contains all the intelligence information included in the modulation signal. It can therefore be seen that either or both sidebands will provide faithful reproduction of the transmitted information from a suitable receiver.

In Fig. 2-4, the carrier frequency is 5,000 kc; however, the RF carrier may be *any* frequency. Any RF carrier mixed with a four-tone audio signal will produce a double-sideband spectrum, with the components related to each other exactly as shown. For example, if the carrier frequency is 50 kc instead of 5,000, the lower-sideband components will be located at 49, 48, 47, and 46 kc. The upper-sideband components will then be at 51, 52, 53, and 54 kc. However, when the sideband signal is generated at a low frequency such as 50 kc, it is then heterodyned to the operating frequency and amplified to the desired power level.

TRANSMITTER EFFICIENCY

In the preceding discussion the relative values of carrier and sideband power was covered, but no mention was made of the power amplifier and over-all transmitter efficiencies. In making comparisons between conventional and sideband transmissions, the relative efficiencies of the two systems must be considered.

The average efficiency of a good Class-C RF amplifier is close to 80% when plate-modulated. Efficiency is determined by the RF power output in watts divided by the DC power input, also in watts. In our hypothetical 1,000-watt transmitter, the input power is equal to 1,000 watts ÷ 0.8 (the efficiency percentage), or 1,250 watts. This 1,250 watts DC is the amount required of the power supply to produce the 1,000 watts of carrier. The 250 watts of DC not converted into RF is largely expended as heat at the plate of the amplifier tube. This energy loss is commonly referred to as the plate dissipation of the tube.

The 500 watts of power in the sidebands is supplied mostly by the Class-B modulator and is in the form of AF power which is developed from a different DC power-supply source.

You have learned that the transmitted carrier contains no intelligence; this information is actually in the two sidebands. You also learned that each sideband contains the same kind and amount of intelligence information. It is then obvious that we can eliminate the carrier and one sideband and still transmit the same amount of information.

CARRIER AND SIDEBAND REMOVAL EFFECTS

The elimination of the carrier will effect a considerable savings in power at the transmitter (Figs. 2-5A and B). In our hypothetical 1,000-watt transmitter, the peak output power at 100% modulation was 4,000 watts but the average power in each sideband was only 250 watts, or a total average sideband power of 500 watts. The power dissipated at the RF-amplifier plate was 250 watts.

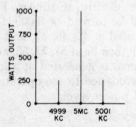

(A) 100% amplitude modulation.

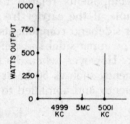

(B) 100% AM double sideband—carrier suppressed.

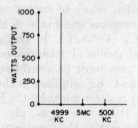

(C) 100% AM single sideband—carrier and one sideband suppressed.

Fig. 2-5. Relative power capabilities of AM, DSB, and SSB transmitters using the same type of RF power amplifier.

The removal of the carrier component and its accompanying high power dissipation will enable us to raise each sideband to 500 watts (1,000 watts of total sideband power). However, when only one sideband is transmitted (as in Fig. 2-5C), the power in that sideband can be raised to 1,000 watts without exceeding the plate-dissipation limits of the amplifier tube. In either case the peak power will remain at 4,000 watts. Remember, though, that the *comunications efficiency* ("talk" power) is contained in the sidebands and to produce 1,000 watts of talk power in *one sideband* of a conventional AM transmitter (no suppressed components), it would be necessary to raise the carrier output to 4,000 watts. A corresponding increase in DC input power would be required, and an RF amplifier with a higher plate-dissipation rating would have to be used.

The removal of one sideband will cut in half the channel space needed to transmit the same intelligence by the conventional AM method. This means the required receiver bandwidth will also be reduced accordingly. Since noise power is proportional to the effective bandwidth required, there will be an improvement in the signal-to-noise ratio of the single-sideband receiver over a receiver receiving conventional AM signals.

Carrier suppression methods and the removal of one sideband will be covered in detail in the next two chapters.

Chapter 3

Carrier Suppression Techniques

In this chapter the actual circuitry effecting removal of the carrier from the AM signal is covered. The techniques used to remove the undesired sideband will be covered in the next chapter.

The device most generally used to suppress the carrier is called the balanced modulator, although it is really better described as a *balanced mixer*. The balanced modulator (or mixer) may use semiconductor (germanium or silicon) diodes, or vacuum-tube diodes, triodes, or pentodes. However, transistors have been used as balanced modulators in some recent circuitry with good results.

PUSH-PULL BALANCED MODULATOR

Fig. 3-1 shows a simple balanced modulator circuit that uses two screen-grid tubes. The two plates are connected to the resonant tank circuit in a push-pull arrangement. The carrier is applied to the parallel control grids, and the AF modulation signal is applied to the push-pull-operated screens through transformer T1. The RF-carrier and audio-modulation signals are kept at low peak values, (usually a few volts), and B+ may or may not be applied to the screens. With some types of tubes, it may be necessary to apply a low negative bias to the screens, as shown in Fig. 3-1. This aids in selecting the operating points for optimum mixer and carrier-suppression action.

With no audio applied to the screens, the positive excursions of the incoming carrier will cause a simultaneous increase in the plate currents of both tubes; and during the negative grid swing, both plate currents will decrease simultaneously. These plate-current pulses, when applied to the push-pull tank circuit, will generate two RF voltages which are equal in value but opposite in phase displacement. These two out-of-phase voltages will cancel each other, and the net carrier output will be

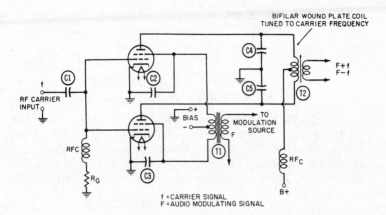

BIFILAR WOUND PLATE COIL
TUNED TO CARRIER FREQUENCY

f = CARRIER SIGNAL
F = AUDIO MODULATING SIGNAL

Fig. 3-1. Balanced modulator with parallel input and push-pull output.

zero. The actual amount of carrier suppression obtained depends on the degree of matching between the two tubes and their associated circuitry. Generally, two *selected* tubes of the same type will give about 20 db of carrier suppression in the circuit of Fig. 3-1. In this case, no adjustments (other than resonating the balanced tank circuit to the carrier frequency) are needed.

Carrier suppression can be further improved by the use of separate bias adjustments (to equalize the two plate currents) and small trimmer capacitors (to balance each grid and plate capacitance to ground). In practical design work, a carrier suppression value of 30 to 35 db is generally considered satisfactory. However, when the balanced modulator is followed by a sideband filter, an additional 20 db of attenuation is obtained. The trimmers, tank circuit tuning, and bias values should all be adjusted for minimum carrier in the output circuit. These various adjustments will interact to some extent; thus it may be necessary to trim them several times before the lowest carrier level can be obtained.

During modulation, the audio voltages on the screens will be 180° out of phase with each other. This will cause the plate current of one tube to increase, and that of the other to decrease, at an *audio rate*. Two RF voltages will then appear across the primary of T2 and, being unequal, will result in a net RF voltage in the secondary. Because the modulator unbalance is occurring at an audio rate, the RF and AF signals will mix (combine) to produce sum and difference RF signals (sidebands) in the output circuit. Since the modulator is balanced for the carrier but not for the sidebands, the output signal will

25

consist of a pair of sidebands and a suppressed carrier. Technically, this output is known as a double-sideband suppressed-carrier signal—or more simply, as a DSB signal.

PARALLEL-OUTPUT
BALANCED MODULATOR

In Fig. 3-2 the carrier is applied to the push-pull-operated control grids and taken off two parallel-operated plates. Since the carrier signal at the grids is 180° out of phase, the plate current of one tube will be increasing as the plate current of the other is decreasing. These two plate-current pulses are applied to a

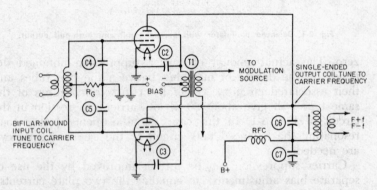

Fig. 3-2. Balanced modulator with push-pull input and parallel output.

common single-ended tank circuit, where each pulse cancels the other. Thus no carrier output is produced. In this circuit, the audio-modulation signal is applied to the screens in the same manner as in Fig. 3-1. Either circuit is equally effective in the production of a suppressed carrier. The choice is determined primarily by constructional, rather than electrical, considerations.

VECTOR ANALYSIS

At this time it may be of interest to compare the power vector of a suppressed carrier signal with that of an ordinary AM signal. The conventional vector resultants of an AM signal are shown in Fig. 3-3A. Here the sideband vectors are considered to revolve around the carrier vector, as indicated by the small curved arrows. The sum resultant of both sidebands and carrier is considered to revolve (at the carrier frequency) around the point represented by the carrier vector origin. The two sidebands are assumed to be of equal amplitude.

During modulation peaks, the sidebands and carrier will add vectorially to produce the maximum power resultant, as shown. The maximum amplitude of the composite signal will then be twice the amplitude of the carrier alone. During the following half-cycle of modulation, the two sideband vectors will have rotated to the point where they combine. Thus their resultant will be equal in magnitude but opposite in polarity to that of the carrier. When this point is reached, the sidebands and carrier cancel, and the net output at that instant is zero. Note that the resultant will reach zero during the modulation cycle, but does not actually swing negative.

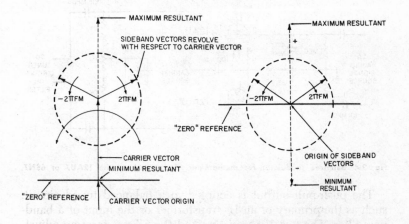

(A) Ordinary AM signal.   (B) Carrier-suppressed signal.

Fig. 3-3. Vector diagrams.

The vector diagram that represents the suppressed carrier is shown in Fig. 3-3B. The origin of the sideband vectors is at the zero reference line, because no signals are present when there is no modulation. The sideband vectors revolve in the directions indicated by the curved arrows. When the two vectors coincide in the positive direction, they will add and from the maximum resultant (shown by the vertical dotted line). When the vectors coincide in the negative direction, they will combine to form the minimum resultant, or "negative peak," as indicated by the same dotted line. Either resultant formed by the sidebands is considered to be of constant phase when both sidebands are of equal amplitude. In the suppressed carrier system, the sideband resultant swings *both positive and negative* during one modulation cycle. This fact will be of considerable interest later when

27

studying product demodulators and also phasing-type sideband generators.

PUSH-PULL INPUT AND OUTPUT

The circuit of a dual-triode balanced modulator is shown in Fig. 3-4. The AF modulation signal is applied to the grids in push-pull from either a phase-inverter stage or the high-impedance secondary of an interstage audio transformer, and the RF carrier is introduced to the common-cathode circuit through a 100-mmf capacitor.

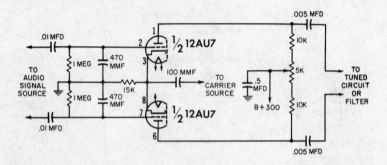

Fig. 3-4. Balanced modulator for medium-mu triodes such as the 12AU7 or 6SN7.

The push-pull output is coupled to a balanced tuned circuit, such as the primary of an IF transformer or the input of a band-pass filter. The two 10K resistors and the 5K pot form an adjustable balanced load for the triode plates. The 5K pot is used to equalize the two plate currents for minimum carrier in the output circuit. Ordinarily no balancing adjustments are required when the incoming audio signals are equal in amplitude.

DIODE MODULATORS

The diode modulator was developed during the early years of carrier-system telephony, but remained comparatively unknown in other communications circles until quite recently. The first balanced modulator used two or more diode rectifiers. The diode, or rectifier, modulator may be of the ring, series, or shunt type—depending on the manner in which its diodes are connected. The main advantage of the diode modulator is its higher stability, compared with its vacuum-tube counterpart. Moreover, diodes require no power, are very compact, and rarely require maintenance or replacement. Originally, the diodes

28

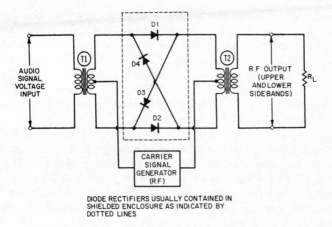

Fig. 3-5. Conventional ring balanced-modulator circuit.

were copper-oxide rectifiers. Today, most are germanium, such as the ordinary type 1N34. When two or more diodes are carefully selected for matched electrical characteristics and mounted in a can or on a terminal board, the unit is known as a *Varistor*. As an example, the popular 1N35 *Varistor* is simply a pair of closely matched 1N34 germanium diodes.

Ring Balanced Type

The ring balanced modulator is the most efficient of the three types, being capable of twice as much output voltage as the shunt or series arrangements. However, the diodes must be very closely matched when used in a conventional ring circuit (Fig. 3-5). Otherwise, it will be impossible to obtain good carrier suppression in the output circuit.

The diode elements in any balanced modulator are arranged so that application of the RF carrier alone does not

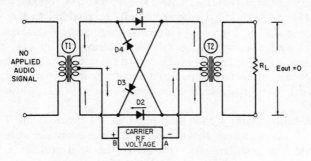

Fig. 3-6. Carrier current in ring modulator.

29

cause a signal to appear in the output. In Fig. 3-6, the carrier balancing action can be analyzed by tracing the carrier current paths as shown. When the carrier voltage is negative at point A, RF current will flow through T2, D1 and D2, T1, and back to the generator at point B. As you can see, the currents through the two halves of the T2 primary are 180° out of phase. As a result, the net RF voltages which are developed cancel each other, and no RF is coupled to the secondary.

On the next carrier half-cycle, the polarity will reverse, and diodes D3 and D4 will conduct. As shown in Fig. 3-7, the carrier current will now reverse direction but the currents in the T2 primary will still be flowing in opposite directions. Thus, the RF voltages developed across the T2 primary will cancel each other, and there will still be no carrier voltage in the output circuit.

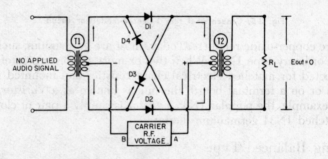

Fig. 3-7. Carrier-current paths when polarity reverses.

The diode balanced modulator can be more easily understood if the diode elements are considered as switches. The simplified schematic in Fig. 3-8A shows diodes D1 and D2 as closed switches, and D3 and D4 as open switches. In this diagram, the circuit conditions correspond to the action occurring in Fig. 3-6. Fig. 3-8B shows the conditions when the carrier-voltage polarity reverses; now D1 and D2 are "open," and D3 and D4 are "closed." These conditions correspond to the action taking place in Fig. 3-7. The switching voltage is the carrier signal, and the switching rate is determined by the carrier frequency. In order to obtain good switching action and to reduce distortion in the modulator output, it is general practice to use a carrier signal which greatly exceeds the audio-signal level.

When an audio signal is applied to the primary of T1, the audio voltage across the diodes will unbalance the modulator circuit. The resultant RF voltage across load resistor R3 will consist of a series of pulses whose polarity and repetition rate

30

are determined by the carrier voltage, and whose amplitude is controlled by the audio voltage. When viewed on a spectrum analyzer, the output signal will be seen to contain an upper and a lower sideband. A similar pair of sidebands (and some other undesired higher-frequency products) will be placed about the

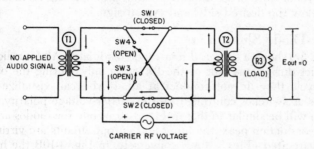

(A) SW1 and SW2 closed.

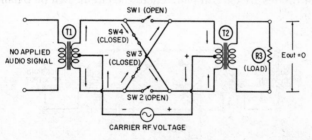

(B) SW3 and SW4 closed.

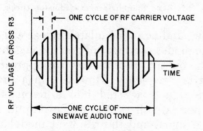

(C) Waveform developed.

Fig. 3-8. Carrier-current paths in ring modulator.

second harmonic of the carrier frequency. The upper and lower sidebands displaced around the carrier frequency are the sum and difference RF signals described in the preceding chapter. A single tone-modulating signal and the resultant waveform of the balanced modulator output are shown in Fig. 3-8C.

Diode balanced modulators are capable of a high degree of carrier balance, and they will retain this characteristic over long periods of time if the components are of good quality and are accurately matched. In a well-designed system, it is not difficult to obtain a carrier suppression figure of 40 db or better, and the level of third-order intermodulation products can be made 50 db below the desired sideband output signal.

Four-Diode Shunt Type

Fig. 3-9 shows a balanced four-diode modulator. All four diodes conduct during one half of the RF cycle only; during the other half-cycle they do not conduct at all. If you can visualize the diodes as switches controlled by the carrier-voltage polarity, the action will be similar to that in Fig. 3-10. While the diodes are at their conduction peak, the input and output circuits are virtually short-circuited (Fig. 3-10A); conversely, in Fig. 3-10B the high-impedance conditions are restored while the diodes are "open." If the four diodes are carefully matched, the circuit will be balanced

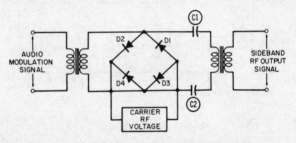

Fig. 3-9. Basic shunt-balanced modulator circuit.

for the RF carrier, and no unmodulated signal will appear in the output. Since the diodes conduct only on the negative portions of the RF cycle, the output currents flow for approximately half a cycle of the carrier frequency. However, in a practical circuit These half-wave signals are fed into a resonant tank circuit and appear as normal full cycles at the output. A single-tone audio-modulation signal and the resultant modulated RF waveform are shown in Fig. 3-10C. As described previously, the modulated RF signal will contain sum and difference signals (sidebands).

Two-Diode Shunt Type

A shunt diode modulator using only two diode elements is depicted in Fig. 3-11. The 1N35 *Varistor* is used in place of the diode elements, and the circuit values are typical for operation

32

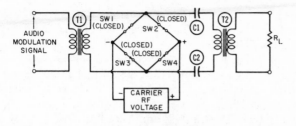

(A) Diodes conducting.

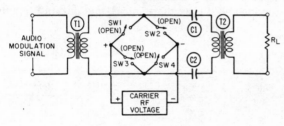

(B) Diodes not conducting.

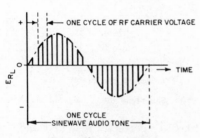

(C) Waveform across R_L.

Fig. 3-10. Diode switching action.

in the 450- to 460-kc region. Notice that D1 and D2 form one half of the bridge circuit, and that resistors R1, R2, and R3 form the other half. The 250-ohm pot (R2) is used to balance the circuit with the RF carrier applied. Known as the "carrier balance" control, it is usually a screwdriver adjustment somewhere on the main chassis. Normally, this adjustment will be made during initial alignment and then left alone. The two 820-ohm resistors, R1 and R3, prevent one side of the carrier source from short-circuiting to ground when the potentiometer arm is rotated to either extreme. A 2,000-ohm pot is sometimes used across the carrier source, instead of the three resistors shown.

The applied carrier signal must be taken from a balanced source. The signal may be supplied to C7 and C8 from an RF-

33

transformer secondary winding or from the output of an RF phase-inverter circuit. (This subject will be covered in more detail in a later chapter.)

Let's suppose, in Fig. 3-11, that there is a carrier signal of about 10 volts across points A and C, but no applied audio. When point A is more positive than B, diodes D1 and D2 will conduct, but will be cut off when point A goes more negative. Current will flow from C, through D2, to B, and from B, through D1, to A and back to the carrier generator. The current will also flow through R1, R2, and R3 as it goes from C to A. The modulator RF output circuit is connected between point B and ground (point D).

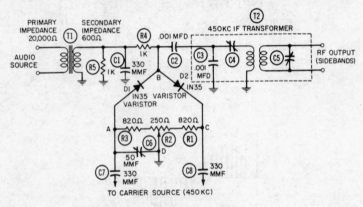

Fig. 3-11. Shunt-type diode balanced modulator.

If the two diodes are perfectly matched and the RF voltages from A to ground and C to ground are equal, the modulator circuit will be well balanced, and no RF carrier will appear in resonant output circuit T2. However, such an ideal condition is rare; in most cases, adjustment of the circuit will be required.

Carrier balance control R2 is now adjusted to obtain minimum carrier signal in the secondary winding of T2. As the control is rotated from one extreme to the other, a definite null should be obtained at or near the center of the balance adjustment range. If no null appears, or if it appears at one extreme of the balance control, then the two diodes do not match closely enough or unequal RF carrier is being applied at points A and C.

Variable capacitor C6 permits adjustment of the carrier so that equal RF voltages will be applied at A and C. It should be turned slowly from its minimum value while balance control R2 is being adjusted. If a satisfactory null is still not obtained, C6 should be removed from point A and connected to point C and the balancing procedure repeated.

34

The 1N35 *Varistor,* which consists of a pair of matched 1N34 germanium diodes, is usually sufficient to permit a good balance with the circuit shown. A pair of 1N34 diodes, selected at random from the dealer's stock, will rarely give optimum balance. If no 1N35 *Varistor* is available, the 1N34's can be roughly matched by selecting those which exhibit similar front and back DC resistances when measured with an ohmmeter. (Measure resistance on the scale where the needle is mid-range.)

When the audio signal from T1 is applied to the diode circuit between B and ground, diodes D1 and D2 will alternately pass RF current during the AF cycle. When point B is more positive than ground (due to the audio signal), D1 will be back-biased and will not conduct until the positive-going carrier voltage exceeds the audio voltage. On the other hand, diode D2 is forward-biased by this positive audio voltage and will conduct over slightly more than half of the RF cycle. Thus, the modulator is unbalanced by the audio signal, and RF voltage will now appear in resonant output circuit T2.

When the audio signal goes negative at point B, the conditions will reverse—D2 will now be back-biased and D1 will conduct. The modulator is again unbalanced by the audio signal, and RF voltage still appears in the output circuit.

Since the modulator unbalance is taking place at an audio rate, the RF carrier and the audio signals will combine, or "mix," to produce sideband signals in the output circuit. If the carrier itself has been satisfactorily suppressed, no carrier component should be present in the output during modulation. If there is, this means the frequency stability of the carrier generator is poor under load. As a result, an FM component will be introduced into the output circuit. This condition rarely occurs when the carrier generator is crystal-controlled, but it can be a serious problem with generators employing self-controlled oscillators. It will be discussed in more detail in Chapter 5.

Any shunt-connected diode modulator must be so designed that the proper impedances are presented to the AF and RF signals. In Fig. 3-11, T1 is a miniature tube-to-line transformer with a primary impedance of 20,000 ohms and a secondary impedance of 600 ohms. The secondary winding is shunted by a 1K resistor and 330-mmf capacitor. Another 1K resistor (R4) is connected in series with the "high" side of the transformer and the junction (point B) of the two diodes. The two resistors form a voltage divider for the audio signal, and R4 offers a relatively high impedance to the RF signal at point B. In some applications, R4 may be replaced by a suitable RF choke. In the direction of the RF output circuit, the audio signal "sees" the high impedance of .001-mfd capacitor C2. The only load for the audio signal is the diodes themselves.

The RF signal at point B, looking toward the output circuit, "sees" the low impedances of C2 and C3 and of the series-resonant transformer primary. The two .001-mfd capacitors, C2 and C3, should be of good quality and have silver mica dielectrics. Variable capacitor C4 is the IF trimmer normally connected across the primary winding.

The shunt type of balanced modulator is more suitable for use in circuits where the output impedance can be made low by series tuning, as has been done here. The Collins series of mechanical filters utilizes a tuned input circuit which may be either series- or parallel-resonated. This circuit may also be used with certain types of crystal lattice filters, which either may employ tuned inputs or can be matched by means of a capacitance voltage divider.

Series Balanced Type

Some filters must be terminated into some definite impedance value. The Burnell S-15000, for example, must be terminated into a 30,000-ohm input impedance in order to retain the proper response characteristics. This input-termination value will not match the output impedance of the shunt modulator; hence some kind of intermediate coupling device would seem necessary, to obtain a satisfactory match between the modulator and filter. However, such a coupling device would not only mean higher cost and additional circuit complexity, but might also increase circuit losses. In circuits using terminated or high-impedance filters after the balanced modulator, a series modulator like the one in Fig. 3-12 is more suitable. Another advantage of the series modulator is that no audio-input iron-core transformer is needed. The AF cathode follower serves the same purpose, but costs less and requires less space.

Two basic requirements of the series balanced modulator are that the impedance across which the AF is developed be low at the carrier frequency, and that the impedance across which the RF is developed be low at the audio frequency. In practice, this requirement is satisfied by the circuit arrangement in Fig. 3-12.

The circuit values shown are suitable for use with the 50-kc Burnell S-15000 filter. Those in Fig. 3-13 are suitable for the 455-kc Collins mechanical filters.

The general theory of operation of the series balanced modulator is similar to that of the shunt type described prior to this discussion.

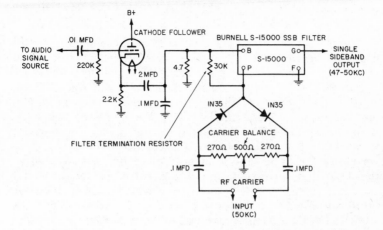

Fig. 3-12. Series-type balanced modulator using a Burnell S-15000 filter.

The balanced modulators described above are considered rather standard arrangements and are used extensively in modern sideband equipment. The actual circuit configurations may vary somewhat with different sets, but the basic functions will remain the same. Any of these circuits, when used properly, will produce a satisfactory suppressed-carrier, double-sideband signal. In most cases, the circuit choice will be determined by the type of components used, such as the sideband filter, and not by any electrical differences between circuits.

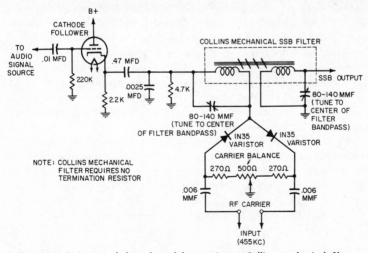

Fig. 3-13. Series-type balanced modulator using a Collins mechanical filter.

37

BALANCED MODULATOR USING A
BEAM DEFLECTION TUBE

Recently a totally different type of balanced modulator circuit has been developed which uses a beam-deflection tube as the modulator. The sheet-beam-switching tube was originally designed for use as a synchronous demodulator in color TV receivers. The first of these tubes produced commercially was the 6AR8, manufactured by GE. The 6AR8 was designed primarily for color TV; the fact that it could also be adapted to sideband generation was merely coincidental. Now a later version of the basic tube is manufactured by RCA. Known as the 7360, it is designed especially for balanced modulator and converter service and is certain to be widely used in the near future. In order to understand the application of the 7360, let's study the basic principles involved in its operation.

The 7360 is a 9-pin miniature type featuring a unique electrode structure which consists of two plates, two deflection electrodes, a cathode, and two grids. The total beam current is determined by the potentials applied to the two grids, and the *portion* of the total beam current collected by each plate is determined by the voltage difference between the two deflection electrodes. The current collected by each plate thus becomes a function of two voltages.

Because of this unique design, the 7360 is particularly useful in modulator, demodulator, and frequency-converter service, in equipment operating at frequencies up to 100 mc. The tube also has inherent long-term stability because the electron flow to each plate is derived from a single beam. Other features of the tube are high transconductance (5,500 micromhos), high deflection sensitivity, low interelectrode capacitances, and good shielding (to prevent interaction between the deflection electrodes and control grid). In carefully designed balanced modulator circuits, the 7360 is capable of providing a carrier suppression of 60 db or better. In balanced mixer (frequency-conversion) circuits, it is possible to obtain at least 40 db of oscillator-signal suppression in the balanced-output tank circuit.

Fig. 3-14 shows the mechanical arrangement of the electrodes in the 7360, and Fig. 3-15 the equivalent circuit symbols and base connections. The balanced modulator circuit recommended by RCA, is shown in Fig. 3-16. A single-sideband generator using one 7360 as a balanced modulator and another as a balanced frequency converter will be featured in a later chapter.

In operation, the sheet of electrons emitted by the cathode passes through the two grids and, if no deflection voltages are

38

present, strike the open space between the two plates. Since the electrons do not strike either plate, no plate current flows and there is no output from the tube. If the RF carrier signal is applied to the control grid, the amplitude of the beam will vary at the RF rate, but there will still be no output since the beam is not striking either plate.

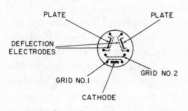

Fig. 3-14. Electrode arrangement in the RCA 7360.

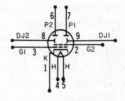

Fig. 3-15. Symbols and connections of RCA 7360.

An electron beam may be deflected by either an electrostatic or electromagnetic field. The construction of the 7360 is such that the electrons are made to pass between the two deflection electrodes (but not contact them). Thus, the application of voltage (either AC or DC) to the electrodes will deflect the beam and cause it to strike one of the plates. When the polarity of the deflection voltage is reversed, the beam will be deflected in the opposite direction and strike the other plate. It is obvious that the beam can be swept back and forth at either an audio-

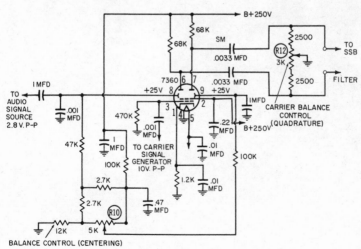

Fig. 3-16. RCA 7360 balanced modulator circuit.

39

or radio-frequency rate by application of a suitable signal at the deflection electrodes.

In balanced modulator service, the audio is applied to the two deflection electrodes. The peak-to-peak audio signal required for full beam deflection is approximately 2.8 volts. The RF carrier signal is applied to the control grid; its peak-to-peak amplitude must be approximately 10 volts. When the 7360 is used as a balanced frequency converter, the conversion oscillator signal is applied to the control grid, and the sideband RF signal is applied to the deflection electrodes. In either case, the RF signal applied to the control grid does not appear in the output.

Because of physical and electrical variations inherent in the manufacture of vacuum tubes, balancing and centering devices must be used with the 7360 in order to obtain optimum carrier suppression and the desired signal output. In Fig. 3-16, a positive DC potential of about 25 volts is applied to the second deflection electrode (terminal 8) by means of a voltage-divider network across the B+. The DC voltage applied to the first deflection electrode (terminal 9) is made adjustable from about 20 to 30 volts by R10 (the 5,000-ohm carrier balance pot). The output circuit balance is adjusted by 2500-ohm pot R12. In operation, R10 and R12 are alternately adjusted for minimum RF signal in the output circuit. When the 7360 is followed by a sharp-cutoff sideband filter, it is possible to obtain carrier suppression of 70 to 80 db below the desired sideband output voltage.

Chapter 4

Sideband Selection

The balanced modulators described in the preceding chapter all produce an output consisting of a pair of sidebands located on either side of the suppressed carrier. Since the objective is to transmit only a single sideband, some means must be used to select one sideband and to suppress the other. In most modern single-sideband systems, this is accomplished by either frequency (filtering) or phase (phase-shift) discrimination.

FILTER METHOD OF SIDEBAND SELECTION

The filter method of sideband selection originated with the carrier system of wire telephony. The filter itself is simply a device which presents a high impedance to unwanted frequencies and thereby weakens (attenuates) them, but offers a relatively low impedance to the desired frequencies. The band of frequencies passed by the filters are generally called the filter *passband*. However, no filter is perfect; they all attenuate the frequencies contained in the passband somewhat. This attenuation is called the filter *insertion loss*. At the upper and lower frequency extremes of the passband, the filter rapidly attenuates those frequencies which lie in both directions away from the filter bandpass. When these frequencies are plotted along the X-axis of an X-Y coordinate system and the attenuation (in decibels) is plotted along the Y-axis, the ratio of frequency change to attenuation is called the *skirt selectivity*. A similar plot of the entire filter response yields the *characteristic curve*. The *bandwidth* of a filter is the difference in cycles (or kilocycles) obtained when the lowest frequency contained in the passband is subtracted from the highest frequency. The two reference frequencies are usually specified at some attenuation point along the skirt, or slope, of the filter response and will vary with different manufacturers. In the Collins F455Y-31 mechanical filter, for example, the bandwidth at 6-db attenuation is specified as 3.1 kc; at 60-db attenuation, the bandwidth is 6 kc. The ratio of the bandwidth at the 6- and 60-db attenuation points is called the *shape factor*. The Collins filter has a shape factor of slightly less than 2.0—which is considered very good.

The original filters developed by commercial telephone companies were designed to operate at very low frequencies (10 to 20 kc). These early filters invariably were derived from combinations of fixed capacitors and high-Q inductors. The characteristic impedances were generally made low to prevent the distributed capacitance of the inductances from deteriorating the over-all filter performance. Some time later the crystal filter came into wide use. Crystal filters were usually based on full-lattice configurations and might contain as many as 80 to 100 individual crystal units. These filters were carefully designed to present a skirt attenuation of 70 to 80 db in less than 50 cycles.

Low-Frequency Filters

Most of the filters in modern single-sideband equipment are considerably simpler than those used in carrier system telephony. However, it is obvious that designing highly selective RF filters requires extremely complex calculations and very precise measurements beyond the scope of this book. For readers interested in this

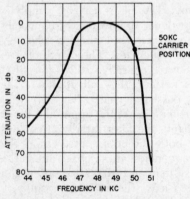

Fig. 4-1. Bandpass characteristics of Burnell S-15000 filter.

subject, there are a number of texts and scientific papers available. With the exception of the relatively simple crystal-lattice filter described later, our discussion will be confined to the various manufactured filters available as stock items.

Burnell S-15000—The most widely known low-frequency filter available to amateurs is the Burnell S-15000, designed for use at a carrier frequency of 50 kc. A careful examination of the response curve in Fig. 4-1 will reveal that this filter passes only those

42

sideband frequencies contained in the region from the 50-kc carrier, down to 47-kc (the lower sideband). All sideband frequencies (upper sideband) higher than 50 kc are rapidly attenuated to the point where virtually none appear at the filter output. The 50-kc carrier is placed at approximately the 20-db attenuation point on the slope of the filter response. At 50.5 kc the upper sideband is down 50 db, and at 51 kc it is down 80 db. For all practical purposes, the upper-sideband frequencies are considered to be completely suppressed, since none appear in the output signal.

Notice that the lower-sideband frequencies are attenuated more gradually. At 47 kc, the lower sideband is down about 5 db, and at 46 kc it is down about 25 db. The 20-db attenuation point on the low-frequency slope occurs at about 46.3 kc. If the filter bandwidth is considered to be the frequency difference between the two 20-db attenuation points, then this filter has a bandwidth (passband) of 3.7 kc. All attenuation figures are given with respect to the maximum (peak) signal output from the filter—which in this case is 0 db. The insertion loss is not indicated for the filter, since all measurements are made at its output terminals.

The carrier is placed at the 20-db attenuation point on the sharp slope of the filter response. This is done to attenuate the speech frequencies below 300 cycles, and also to give another 20 db of carrier suppression in addition to that of the balanced modulator. If the carrier is placed too high on the filter slope, or if the filter attenuation is too slow in the direction of the unwanted sideband, a portion of the unwanted sideband will appear in the output signal. Because of the filter-response slope, the two sideband components closest to the carrier will be unequal in amplitude. As a result, angle modulation will take place. In single-sideband transmitters it causes a rapid increase in distortion products and usually can be identified by the lack of quality in the transmitted signal. Angle modulation can also be caused by 60- or 120-cycle hum components reaching the audio circuit of the balanced modulator. This condition is especially serious when the carrier-generator frequency stability is poor under load.

In addition to extremely accurate and stable carrier generators and filters, most modern single-sideband systems also make use of bandpass filters to restrict the AF range. The band of audio frequencies between 300 and 3,000 cycles is generally considered adequate for the transmission of intelligible speech. Those below 300 cycles waste transmitter power and contribute virtually nothing to signal intelligibility. The main reason for restricting the audio-frequency range to 3,000 cycles is to prevent adjacent-channel interference. The design of single-sideband audio circuitry will be covered in detail in a later chapter.

The Burnell S-15000 sideband filter is of unbalanced input type, where the input must be terminated in a resistance of 30 k ohms in order to retain the characteristic response. Because of the unbalanced input termination, the filter cannot be used with balanced modulators (such as the 7360) unless an intermediate balance-to-unbalanced coupling device is employed. Fig. 4-2 shows the method of using the S-15000 filter with a push-pull output type of balanced modulator.

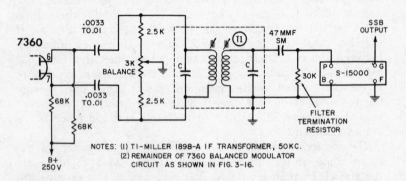

NOTES: (1) T1–MILLER 1898–A IF TRANSFORMER, 50 KC.
(2) REMAINDER OF 7360 BALANCED MODULATOR
CIRCUIT AS SHOWN IN FIG. 3-16.

Fig. 4-2. Burnell S-15000 filter used in 7360 balanced modulator circuit.

Hammarlund HX-500—The sideband filter in the Hammarlund HX-500 single-sideband transmitter is designed for a 60-kc. carrier It is composed of eight individually shielded high-Q tuned circuits, a carrier-frequency trap, and a 6EW6 amplifier tube. Since it is not a single unit, this very interesting and unusual sideband filter will be described in a later chapter on commercial single-sideband generator design.

Barker and Williamson "360" and "361"—The Barker and Williamson Company also produces two types of low-frequency precision toroidal filters. One is the "360" filter, designed for receiving purposes. The same manufacturer can supply (on special order) a combination transmitting and receiving type known as the "361," which contains balanced coupling windings of 500 and 10,000 ohms. Otherwise, its bandpass, attenuation characteristics, and physical dimensions resemble those of the "360."

Eight stabilized toroidal inductances and precision silver mica capacitors are used in the "360" to provide passband and attenuation characteristics that remain constant, even under changing operating temperatures. The amplitude characteristic

44

(Fig. 4-3) is relatively flat across the nominal 3-kc passband, with sharp skirt selectivity on *both* sides of the bandpass region. The high input and output impedances (20,000 ohms each) permit the filter to operate as an interstage coupling device. The carrier position, at 20 db down on the low-frequency slope, is 17 kc. The corresponding 20-db attenuation point on the high frequency slope is located at about 20.1 kc.

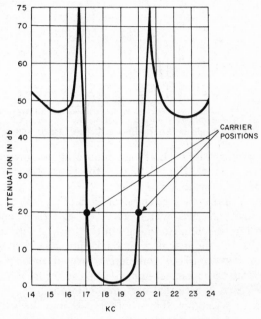

Fig. 4-3. Bandpass characteristics of B&W "360" filter.

Since the carrier frequency is 17 kc and the passband extends from 17.2 to 20.2 kc, the filter rejects the lower but passes the upper sideband. The insertion loss, measured at 18.5 kc, is about 6 db. The "360" is housed in a hermetically sealed tinned steel case which measures 2⅝" × 2¼" × 3¾" (exclusive of mounting studs and terminals).

Medium-Frequency Filters

The early crystal-lattice filters, constructed by amateurs from war surplus FT-241-A crystals, were generally in the 450- to 470-kc region. The coupling devices were usually made from ordinary 455-kc IF transformers. Commercially, the most widely known 455-kc single-sideband filter is the one made by Collins. Produced in a number of shapes and bandwidths, Collins filters

45

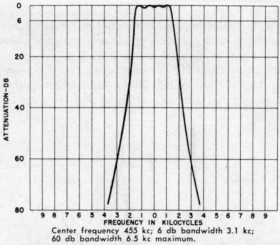

Center frequency 455 kc; 6 db bandwidth 3.1 kc;
60 db bandwidth 6.5 kc maximum.

Fig. 4-4 Bandpass characteristics of Collins "455-31" filter.

are used extensively in both amateur and commercial single-sideband equipment. Fig. 4-4 shows the characteristic curve for the Collins miniature F455-31 filter.

Mechanical Filters—A mechanical filter (Fig. 4-5) is a mechanically resonant device which receives electrical energy and converts it into mechanical energy in the form of vibrations, then converts the mechanical energy back into electrical energy at the output. Although the commercial use of mechanical filters is of comparatively recent origin, their basic principles have been known for years. Notice that each end contains both a transducer coil and a bias magnet. Thus, either end may be used for the source or load. The transducer coils are series- or parallel-resonated (depending on the requirements of the associated circuitry) to a specified frequency at the center of the passband. When an RF signal of that frequency is applied to the resonant input circuit, the alternating magnetic field from the coil causes the magnetostrictive material of the core to stretch or shrink with changes in the magnetic flux. In this manner, the

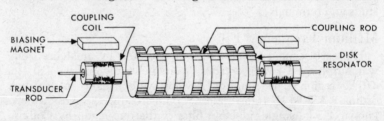

Fig. 4-5. Construction of a typical mechanical filter.

46

electrical oscillations are converted into mechanical oscillations, which then drive the mechanical elements of the filter.

The center frequency of the filter is determined by the metal discs. Since each disc appears as an individual series-resonant circuit, it is apparent that the skirt selectivity of the filter can be improved by increasing the number of the discs. As mentioned at the beginning of this chapter, the skirt selectivity is related to the shape factor (the ratio of the bandwidth at the 6- and 60-db attenuation points). A mechanical filter containing six discs will have a shape factor of approximately 2.2, and adding a disc will lower the shape factor to approximately 1.85. A filter with nine discs will have a shape factor of approximately 1.5. At the present time, nine is the limit. However, it

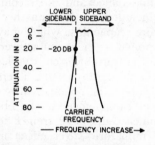

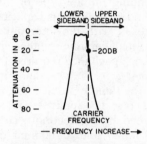

(A) Passing upper sideband only. (B) Passing lower sideband only.

Fig. 4-6. Sideband-selection characteristics of the mechanical filter.

seems likely that future improvements in manufacturing techniques will make possible the production of units with more discs and thus even better skirt selectivity.

Since the bandwidth varies approximately as the total area of the coupling rods, the bandwidth of the filter can be varied by making the coupling rods larger or smaller. Some single-sideband mechanical filters have a bandwidth as narrow as 0.5 kc.

The symmetrical bandpass characteristic of the mechanical filter simplifies the over-all single-sideband generator design to some extent. To change the signal passed by the filter from an upper to a lower sideband or vice versa, it is only necessary to change the frequency of the carrier-generator oscillator. As shown in Fig. 4-6, an upper-sideband signal will be passed when the carrier frequency is at the 20-db attenuation point on the low-frequency slope. Likewise, the lower sideband will be passed when the carrier frequency is at the 20-db attenuation point on the high-frequency slope. In single-sideband generators designed around the mechanical filter, the carrier frequencies are usually controlled by two crystals in the generator oscillator.

47

The two crystals are usually connected to a "sideband selector" switch controlled from the front panel. Its two positions are generally marked "LSB" and "USB," for the lower- and upper-sideband transmissions, respectively. (Note, however, that the panel markings on most commercial equipment refer to the characteristic of the sideband transmission from the output terminals of the transmitter, and not necessarily to the sideband being passed by the filter. This subject will be discussed further in the chapters on equipment design.)

The input and output impedances of the mechanical filter are largely resistive, since the input and output circuits are tuned to resonance at the center of the passband. The actual impedance values will range from 1,000 to 50,000 ohms, depending on the type of filter. The impedance and the recommended resonating capacitance are included on the data sheet packed with the filter unit. The tuning capacitors, which may be small ceramic trimmers, are not supplied by the manufacturer. The capacitance required to resonate the transducer coils varies from type to type, and may even vary slightly among filters of the same type. In most mechanical filters, the nominal capacitance is 120 mmf. A suitable value of capacitance can be obtained by connecting a ceramic trimmer (adjustable from 8 to 50 mmf) and a 100-mmf capacitor (miniature, silver mica) in parallel. The use of air-dielectric tuning capacitors, particularly relatively large ones, is not recommended. The large mass of metal in the stator-plate assembly may cause signal radiation or coupling around the filter. Either will result in incomplete suppression of the unwanted sideband, or other deterioration of the filter characteristic response.

The smallness of the mechanical filter makes it especially attractive for use in compact equipment such as portable or mobile transmitters and receivers. One of the recently developed tubular mechanical filters is only about ½ inch in diameter by 1¾ inches in length.

Lattice—The lattice-type filter using quartz crystals has been very popular with amateurs, as evidenced by the many articles written about them in amateur radio publications during the past few years. There is little doubt that the lattice filter (constructed from war surplus FT-241-A crystals) played a large part in the enthusiastic response of amateurs to single-sideband technology. FT-241-A crystals are still available from surplus houses for only a few cents each. Some of these outlets even offer "matched sets" at a slightly higher cost. If the crystals are properly selected and the filter is carefully constructed and aligned, the over-all performance of the home-

48

made filter will approach that of the more expensive manufactured variety. While the construction of a good crystal-lattice filter is a tedious task, it is an excellent project for the experimenter, especially those who desire practical experience in the design and construction of single-sideband equipment.

FT-241-A crystals are of the plated-electrode type and are mounted in *Bakelite* holders with pins 0.093 inch in diameter and spaced 0.486 inch apart. The crystals were manufactured in two groups within the fundamental frequency range from 370 to 540 kc. Each group is identified by a two- or three-digit number on the label of the crystal holder. The two-digit group is for Channels 0 to 79 inclusive, and the three-digit group, Channels 270 to 289 inclusive. The equipment containing these crystals multiplied the fundamental frequency 54 times for the two-digit and 72 times for the three-digit crystals. The channel number indicates the output frequency of the equipment. For example, an FT-241-A two-digit crystal marked "CHANNEL 48, 24.8 MC" has a fundamental frequency of 459.259 kc (24.8 mc divided by 54). In like manner, a crystal marked "CHANNEL 49, 24.9 MC" has a fundamental frequency of 461.111 kc.

For three-digit channel crystals the channel designation (in megacycles) is divided by 72. For example, take an FT-241-A three-digit crystal marked "CHANNEL 326, 32.6 MC." Its fundamental frequency is 32.6 mc divided by 72, which gives 452.777 kc.

The frequency difference (at the fundamental) between any two FT-241-A crystals marked with consecutive two-digit channel numbers is 1.85 kc. For three-digit channel numbers the difference is 1.39 kc.

Two-digit channel-number crystals are mounted in *black Bakelite* holders, and the three-digit ones in *brown Bakelite* holders.

Full-lattice—When FT-241-A crystals are used in a lattice filter configuration (as in Fig. 4-7), the bandwidth of the filter is determined by the frequency separation between crystals X1 and X2. This crystal arrangement is known as a full-lattice filter and is used extensively in single-sideband telephone equipment. Probably the greatest difficulty in the construction of a full-lattice crystal filter is obtaining matched pairs of crystals. Each pair designated X1 or X2 must be within 10 to 20 cycles of the same frequency. Although crystals with a slightly greater frequency difference are usable, the filter response characteristic will deteriorate rapidly as the frequency separation increases.

The most practical method of accurately measuring the fundamental frequency of an FT-241-A crystal in the vicinity of 455

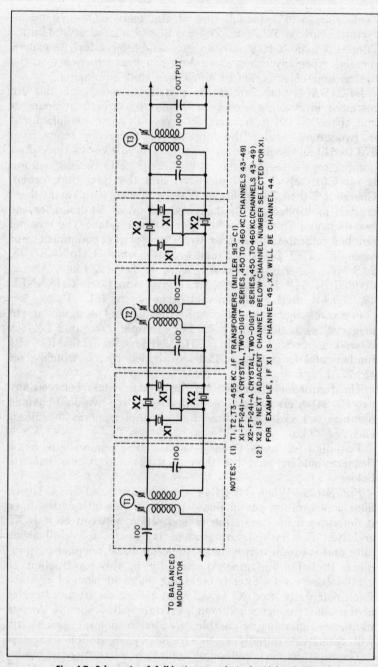

NOTES: (1) T1, T2, T3—455 KC IF TRANSFORMERS (MILLER 913-C1)
X1—FT-241-A CRYSTAL, TWO-DIGIT SERIES, 450 TO 460 KC (CHANNELS 43-49)
X2—FT-241-A CRYSTAL, TWO-DIGIT SERIES, 450 TO 460 KC (CHANNELS 43-49)
(2) X2 IS NEXT ADJACENT CHANNEL BELOW CHANNEL NUMBER SELECTED FOR X1.
FOR EXAMPLE, IF X1 IS CHANNEL 45, X2 WILL BE CHANNEL 44.

Fig. 4-7. Schematic of full-lattice crystal single-sideband filter.

50

kc is to place it into a suitable oscillator-frequency-multiplier circuit and read the harmonic frequency on a calibrated receiver. For example, take an FT-241-A crystal marked "CHANNEL 43, 24.3 MC." Since it is designated by a two-digit channel number, you divide the 24.3 mc by 54 to obtain the fundamental frequency of 450 kc. If this 450 kc is now multiplied by 16, the sixteenth harmonic will appear at 7,200 kc (which is within the 40-meter amateur band). Virtually all modern amateur and commercial communications receivers include a 100-kc crystal calibrator as standard equipment, and 7,200 kc is one of the 100-kc check points on the dial scale. Ordinarily, the 100-kc frequency standard is checked and adjusted for accuracy against the transmission of U. S. Bureau of Standards radio station WWV before the receiver dial is calibrated. However, the exact frequency of the crystal-oscillator harmonic is not too important. Our primary interest is in determining which pairs of crystals are closest to the same frequency.

This is done by placing one of the crystals into the oscillator circuit and tuning the calibrated receiver to zero-beat with the harmonic signal at or near 7,200 kc. (Before making any measurements, allow the receiver beat-frequency oscillator (BFO) enough time to become stabilized after it is turned on). After tuning the receiver until it zero-beats with the harmonic, remove the crystal from the oscillator, insert another 450-kc crystal, and note the pitch of the beat note if audible. If no beat note is heard, the second crystal has the same frequency as the first, or else is not oscillating. Continue to insert crystals into the oscillator and listening to the pitch of the audible beat note. The crystals which produce similar-sounding audio beat notes should be segregated and their frequencies measured more closely. After obtaining a half-dozen crystals or so with similar beat frequencies, select one of the crystals as a standard, accurately tune its harmonic to zero-beat with the calibrated receiver, and note the dial-scale reading. On some modern communications receivers, dial scales are calibrated to an accuracy of 100 cycles or better. If the individual crystals are sufficiently close in frequency that they can be used as matched pairs, their frequency differences at the sixteenth harmonic will be 300 cycles or less. Even with a deviation of 300 to 500 cycles at the harmonic frequency, the crystals will still be usable as matched pairs, but over-all filter performance will be degraded.

It may be argued that the oscillator-harmonic method of selecting matched pairs of crystals is questionable, since the crystals may not have exactly the same resonant frequencies

Nominal Crystal Freq. kc	Chan-nel No.	Nominal Crystal Freq. kc	Chan-nel No.	Nominal Crystal Freq. kc	Chan-nel No.	Nominal Crystal Freq. kc	Chan-nel No.	Nominal Crystal Freq. kc	Chan-nel No.	Nominal Crystal Freq. kc	Chan-nel No.
370.370	0	398.611	287	424.074	29	450.000	324	477.778	58	505.556	73
372.222	1	400.000	16	425.000	306	451.388	325	479.166	345	506.944	365
374.074	2	400.000	288	425.926	30	451.852	44	479.630	59	507.407	74
375.000	270	401.388	289	426.388	307	452.777	326	480.555	346	508.333	366
375.926	3	401.852	17	427.777	308	453.704	45	481.481	60	509.259	75
376.388	271	402.777	290	427.778	31	454.166	327	481.944	347	509.722	367
377.777	272	403.704	18	429.166	309	455.555	328	483.333	61	511.111	76
377.778	4	404.166	291	429.630	32	455.556	46	483.333	348	511.111	368
379.166	273	405.555	292	430.555	310	456.944	329	484.722	349	512.500	369
379.630	5	405.556	19	431.481	33	457.407	47	485.185	62	512.963	77
380.555	274	406.944	293	431.944	311	458.333	330	486.111	350	513.888	370
381.481	6	407.407	20	433.333	34	459.259	48	487.037	63	514.815	78
381.944	275	408.333	294	433.333	312	459.722	331	487.500	351	515.277	371
383.333	7	409.259	21	434.722	313	461.111	49	488.888	352	516.666	372
383.333	276	409.722	295	435.185	35	461.111	332	488.889	64	516.667	79
384.722	277	411.111	22	436.111	314	462.500	333	490.277	353	518.055	373
385.185	8	411.111	296	437.037	36	462.963	50	490.741	65	519.444	374
386.111	278	412.500	297	437.500	315	463.888	334	491.666	354	520.833	375
387.037	9	412.963	23	438.888	316	464.815	51	492.593	66	522.222	376
387.500	279	413.888	298	438.889	37	465.277	335	493.055	355	523.611	377
388.888	280	414.815	24	440.277	317	466.666	336	494.444	67	525.000	378
388.889	10	415.277	299	440.741	38	466.667	52	494.444	356	526.388	379
390.277	281	416.666	300	441.666	318	468.055	337	495.833	357	527.777	380
390.741	11	416.667	25	442.593	39	468.519	53	496.296	68	529.166	381
391.666	282	418.055	301	443.055	319	469.444	338	497.222	358	530.555	382
392.593	12	418.519	26	444.444	40	470.370	54	498.148	69	531.944	383
393.055	283	419.444	302	444.444	320	470.833	339	498.611	359	533.333	384
394.444	13	420.370	27	445.833	321	472.222	55	500.000	70	534.722	385
394.444	284	420.833	303	446.296	41	472.222	340	500.000	360	536.111	386
395.833	285	422.222	28	447.222	322	473.611	341	501.388	361	537.500	387
396.296	14	422.222	304	448.148	42	474.074	56	501.852	71	538.888	388
397.222	286	423.611	305	448.611	323	475.000	342	502.777	362	540.277	389
398.148	15			450.000	43	475.926	57	503.704	72		
						476.388	343	504.166	363		
						477.777	344	505.555	364		

Courtesy of Texas Crystals

Fig. 4-8. Channel numbers and fundamental frequencies of FT-241-A crystals from 370 to 540 kc.

in the filter that they had in the oscillator. While this is true to some extent, crystals that bear a certain relationship to each other, when measured as described above, will exhibit a similar relationship when placed in the filter. The activity of the individual crystals can be checked by noting the amplitude of the harmonic signal, as indicated by the signal-level meter of the receiver. The matched pairs of crystals should have approximately equal degrees of activity.

The frequency separation between crystals X1 and X2 in Fig. 4-7 determines the bandwidth of the filter. In most lattice filters constructed from FT-241-A crystals and standard IF transformers, the bandwidth has been about one and one-fourth times the frequency difference between the X1 and X2 fre-

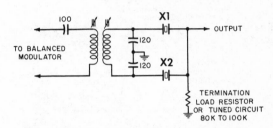

Fig. 4-9. Half-lattice crystal filter.

quencies. If two consecutive two-digit channel crystals are selected for the X1 and X2 frequencies, then the bandwidth will be approximately 2.3 kc. This is very close to the 2.1-kc bandwidth of the filters used in some recent commercial single-sideband transmitters. If consecutive three-digit channel crystals are used, the bandwidth of the filter will be approximately 1.75 kc; this is generally considered too narrow for readable speech quality. It is possible, by using combinations of the two- and three-digit channel crystals, to produce filters with various bandwidths. The chart in Fig. 4-8 gives the channel numbers and fundamental frequencies of all FT-241-A crystals from 370 to 540 kc.

Half-lattice—The "half-lattice" filter in Fig. 4-9 is similar to the single-crystal filter used in older communications receivers, except that the phasing capacitor has been replaced by a second crystal. The shunt capacitances of the two crystals balance each other and produce a bandpass response similar to that shown in Fig. 4-10A. When the tuned circuits are properly adjusted, the response curve should have a flat top. However, its final shape will be due to a compromise between good skirt selectivity and a flat bandpass response. Most lattice filters will

53

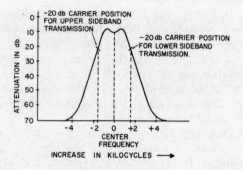

(A) Without trimmer.

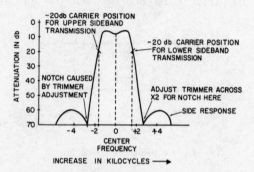

(B) With trimmer.

Fig. 4-10. Half-lattice filter-response curves.

have two peaks, separated by about 2 kc and with a dip of 3 to 6 db at the center, between the two peaks. The shape factor (ratio of the bandwidth at the 6- and 60-db attenuation points) of the filter shown in Fig. 4-9 is about 4 or 5—which indicates a rather poor skirt selectivity. However, the shape factor can be improved considerably by the use of a 2-mmf trimmer across

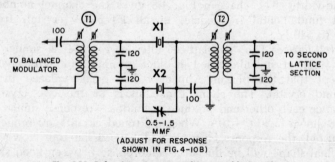

Fig. 4-11. Balancing trimmer used in crystal-lattice filter.

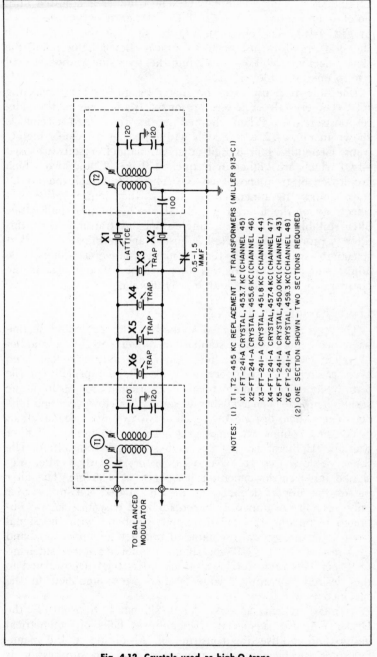

NOTES: (1) T1, T2 — 455 KC REPLACEMENT IF TRANSFORMERS (MILLER 913-C1)
X1—FT-241-A CRYSTAL, 453.7 KC (CHANNEL 45)
X2—FT-241-A CRYSTAL, 455.6 KC (CHANNEL 46)
X3—FT-241-A CRYSTAL, 451.8 KC (CHANNEL 44)
X4—FT-241-A CRYSTAL, 457.4 KC (CHANNEL 47)
X5—FT-241-A CRYSTAL, 450.0 KC (CHANNEL 43)
X6—FT-241-A CRYSTAL, 459.3 KC (CHANNEL 48)
(2) ONE SECTION SHOWN — TWO SECTIONS REQUIRED

Fig. 4-12. Crystals used as high-Q traps.

55

crystal X2, as shown in Fig. 4-11. The trimmer is adjusted until notches appear at the sides of the response curve, as shown in Fig. 4-10B. The optimum adjustment is at the point where the side responses just begin to appear. Beyond this point, the skirt selectivity will improve, but the two side responses will rise to unacceptable values.

The side responses can be made insignificant by selecting FT-241-A crystals with series-resonant frequencies in the side-response region. When shunted across the tuned circuit as shown in Fig. 4-12, the crystals will appear as extremely high-Q traps. Generally, four 3-digit adjacent-channel crystals are used —two which are higher in frequency than X2, and two which are lower in frequency than X1. The addition of the crystal traps across the tuned circuit will further improve the skirt selectivity of the filter. Fig. 4-13 shows a practical half-lattice filter suitable for use in a single-sideband transmitter. If this filter is properly constructed, adjusted and terminated, its skirt selectivity will approach that of many commercial filters. The adjustment procedure for this filter will be covered later in the chapters on single-sideband test equipment.

High-Frequency Filters

The crystal-lattice filters described in the preceding section have been more or less standard arrangements for a number of years. During the past few years, however, there has been even greater interest in crystal-lattice filters, especially in the 5- to 30-mc region. Commercial filters designed for up to 50 mc and higher have been available for some time. However, their high cost places them beyond the reach of the average radio amateur.

The first commercial amateur transmitter to use a HF filter was the Hallicrafters HT-32 single-sideband transmitter. The later version, the HT-32A, used a crystal-lattice filter designed for a carrier-generator frequency of 4.95 mc. The filter passes the upper sideband of the modulated 4.95-mc carrier only. A choice of upper- or lower-sideband transmission was obtained by mixing the 4.95-mc upper sideband with the signal from a 4.05-mc crystal oscillator to produce an *upper* sideband of 9 mc, or with a 13.95-mc signal to obtain a *lower* sideband of 9 mc. This upper or lower sideband is then heterodyned to the desired operating frequency and *then* amplified to the specified power level.

A more recent amateur single-sideband transmitter, the Drake T-4, uses a special HF bandpass filter of symmetrical design and multisection construction. According to the manufacturer's specifications, the unwanted sideband suppression is

56

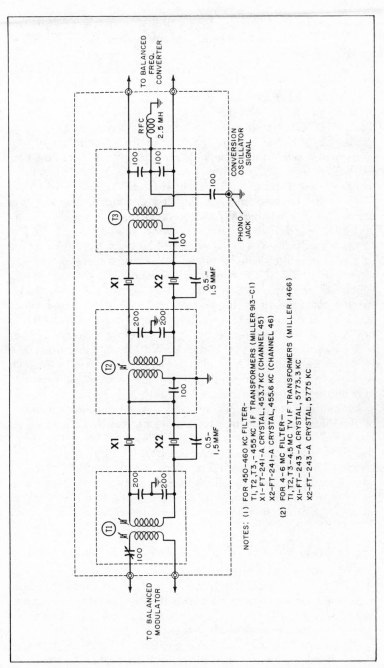

Fig. 4-13. Schematic of lattice filter using war surplus crystals.

NOTES: (1) FOR 450-460 KC FILTER—
T1, T2, T3, – 455 KC IF TRANSFORMERS (MILLER 913-C1)
X1–FT–241–A CRYSTAL, 453.7 KC (CHANNEL 45)
X2–FT–241–A CRYSTAL, 455.6 KC (CHANNEL 46)

(2) FOR 4-6 MC FILTER—
T1, T2, T3–4.5 MC TV IF TRANSFORMERS (MILLER 1466)
X1–FT–243–A CRYSTAL, 5773.3 KC
X2–FT–243–A CRYSTAL, 5775 KC

TO BALANCED FREQ. CONVERTER

RFC 2.5 MH

CONVERSION OSCILLATOR SIGNAL

PHONO JACK

100

100

100

T3

X1

X2

0.5 – 1.5 MMF

200

200

T2

100

X1

X2

0.5 – 1.5 MMF

200

200

T1

100

TO BALANCED MODULATOR

60 db or better. The crystal-controlled carrier-generator frequency is 5645. This interesting new transmitter will be described in more detail in a later chapter.

The lattice configurations and general design procedures for high-frequency crystal filters are similar to those of the filters which use the FT-241-A crystals. The most suitable surplus crystals for high-frequency filters are the FT-243 types, in the 2905- to 8650-kc range.

The FT-243 crystals were manufactured for a number of odd frequencies and, unlike the FT-241-A, do not follow any particular channel order. However, there are some frequencies available which have an "adjacent-channel" crystal only 1.7 kc away from the frequency of the first crystal. A few of these are 5773.3 and 5775 kc, 5973.3 and 5975 kc, 6673.3 and 6675 kc, and 7973.3 and 7975 kc. If the lower-frequency crystal in any of these groups is used as X1 and the higher as X2, the bandpass of the lattice filter will be about 2.1 kc. In some experimental filters using 5773.3-kc crystals as X1 and 5775-kc ones as X2 (such as the two-section half-lattice circuit of Fig. 4-13), the bandpass measures approximately 2.5 kc at 6 db and about 10 kc at 60 db down. The resultant shape factor is 4, which is fairly good at this frequency. The coupling transformers in this experimental filter are the J. W. Miller 1466 interstage IF type. In building this filter, it was necessary to remove two or three turns from all primary and secondary windings in order to obtain resonance at 5.775 mc.

As might be expected, the stray capacitance and leakage of this filter proved to be much more critical than those of its low-frequency counter-part, the FT-241-A. The entire filter should be enclosed in an aluminum box. The input and output terminals must be kept well separated, and also must be shielded from each other by a metal plate at least two inches high and three or four inches long. All terminal leads must be kept as short as possible, to prevent signal radiation around the filter.

PHASE-SHIFT SIDEBAND SELECTION

Two balanced modulators are used in the phase-shift method of sideband selection. The exciting signals are made to have phase relationships such that, when the outputs of the two modulators are combined, the desired sideband components are reinforced and the undesired ones canceled out.

The phase-shift single-sideband generator requires no selective filters. It also has the advantage of being able to generate the single-sideband signal at the operating frequency without the frequency conversion required by the filter method. The phase-shift and amplitude properties of the circuit, however, are very critical and must be held to close tolerances. This characteristic, and the requirement of two balanced modulators, tend to make the system somewhat more complex than the filter method.

Block Diagram

Fig. 4-14 illustrates the generation of a single-sideband signal by the phase-shift method. The carrier is applied directly to balanced modulator A with no phase shift. The carrier signal applied to balanced modulator B is shifted in phase by 90°. In

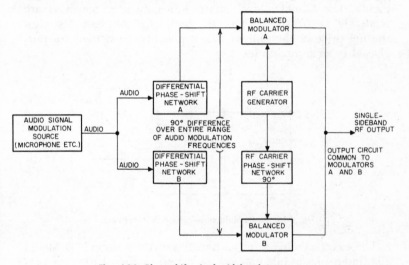

Fig. 4-14. Phase-shift single-sideband generator.

other words, at any given instant the carrier signals applied to the two balanced modulators will be 90° out of phase. The 90° carriers are adjusted so that their amplitudes are equal. The two balanced modulators have a common output tuned circuit, which is resonated to the carrier frequency. When the usual balancing and tuning procedures are carried out, no RF carrier will appear in the tuned output circuit.

In order for the system to function as a single-sideband generator, it is necessary to divide the AF signal of the balanced modulators into two components 90° out of phase. If the audio signal were a single tone of, say, 1,000 cycles and no other tones were to be transmitted, the 90° audio phase-shifting device would be relatively simple. In this case, the single-tone audio signal would be applied directly to modulator A with no phase change, and the 90° phase-displaced audio signal would be applied to modulator B. In a practical single-sideband transmitter, however, it is generally desired to transmit a band of audio frequencies rather than a single tone. At this time, there is no known means for obtaining a 90° phase shift over a wide range of audio frequencies. In actual practice, "two" phase-shift networks with a differential phase shift of 90° are inserted between the AF source and balanced modulators. This phase-shift difference can be maintained over a frequency range of about seven octaves with a deviation of not more than ±2°. The phase-shift networks are made up of high-precision resistors and capacitors, and require the use of laboratory instruments for adjustments and measurements. The manufactured phase-shift networks, however, are relatively inexpensive. In fact, the completed unit costs less than the net price of the individual components when they are purchased in small quantities.

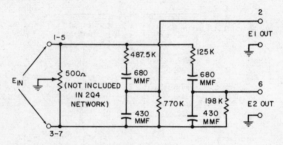

Fig. 4-15. Audio differential phase-shift network.

The electrical circuit of the Barker and Williamson 2Q4 Model 350 audio phase-shift network is shown in Fig. 4-15. This network is designed to function within the range of 300 to 3,000 cycles and with a phase differential of 90°±1.5°. Its components are mounted within an octal-based metal tube shell, and the unit requires the same space as a 6J5 metal tube.

The vector diagram in Fig. 4-16 shows the carrier and sideband relationships at the output of the balanced modulators. The amplitudes of the two carrier vectors have been exaggerated in order to simplify the explanation. These vectors are considered to be rotating counterclockwise around their common origin, with the vector at A leading the vector at B by 90°. At the instant shown, carrier vector A and its upper and lower sidebands are adding, whereas the sidebands at B appear to be canceling. It must be understood that the sideband energy of both carrier components exists in a common tuned circuit. The lower sideband at A is generated at the same frequency as the one at B but because of the 90° phase difference in *both* the carrier and the audio signals, the two lower sidebands will be 180° out of phase. At the instant shown, the lower sideband at A is at a maximum of 90° and that at B, 270°. The two lower-sideband vectors rotate in the same direction and at the same rate, since the frequency is the same for both. Thus, the 180° phase difference will be maintained. When two AC sine waves are equal in amplitude but exactly 180° out of phase, they will cancel each other, and their combined net amplitude will be zero.

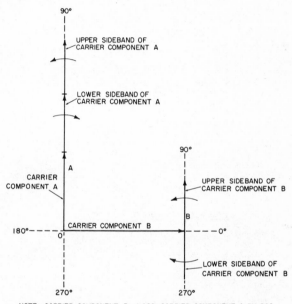

NOTE: CARRIER COMPONENT B LAGS CARRIER COMPONENT A BY 90°

Fig. 4-16. Vector diagram, showing a single-sideband signal.

The upper-sideband components at A and B are at 0° phase difference, or in phase. The sum of these two will be twice the amplitude of either sideband alone. Since the amplitude of the upper sideband has doubled and that of the lower has been reduced to zero, the RF output will consist of the upper sideband only.

In order for a lower-sideband signal to be generated, the phase of *one* of the audio components must be shifted by an additional 180°, as shown in Fig. 4-17. Notice that the two lower sidebands are now in phase, and that the two upper side-

61

bands are 180° out of phase. It is obvious, then, that the two lower sidebands will add and the two upper sidebands will cancel, leaving an RF output consisting of the lower sideband only. The required 180° phase shift is generally brought about by reversing the connections of one audio-transformer primary winding, as shown in Fig. 4-18.

Practical Generator

In Fig. 4-18 a typical balanced modulator section of a phase-shift single-sideband generator is shown. The sideband signal

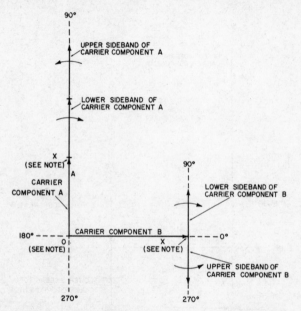

NOTE: CARRIER COMPONENTS A AND B ARE ACTUALLY SUPPRESSED IN PRACTICE, BUT SIDEBAND RELATIONSHIP IS AS SHOWN. THE POINTS MARKED X COINCIDE AND ARE LOCATED AT THE ORIGIN O IN PRACTICAL CIRCUIT APPLICATION.

Fig. 4-17. Vector diagram, showing a lower-sideband signal.

is generated with a 9-mc carrier. The 9-mc upper- or lower-sideband signal is then mixed in a frequency-conversion circuit, together with an appropriate RF oscillator signal, and hetero-dyned to the operating frequency.

Although the audio differential phase-shift networks are generally beyond the design and measurements of the amateur, the RF phase-shift networks are not. The primary function of the RF phase-shift network is to accept a signal from the carrier generator (usually a crystal-controlled oscillator) and

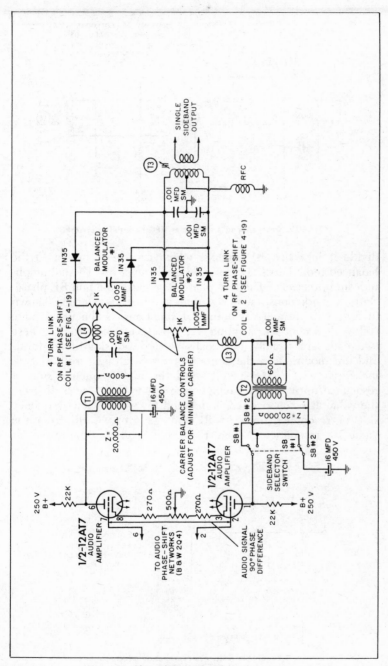

Fig. 4-18. Phase-shift single-sideband generator.

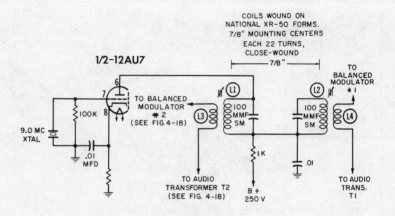

Fig. 4-19. Double-tuned transformer RF phase-shift network.

divide it into *two* RF signals, which are then applied to the balanced modulators. These two signals must be of equal amplitude and precisely 90° out of phase. The most common RF phase-shift network consists of the double-tuned transformer shown in Fig. 4-19. Primary winding L1 functions as the usual plate coil with secondary winding L2 loosely coupled to it. These two coils are usually identically wound on slug-tuned forms and are mounted so the centers of the windings are about 7/8 inch apart. L1 is detuned toward the high-frequency side of resonance until the RF voltage across it is down by 3 db from the value at resonance. L2 is detuned toward the low-frequency side of resonance until its RF voltage drops 3 db from the value at resonance. When these two coils are adjusted as

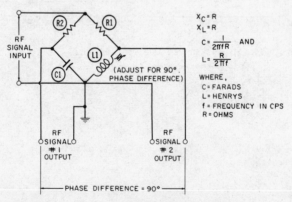

Fig. 4-20. Simple resistance-capacitance-inductance RF phase-shift network.

described, the voltages across link windings L3 and L4 will be approximately 90° out of phase.

Resistance-Reactance Networks

Fig. 4-20 shows a simple phase-shift network composed of resistance, capacitance, and inductance. R1 and R2, which are equal in value, determine the impedance of the network. The inductive and capacitive reactances must equal the resistances of R1 and R2, respectively, at the operating (carrier) frequency. When an AC signal (RF in this case) is applied to a pure inductance, the voltage across the circuit will *lead* the current by 90°. When the same signal is applied to a pure capacitance, the voltage across the circuit will *lag* the current by 90°. When a reactance and a resistance are used in combination, the resulting phase angle of the voltage and current will be somewhere between ±90° and 0°, depending on the relative values of the total reactance and resistance. In this network, where each reactance is equal to each resistance, the voltage across L1 will *lead* the current by 45°, and the voltage across C1 will *lag* the current by 45°. The phase difference between the two voltages will then be 90°. Their amplitudes will be equal only at the frequency where the reactance values are equal. When the carrier frequency is increased, the voltage drop will increase

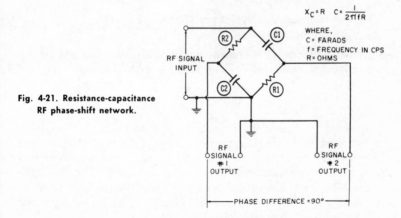

Fig. 4-21. Resistance-capacitance RF phase-shift network.

across L1 and decrease across C1. Conversely, when the carrier frequency is decreased, the opposite will occur. The phase relationship of this circuit will remain at 90° for a reasonable range of frequencies above and below the design frequency. The output impedance is high and should not be terminated in resistances of less than 1 or 2 megohms. The

65

network is used most generally with vacuum-tube balanced modulator circuits.

Another simple RF phase-shift network is shown in Fig. 4-21. The two resistors are of equal value, usually 50 to 100 ohms, and each capacitor must have a reactance equal to the value of one of the resistors at the carrier frequency. At the design center frequency, where the X_C of C1 is equal to the value of R1 and the X_C of C2 to the value of R2, the voltage drops across R1 and C2 will be equal. The RF voltage across R1 will be in phase with the current through R1. The RF voltage across C2, however, will lag the current through C2 by 90°. The phase difference between the two RF voltages at the output terminals will then be 90°.

The inductive reactance for the network shown in Fig. 4-20, and the capacitive reactances for the networks shown in Fig. 4-20 and Fig. 4-21, are calculated according to the usual formulas, or may be determined from a reactance chart for radio frequencies. The inductive reactance (X_L) or capacitive reactance (X_C) must equal the resistance (R). The formula for inductive reactance is:

$$X_L = 2\pi fL$$

where,

X_L is the reactance in ohms,
π is equal to 3.1416,
f is the frequency in cycles per second,
L is the inductance in henrys.

Since the value of X_L is known (equal to R), the equation can be rearranged to solve for L. The formula now becomes:

$$L = \frac{R}{2\pi f}$$

When the value of the inductance (in microhenrys) has been determined, a suitable slug-tuned coil may be wound according to instructions given later in this book, or a manufactured coil which can be adjusted to the required inductance may be used. Ordinarily, one reactive element of the phase-shift network is made adjustable. The network phase correction adjustments will be covered in a later chapter.

The values of C1 and C2 in Fig. 4-21, and the value of C1 in Fig. 4-20, are calculated by rearranging the basic capacitive reactance formula:

$$X_C = \frac{1}{2\pi fC}$$

where,

    X_C is the reactance in ohms,
    f is the frequency in cycles per second,
    C is the capacity in farads.

Since the value of X_C is known (equal to R), the equation can be rearranged to solve for C. It now becomes:

$$C = \frac{1}{2\pi fR}$$

The resistors used in RF phase-shift networks should be of the precision metal-film type with a tolerance of ±1% or better. Carbon resistors are not suitable, even though their tolerances are within the limits. The ordinary carbon resistor is frequency-sensitive, and its resistance at RF may differ considerably from the value obtained by DC measurements. Wirewound resistors should not be used either, because of their inductive-reactance effect at radio frequencies.

Chapter 5

Carrier Generators

The frequency accuracy requirements for single-sideband carrier-frequency generators are very precise, because any drift or other changes will deteriorate the transmitted signal. With most filters in use today, a carrier-frequency error of 20 cycles or less will give satisfactory voice reproduction. However, at an error of 50 cycles the distortion will readily become apparent; and when the error is greater than 50 cycles, the distortion increases so rapidly that the intelligibility is seriously impaired. It is quite likely that carrier-frequency control requirements will become more stringent as filters with better skirt selectivities are developed.

The exact circuitry of the generator will depend on the frequency at which the single-sideband signal is generated, and on the type of balanced modulator used. The low-frequency carrier generator (for operation in the 20- to 50-kc region) will be discussed first.

LOW-FREQUENCY GENERATORS

The simplest method of producing a balanced RF signal is to use a push-pull oscillator, as shown in Fig. 5-1. This oscillator is very stable and reliable when carefully constructed from quality components. In addition to a very high-Q, toroidal coil L1 has a restricted external magnetic field which aids in preventing carrier signal leakage. All fixed capacitors are silver mica dielectrics and have at least a ±5% tolerance. Variable capacitor C1 is a double-bearing miniature type with a maximum capacitance of about 250 mmf. The oscillator tube is a 12AU7 with a plate voltage of 105 volts regulated.

This experimental generator (with the exception of the 12AU7 and its socket) was contained in an aluminum box about 4″ × 4″ × 4″, and the components were rigidly mounted on heavy-duty terminal strips. A number of tests over a long period indicated that the frequency drift (after warm-up) would remain well within the 50-cycle drift limit. A single-sideband (SSB) transmitter using this carrier generator was operated for over a year; yet the generator required only occasional readjustment.

Instead of a toroidal coil, L1 may be a slug-tuned TV width coil adjustable to 5 mh. Variable capacitor C1 is not required when an adjustable coil is used. In this case, a silver mica, 300-mmf capacitor should be connected directly across the coil. The coil slug is then adjusted for an oscillator frequency of 50 kc.

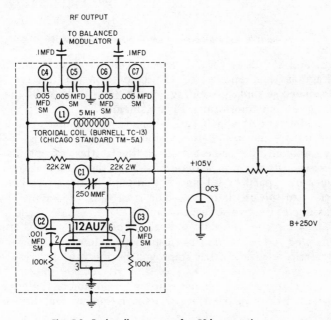

Fig. 5-1. Push-pull generator for 50-kc operation.

Fig. 5-2 shows the 60-kc carrier generator used in the Hammarlund HX-500 transmitter. The oscillator circuit is a tapped-coil Hartley type, with the tank-circuit capacitance to inductance ratio being large in order to minimize any changes in the interelectrode capacitances of the 6AU6 (due to power-supply variations or an aging tube). The oscillator circuit proper uses the cathode, control grid, and screen grid of the 6AU6. The plate circuit is electron-coupled to the oscillator section to further improve the frequency stability. The primary of output transformer T1 has a high Q to reduce the harmonic content of the output signal and to improve its waveform. A 33K load resistor, connected across the primary, further improves the wave-

69

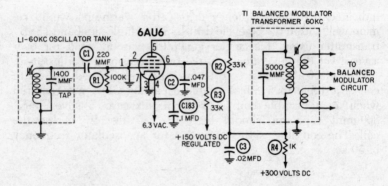

Fig. 5-2. 60-kc generator used in Hammarlund HX-500.

form and stabilizes the RF output voltage. The balanced RF voltage is then applied to the modulator via the two low-impedance secondary windings of T1. Both 60-kc oscillator coil L1 and output transformer T1 are shielded.

Another circuit which can be made very stable at low and medium frequencies is the Colpitts oscillator in Fig. 5-3. It has essentially the same circuit as the Hartley, except that the effective cathode tap is determined by the ratio between the values of capacitors C1 and C2 instead of by an actual connection to the oscillator coil. The total tank capacitance is the net value of the two series capacitors.

The Colpitts circuit is generally free from spurious oscillations and other waveform distortions. However, the output waveform may be further improved by the use of a resistor in the cathode circuit, instead of the RF choke shown. Since cathode current does not pass through a portion of the oscillator coil (as it does in the Hartley), the frequency stability of the

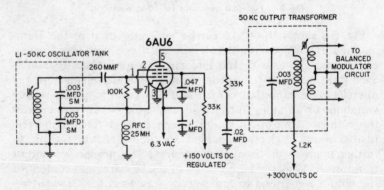

Fig. 5-3. 50-kc generator using Colpitts oscillator.

tank circuit will be much better. In the design of commercial transmitters, it is common practice to use special coil forms and material (as well as fixed capacitors and other components) with specified temperature characteristics.

The stability of any self-controlled oscillator will depend as much (if not more) on the mechanical design than on the selection of the oscillator circuit itself. It is almost impossible to determine the relative stabilities of oscillators from their circuit diagrams alone. The secrets of stability are contained in the component specifications and the mechanical design. In any oscillator,—either fixed or variable in frequency—a high degree of stability is usually attained only after many tedious experiments and measurements have been completed.

Hartley and Colpitts oscillators normally operate best when the feedback tap is at about one-third of the distance from the bottom of the coil. With stock slug-tuned coils, however, it may be somewhat difficult to position the feedback tap for proper oscillation. In the Colpitts circuit, no physical connection is required; in effect, the electrical tap is moved up or down by varying the capacitance ratio between the two tank capacitors.

MEDIUM-FREQUENCY GENERATORS

The carrier generator for use in the 200- to 500-kc region generally has the same circuitry as the oscillators just described. The higher the frequency, however, the more pronounced the factors which cause instability become. Although some manufacturers have used self-controlled oscillators for generation in the 450- to 460-kc region, the tendency is toward precision crystal-controlled oscillators.

In any variable-frequency oscillator circuit, the tube- and stray-circuit capacitance effects should be minimized and the frequency should then be determined by the tuned-circuit LC components. From an electrical point of view, the series-tuned Colpitts in Fig. 5-4 offers excellent isolation of the tube capacitance—and its associated effects—from the series-resonant tuned circuit. Capacitors C4 and C5 are of such a value that their reactance at the oscillation frequency will be 40 to 100 ohms. In the 450- to 460-kc region, C4 and C5 will range from .003 to .005 mfd. The main purpose of this circuit configuration is to present a very low impedance (in parallel with the tube input capacitance) at the oscillation frequency. Since the tube has an input capacitance of only a few micromicrofarads when connected across a 1500- to 2500-mmf capacitance, the net effect of tube capacitance changes on the tuned circuit will be negligible.

71

At the LC resonant frequency, the internal impedance will be minimum. Thus, maximum RF current will flow, creating an appreciable voltage drop across C4 and C5. The drop across C4 is applied to the grid as excitation, and the amplified output across C5 is applied to the cathode as driving power to maintain oscillation. These LC components will have approximately the same values as those in a parallel-resonant circuit of the same frequency. The coil, however, must have a high Q. C4 and C5 would have the largest values that will permit oscillations over the entire tuning range of C1. The larger the values of C4 and C5, the smaller the effect of the tube capacitance on the oscillating circuit. Therefore, the better the oscillator stability will be with respect to any tube variations.

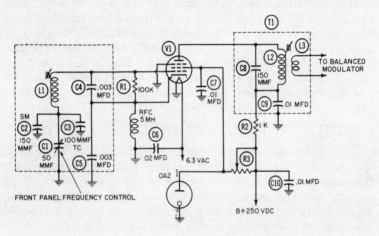

Fig. 5-4. Series-tuned Colpitts suitable for 450- to 460-kc generator.

Larger capacitances require an oscillator tube with a high mutual conductance. The preferred types are the 6AH6 and 6CB6, in that order. If tubes such as the 6AU6 or 6BA6 are used, the values of C4 and C5 must be reduced in order to sustain oscillation. Accordingly, the frequency stability of the oscillator, with respect to tube variations, will also be reduced.

The power output of the series-tuned Colpitts varies rapidly with changes in the LC ratio. In fact, oscillations may cease if the resonant circuit capacitance is too low. It is desirable to limit the frequency range of the oscillator by making C1 just large enough to tune about 3 or 4 kc higher and lower than the center frequency of the filter bandpass response. In addition, a fixed capacitor (C2 in Fig. 5-4) should be paralleled across C1, to maintain sufficient minimum capacitance to sustain oscil-

72

lation. The value of C2 depends on that of temperature-compensating capacitor C3. In turn, the capacitance and thermal characteristics of C3 are determined by the amount and type of temperature compensation required. Between 450 and 460 kc, the minimum capacitance usually is 200 to 250 mmf, provided the coil has a reasonably high Q.

Construction

The mounting and location of LC components is an important factor in the over-all frequency stability of the oscillator. In several experimental oscillators, the best frequency stability was obtained by placing the components (enclosed by the dotted lines in Fig. 5-4) inside the 4″ × 4″ × 4″ aluminum box. The box was then mounted in one corner of the main generator chassis, flush against the front panel. Tuning capacitor C1 was mounted in a ⅜-inch hole drilled through both the side of the box and the panel. C1 must be small in size and ruggedly constructed. The VHF type of tuning capacitor with thick plates is recommended, but the single-bearing type is satisfactory if the capacitor is of good construction.

Coil L1 is mounted in the center of the aluminum box. Not only should it be equidistant from all four sides, but also equally spaced between the top and bottom plates of the box. The coil should be rigidly mounted on the bottom of the box (and chassis), but should not be fastened to the sides. In other words, the coil should be mounted in such a manner that any expansion or contraction of the box will cause the coil to move as a unit. If the coil mounting places a torque on the form or windings during normal expansion or contraction of the metal, the oscillator warm-up frequency drift will be excessive, and temperature compensation of the circuit may be more difficult to achieve. The exact mechanical mounting of L1 will depend on the type of coil used. There are a few iron-core 2.5-mh RF chokes available which are suitable for use as L1. These generally have a ceramic form tapped for a small-diameter machine-screw thread. If the end of the tapped form is placed directly on the bottom plate, the proximity of the plate may reduce the Q of the coil. The use of a small porcelain stand-off insulator is recommended. However, the porcelain will act as a heat insulator and increase the warm-up time somewhat. The J. W. Miller "6300," (a high-Q ferrite-rod antenna coil) is excellent for use as L1 except that it may be found somewhat difficult to mount rigidly.

Capacitors C2, C4, and C5 should be mounted on a heavy-duty terminal board securely fastened to the bottom plate of the box. Temperature-compensating capacitor C3 is generally placed across the terminals of variable C1. In some circuits, more than one capacitor, with different temperature-coefficient characteristics, may be required. The use of temperature-compensating components will be covered later.

The flexible copper braid connecting C1 to L1, and L1 to C4, should have a slight amount of slack. If it is too rigid, its expansion and contraction will affect the frequency stability of the oscillator.

Once the component values of the resonant circuit and the temperature compensation are both correct, the top plate of the box should be secured along all four edges with ¼-inch self-tapping screws spaced about a half inch apart. The screws must be tightened down to prevent air circulation through the box and over the sensitive frequency-determining components.

The tube socket, and the terminal strip for mounting R1 and the RF choke, are mounted on the main chassis. The socket should be at least two inches away from the aluminum box, to minimize heating effects. The leads from the tuned circuit to the cathode and grid should be made of flexible, insulated hook-up wire and not be too taut nor dressed along the metal chassis. Miniature feedthrough insulators should be used for the connections through the metal box and chassis.

The tuned output transformer (T1) is a good-quality, 455-kc, IF replacement type. Its regular primary winding is coil L2. The secondary winding has been removed and coil L3, which consists of 40 to 50 turns of No. 30 enameled d.c.c. copper wire, is random-wound around the form, about a half inch below the "cold" end of the tuned primary. With certain types of balanced modulators (the shunt modulator of Fig. 3-11, for example), it may be necessary to center-tap L3 in order to obtain equal RF output voltages. The use of a bifilar winding at L3 usually gives the best balance between the two RF output voltages.

In most recent amateur single-sideband transmitters, the carrier generator uses a crystal-controlled oscillator. The crystals are manufactured to precise tolerances and, when used in the proper circuitry, will have negligible frequency drift.

Nearly all crystals are manufactured by the same process. The selected quartz is first X-rayed to determine the desired type of cut and hence the correct cutting angle. The quartz is then cut (with diamond saws) into thin wafer slices, which are diced into various sizes and rough-lapped. As the process continues, each wafer is fine-lapped to the approximate frequency desired, and then etched and polished to the exact frequency. Finally, the finished crystal is mounted in a holder.

74

Pressure-type crystals are mounted between two stainless-steel electrodes, which hold the crystal by its four corners. An air space is provided between the crystal and electrodes, to permit the crystal to oscillate freely. The crystal and electrodes are placed into the holder and held in position by a spring. The holder is then sealed with a neoprene gasket and the nameplate applied.

Type HC6/U crystals are gold- or silver-plated on both sides and polished to a high gloss. (The plating acts as an electrode.) The crystal is mounted in the holder and cemented on each side to springs. The case is then hermetically sealed in a vacuum or is filled with nitrogen or helium. Unless abused electrically or physically, today's crystals will retain their accuracy almost indefinitely. However, to insure that this accuracy is maintained, and to prevent damage to the crystal, the manufacturer will usually recommend specific oscillator circuitry for the various crystals.

Table 5-1.
Frequency changes versus input capacitance.

	10 MMF	20 MMF	32 MMF	50 MMF
	2,000.200	2,000.060	2,000.000	1,999.950
Crystal	3,000.600	3,000.200	3,000.000	2,999.800
Frequency	4,001.000	4,000.400	4,000.000	3,999.700
in	7,003.300	7,001.200	7,000.000	6,999.200
Kilocycles	14,008.100	14,003.100	14,000.000	13,998.000

Note: The input capacitance of the crystal test oscillator is standardized at 32 mmf.

The input capacitance of the circuit affects the frequency at which the crystal will oscillate. Any added capacitance lowers the frequency, as shown in Table 5-1. During manufacture, all modern crystals are tested in an oscillator circuit having an input capacitance of 32 mmf (included in this value are the input capacitance of the tube and the stray capacitance of the circuit). The oscillator frequency can be changed, if desired, by changing the input capacitance of the circuit. Most carrier generator circuits are designed to present a capacitance of about 32 mmf to the crystal. In such circuits, the crystals should have a frequency tolerance of .005%.

Crystal Oscillators

The oscillator circuit shown in Fig. 5-5 is suitable for crystals having fundamental frequencies in the region from 80 to 800 kc. The circuit will give satisfactory performance with either army-surplus FT-241-A low-frequency crystals or the more re-

75

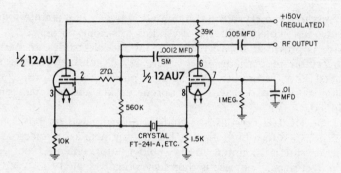

Fig. 5-5. Oscillator for 80- to 800-kc crystals.

cent hermetically sealed types. As you can see, the basic circuit is essentially a multivibrator. A 12AU7 is used here, although the circuit performs well with other double triodes such as 12AX7 or 12AT7. The plate voltage must be kept within 100 to 150 volts. Where a balanced RF output voltage is required, the oscillator signal may be applied to a resistance-coupled RF phase-inverter stage. The balanced RF voltages for the modulator are then taken from the plate and cathode circuits of the phase inverter.

The crystal oscillator shown in Fig. 5-6 is similar to that used in the carrier generators of commercial transmitters. The circuit is a modified Pierce oscillator in which the screen of the tube acts as the anode of the crystal oscillator. With the constants shown, satisfactory performance will be obtained by using 70- to 500-kc crystals. Variable capacitor C1, normally a small air-dielectric trimmer, permits the frequency to be raised or lowered about 20 to 30 cycles. This adjustment is useful for placing the carrier at the precise point on the filter response slope specified by the manufacturer. In circuits where two crystals are

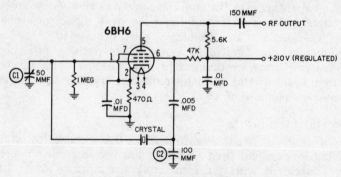

Fig. 5-6. Oscillator for 70- to 500-kc. crystals.

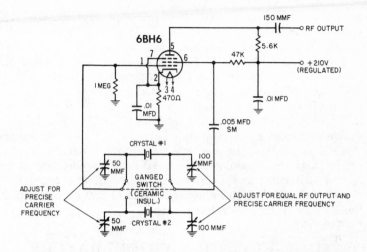

Fig. 5-7. Crystal-controlled carrier generator for symmetrical-bandpass, single-sideband filters.

used (for sideband selection), each crystal should have its own trimmer. A practical carrier generator for use in the 450 to 460-kc region is shown in Fig. 5-7. It features sideband selection and individual frequency-adjustment trimmers, and is designed for use with filters having a symmetrical bandpass response.

Fig. 5-8 shows a dual-crystal-controlled carrier generator like the one in the Collins 32S-1 SSB transmitter. The basic circuit is a Pierce oscillator, and the crystal is connected between the control and screen grids. A 6U8A tube is used,—the pentode section serving as the oscillator, and the triode (not shown) as an audio cathode follower in the speech-amplifier

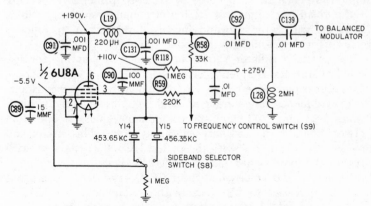

Fig. 5-8. Carrier generator and sideband-selector circuit.

77

section of the transmitter. The precision crystals are type CR46/U'S in HC6/U holders and have a frequency tolerance of .01%. The specified frequency is 453.65 kc for the Y14 crystal, and 456.35 kc for the Y15. These frequencies indicate that the mechanical filter in the 32S-1 transmitter has a bandwidth of 2.7 kc at −20 db down, and 2.1 kc at the top of the curve.

The circuit in Fig. 5-8 contains a low-pass RF filter network in its output circuit. This network (C91, C131, and L19) is designed to pass the crystal fundamentals, but to attenuate any carrier harmonics in the plate circuit before the signal is applied to the balanced modulator. This will aid considerably in reducing distortion and spurious responses in the transmitted signal. Coil L19 has an inductance value of 220 μh and capacitors C91 and C131 are .001 mfd each.

HIGH-FREQUENCY GENERATORS

Carrier generators designed for operation in the 2- to 30-mc region invariably have crystal-controlled oscillators with fundamental-frequency crystals up to about 15 mc and the overtone type *above* 15 mc. At this time, only a few single-sideband transmitters are being manufactured that use filters and carrier generators in the high-frequency region. The recent Johnson *Invader* transmitter generates a SSB signal at 9 mc, and the Hallicrafters HT-32A generates one at 4.95 mc (which, however, is converted to 9 mc before being heterodyned to the operating frequency).

HF single-sideband generators offer some very definite advantages, particularly in reducing circuit complexity and over-all size of the equipment. Up to this time, there has been only slight difference in cost between systems, principally because of the relatively high cost of high-frequency sideband filters. However, with wide use and improved production techniques their cost will undoubtedly be reduced.

The crystal oscillator shown in Fig. 5-9 is suitable for use with fundamental-frequency crystals in the 1- to 16-mc region. The input capacitance of this circuit—when the proper constants for the frequency range are used—will be approximately 32 mmf. Tables 5-2A and 5-2B show the component values for operation between 1 and 3 mc and between 3 and 16 mc. This circuit will give good performance with the plated HC6/U crystals, or with pressure-mounted types like the FT-243. Plate voltage should be limited to 100 volts when the HC6/U crystals are used, but may be increased to 250 volts without damaging an FT-243. As a general rule, however, it is advisable to operate the oscil-

78

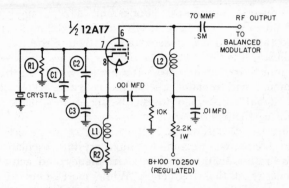

Fig. 5-9. Oscillator circuit for 1- to 16-mc crystals.

lator at the lowest plate voltage consistent with the required level of output power.

Fig. 5-10 shows the carrier-generator circuit of the Johnson *Invader* SSB transmitter. Its basic oscillator circuit is similar to that of Fig. 5-9, except that the component values have been selected for optimum performance at the carrier frequencies. Each section of the 12AU7 serves as a separate crystal oscillator. Sideband selection is accomplished by switch SW3B, which is controlled from the front panel. From a design standpoint, the

Table 5-2.
Component values for 1 to 16 mc fundamental frequency crystal oscillator circuit.

1 to 3 mc	3 to 16 mc
R1—1 megohm	R1—.1 megohm
R2—3,900 ohms	R2—330 ohms
C1—22 mmf	C1—22 mmf
C2—12 mmf	C2—12 mmf
C3—75 mmf	C3—75 mmf
L1—7.5 mh	L1—5 mh
L2—5 mh	L2—2.5 mh
(A)	(B)

method of carrier and sideband frequency selection is unique. The two crystals and associated components are permanently connected into the oscillator grid circuits. Cathode RF choke L1 is common to both oscillators; and the grid of each oscillator is returned, through an 820K resistor, to SW3B. This switch is returned to the—150-volt supply in such a manner that, when one oscillator is operating, the other will be inoperative due to the high negative bias applied to its grid. In this manner, either crystal frequency may be selected without disturbing the elec-

79

trical connections in the oscillator circuit. This arrangement also has the advantage that C1 and C10 (the 3- to 32-mmf trimmers) may be permanently connected across their respective crystals and adjusted for the precise carrier frequencies required. Since the trimmers are isolated from the mode switch, the frequency adjustments will remain precise much longer. The generator output signal is coupled to the balanced modulator through 100-mmf capacitor C5.

During the past few years, the use of overtone crystals has become increasingly common. Such crystals oscillate at the overtone rather than fundamental frequency and actually generate energy at that frequency. While most standard crystals (such as the FT-243) can be made to operate on their overtone frequencies, the overtone crystal is designed for this type of operation only. The overtone (or third or fifth mode) of a

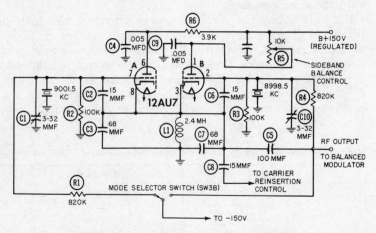

Fig. 5-10. Johnson INVADER carrier-generator circuit.

crystal is not the *exact* third or fifth harmonic of the fundamental, but rather a frequency which may differ from the harmonic by several kc. All such crystals are calibrated at their overtone frequencies, and must be used in an oscillator whose plate circuit is tuned to that frequency. Most amateurs do not consider the overtone crystal a precision frequency-control device. However, these crystals are currently being used in some 2.5- and 5-mc laboratory frequency standards. At the present time, no overtone crystals are known to be used in carrier generators of commercial SSB transmitters. However, as the development of higher-frequency sideband filters continues, it is quite likely that overtone oscillators may be used extensively for this purpose.

A simple oscillator circuit—suitable for overtone crystals from 10 to 60 mc—is shown in Fig. 5-11. Resonant tank circuit L1 and C1 is turned to the overtone frequency of the crystal. The tube most generally used in this circuit is the 12AT7, although the circuit will give good performance with the 12BH7 or the triode section of a 6U8. Plate voltage should not be greater than 125 volts and, if possible, should be regulated at 75 or 105 volts by using a VR tube. The grid resistor is determined by the type of crystal used; its value should be sufficiently high that stable oscillation is obtained, but not so high that the RF voltage across the crystal will be excessive. If excessive RF voltage is developed, large amplitudes of crystal vibration will occur which, in turn,

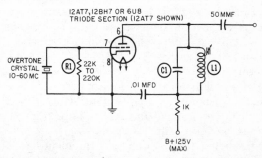

Fig. 5-11. Oscillator circuit for 10- to 60-mc overtone crystals.

will cause frequency drift and heating of the crystal element. At a certain high value of RF voltage (depending on the type of crystal used), the crystal element will fracture and stop oscillating. When the plate voltage is regulated at 105 volts, a value of about 0.1 meg for grid resistor R1 will be satisfactory for most overtone crystals. The power output from this simple overtone oscillator is very low; so the loading of the output circuit must not be heavy. If an appreciable RF voltage swing is required from the oscillator, it should be followed by a tuned RF amplifier using a miniature pentode (6AU6).

GENERATOR DESIGN PRECAUTIONS

The ideal carrier generator for a single-sideband communications system would not only provide an exact signal of the required frequency and amplitude, but would maintain these characteristics indefinitely. The frequency and amplitude of the signal should be of the proper values at the instant power is applied to the equipment, and these values should not change due to heating effects, time, variations in the load during modula-

81

tion, or variations in the supply voltages. The RF signal should appear only in that portion of the circuit where it performs a useful function. Unfortunately, no such perfect generator exists, but the design engineer must constantly strive for this ideal.

Frequency Drift

The greatest single problem in carrier generator design is frequency drift, both "short term" and "long term." Short-term drift—as the term implies— is most generally a rapid change of frequency within a relatively short time (a good example is the drift that takes place during the oscillator warmup.) In commercial equipment, this drift is almost always specified as "after warm-up," with no time given. However, the warm-up period is generally regarded as the first 30 minutes after the equipment is turned on in a room with normal temperature. In a typical SSB receiver, the specified frequency stability— after warm-up—is 100 cycles.

"Long-term" frequency drift is the gradual change in the frequency of an oscillator over a longer period of time—possibly days, weeks, or months. In specifying long-term drift, it is assumed that the equipment has reached operating temperature and that the short-term drift has ceased.

Most of the better single-sideband equipment has some means (usually a movable hairline) by which the tuning-dial calibration accuracy may be restored. This does not mean that the engineer has been negligent in the design of the frequency-generating portions of the equipment; it simply indicates he is facing the fact that there will be some change in the frequency of the oscillator over long periods. However, the main efforts of the design engineer are directed toward determining the best means of minimizing this frequency change.

Carrier frequency drift in amateur or commercial SSB transmitters is evidenced by a deterioration of the speech quality. In general, the better the shape factor, of the filter, the more stringent will be the stability requirements of the generator. If the carrier frequency drifts away from the filter bandpass, the speech quality will become very shrill. Excessive drift causes the midrange voice frequencies to be lost and, as a result, the transmitted signal may not be intelligible. If the carrier frequency drifts in the direction of the bandpass, the upper midrange voice frequencies will be attenuated by the filter and cause the transmitted signal to sound very bassy. Should the carrier actually be inside the bandpass of the filter, the undesired sideband will not be completely suppressed, and unless the carrier to the balanced modulator has been completely suppressed, some of the carrier components will be present in the transmitted signal. This carrier component, and the two unequal sidebands will combine in the transmitted signal to give an effective angle or phase modulation, in addition to the reduced carrier AM. In some transmitters, the presence of the carrier may even cause the idling dissipation limits of the linear amplifiers to be exceeded.

Crystal-controlled oscillators are recommended in amateur single-sideband transmitters. While precision crystals may be somewhat expensive, any deviation of the carrier frequency over the useful life of the transmitter will be negligible, if reasonable care is used in the generator design. The oscillator circuit will depend on the type of crystal used and its frequency. However, if we wish to build a crystal-controlled carrier generator for use with a Collins mechanical filter, the circuit shown in Fig. 5-7 will be suitable.

Before the two necessary crystals can be purchased, the frequencies of the −20-db filter attenuation points must be known. This information is packed in the box with the individual filter. In general, it is advisable to order crystals with a frequency tolerance of .005%. In Fig. 5-7, the individual trimmers will usually permit the crystals to be adjusted to the exact point on the filter slope specified by the manufacturer. The FT-241-A crystal may be used if its fundamental frequency is sufficiently close to the specified point on the filter slope. However, it is much easier to lower the frequency of the FT-241-A than to increase it. If C1 and C2 are increased to an approximate maximum of 200 mmf and C3 and C4 are increased to about 370 mmf, it is possible to lower the fundamental frequency of some FT-241-A crystals by as much as 50 to 100 cycles. When these capacitance values are further increased, the crystals may either oscillate sluggishly or not at all. In most instances when sufficient FT-241-A crystals are available, it is possible to select crystals which are 20 to 50 cycles lower than the nominal fundamental frequency indicated by their markings. The crystal frequencies can then be lowered another 50 to 100 cycles by adjusting the values of the trimmers and fixed capacitors.

Crystal oscillators, particularly those which use low-frequency crystals, present no serious frequency-drift problems. In general, if the proper circuit is used for the type of crystal involved, and if the plate and screen voltages are kept as low as possible, any deviation from the nominal crystal frequency will be negligible.

Frequency drift in self-controlled oscillators is most generally due to changes in the electrical characteristics of the components. The most common cause of such changes is distortion of their physical dimensions by temperature variations. These effects can be minimized by selecting components with known temperature characteristics, and by careful electrical and mechanical design of the circuitry. In general, an oscillator circuit should be selected in which variations in the tube interelectrode capacitances will have little or no effect on the resonant circuit. The conventional Colpitts circuit, and also its series-tuned version, are excellent for use as a variable-frequency carrier-generator oscillator. Since the interelectrode capacitances of a vacuum tube vary with changes in the electrode potentials, the plate and screen voltages must be held at a constant value. Voltage regulation of these potentials is most easily accomplished by using a miniature gaseous VR tube such as the OA2 or OB2. While the selection of a proper circuit is important, most design problems will be centered around the components themselves and in the physical construction of the oscillator itself.

Although the carrier generator is usually an integral part of the main chassis, it is generally considered good practice to design this oscillator as a complete subassembly. Most carrier generators will be completely shielded. The actual physical dimensions of the subassembly are usually determined by the space available on the main chassis.

In commercial design work it is customary, after the physical dimensions of the generator subassembly have been determined, to build a laboratory model for tests and measurements. This preliminary model is then subjected to the environmental conditions likely to be encountered in normal operation. The frequency drift, both short- and long-term, is carefully recorded. Once a series of measurements have been recorded, the data obtained will usually indicate which components are responsible for the drift. From this point on, the general procedure consists of replacing components, changing the layout, or adding temperature-compensating components in various parts of the circuit. When a change of any kind is made, another series of measurements are recorded. It is not at all unusual for a design engineer to spend several weeks on a relatively simple oscillator before it is ready for production. At the end of this time, the schematics of the preliminary model and the finished product may be identical, but the characteristics of the components in each may be entirely different.

Most of the frequency drift in the self-controlled oscillator is caused by changes in the physical properties of the tank coil form and in the mechanical structure of the variable

84

tuning capacitor. The ordinary *Bakelite* and porcelain coil forms sold in most parts houses will change their dimensions to a considerable degree. If the carrier frequency is 50 kc or lower, the best type of coil to use is a miniature toroid. However, with a carrier of approximately 455 kc, the high-Q ferrite, loop-stick coil will be more suitable.

In order to maintain its high-Q, the ferrite-rod coil should be kept away from the metal shielding, because it is quite sensitive to any expansion in the shielding due to heat. The shield box should be constructed of fairly heavy-gauge aluminum. Unless the box seams and the top and bottom plates maintain a good electrical connection during expansion of the metal, the coil field will be disturbed and cause the oscillator frequency suddenly to increase from time to time. This condition can usually be eliminated by securing the top and bottom plates firmly to the sides of the box.

The coil should be mounted by one side only, so that any expansion of the box will cause the coil to move as a single unit. If the coil is mounted at more than one point, the expansion of the metal will distort the coil and the oscillator will tend to change suddenly in frequency during operation. The coil tuning slug should *not* be cemented in place. In a number of experiments with oscillators operating in the 455-kc region, it was found that application of coil cement to the windings and the ferrite slug caused a rapid increase in the frequency drift.

Most self-controlled oscillators tend to drift lower, (rather than higher) in frequency as the components of the frequency-determining circuit heat up. An oscillator that drifts lower in frequency is said to have a *positive temperature coefficient*. In order to stabilize the oscillator, it will be necessary to introduce some component into the resonant circuit which, as it becomes heated, will cause the frequency to increase. Such a component is said to have a *negative temperature coefficient*. If the rate of frequency change caused by the negative-coefficient component is exactly equal to the normal positive-coefficient component drift, then the two coefficients will balance (cancel), and the oscillator frequency will remain constant.

The most common negative temperature-coefficient components are small ceramic capacitors. Before an oscillator can be compensated for frequency drift, the rate of drift must be known. The usual procedure is to measure the amount of frequency change at the end of the first 30-minute period after the oscillator is turned on. The oscillator is then turned off and allowed to cool down, and the temperature-compensating capacitor

85

placed in the tuned circuit. The negative-coefficient component must be placed where its temperature will rise and fall at the same rate as the temperature of the other components of the tuned circuit. In the circuit of Fig. 5-4, for example, capacitor C3 may actually consist of two or three temperature-compensating units with different negative-coefficient rates. Actually, the best point in the tuned circuit to begin the compensation process is at the variable tuning capacitor.

In general, best results are obtained by adding the negative-coefficient capacitors in steps of 10 mmf each. A suitable capacitor for this purpose is the Centralab TCN-10. This small ceramic capacitor is soldered across the terminals of the trimmer, and the oscillator placed in normal operation for 30 minutes. At the end of that period, the oscillator frequency is accurately measured, and the amount of drift compared with that of the uncompensated oscillator. If the drift is still in the low-frequency direction, more negative-coefficient compensation is indicated. Another TCN-10 should be connected in parallel with the variable tuning capacitor, and the oscillator operated for another 30 minutes.

It is advisable to make long-term drift measurements over hours or days. However, if the carrier generator attains normal operating temperatures at the end of 15 to 20 minutes, the frequency drift will generally be negligible. Some experimental oscillators have actually drifted less than 50 cycles over a period of several days.

Chapter 6

Speech Amplifiers
and Filters

Compared with the complex circuitry used for carrier and sideband suppression, the audio amplifiers used in single-sideband transmitters are relatively simple. Since single-sideband transmission requires very little power from the audio system, the entire speech amplifier may consist of nothing more elaborate than a single pentode. In most commercial single-sideband transmitters, however, special circuitry and possibly a number of stages are employed in the speech amplifier, because the voice signal is also used to automatically operate relays which control the transmitter and receiver. The actual design of the speech circuit will depend on the type of balanced modulator used and, to some extent, on the bandpass characteristics of the single-sideband filter. Also, the speech-amplifier circuits of the phase-shift type of transmitter will differ from those of a filter-type transmitter. Before either speech system can be successfully designed, it will be necessary to clearly understand the basic principles involved.

AMPLIFIER FREQUENCY RESPONSE

In a single-sideband transmitter designed for voice transmission, the AF response of the speech amplifier is generally limited to a bandpass of less than 3,000 cycles. In voice communications, the primary objective is to attain the most effective means of transmitting the intelligence. This means that the transmitted message must be received and understood in spite of adverse conditions like noise or interference. Such other considerations as fidelity of tone quality of the voice are definitely secondary to the intelligibility of the signal. The voice frequencies which contribute most to intelligibility are those between 500 and 2,000 cycles. Other frequencies greatly contribute to the fidelity, but add very little to the intelligibility. In most commercial single-sideband transmitters, however, the audio-fre-

87

quency response is not abruptly cut off at these two points, because to do so would make the transmitted voice signal flat and monotonous. It is customary, in speech-amplifier design, to gradually attenuate the frequencies from 500 to 300 cycles, and to sharply attenuate those below 300 cycles. At the high-frequency end of the amplifier, the frequencies from about 2,500 to 3,000 cycles are gradually attenuated and those above 3,000 cycles are rapidly attenuated. The graph in Fig. 6-1 shows the speech-amplifier response curve of a typical single-sideband transmitter.

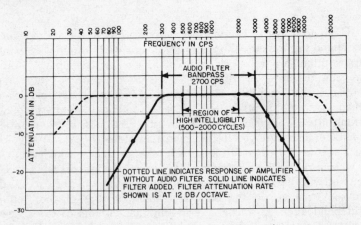

Fig. 6-1. Speech-amplifier frequency response, with and without filter.

Fortunately a high degree of intelligibility can be maintained in a relatively narrow band of audio frequencies, since the width of the RF channel is directly proportional to the width of the AF bandpass of the speech-amplifier circuit. It is desirable to keep the channel width as narrow as possible, in order to reduce unnecessary interference with adjacent-channel stations. Current practice is to regard as broad any single-sideband signal which occupies a channel width of more than 3,000 cycles.

As shown in Fig. 6-2, the channel width of the single-sideband signal is determined largely by the bandwidth of the sideband filter. Broadness of the transmitted signal can also be caused by distortion products generated during frequency conversion, or by poor linearity in the RF amplifiers following the sideband generator. This problem will be thoroughly discussed in a later chapter on linear-amplifier design.

The AF response of a typical resistance-coupled Class-A amplifier is shown at A in Fig. 6-2, and the response of a typical single-sideband RF filter, appears at B in Fig. 6-2. The curve in Fig. 6-2

88

at C represents the response of the AF signal recovered after passing through the sideband filter.

At first glance there apparently is little reason to be concerned about the audio-frequency response of the speech amplifier, since the sideband filter will automatically cut off the undesired frequencies in the transmitted signal. While this is true to some extent, no sideband filter is perfect and some may actually respond to frequencies outside their normal bandpass. Today's

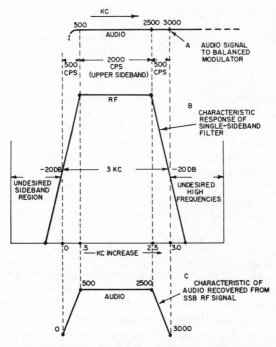

Fig. 6-2. Attenuation of high- and low-frequency audio response by single-sideband filter.

filters are precision devices, but in order to do their work efficiently, the associated circuits must also be properly designed.

In a filter-type single-sideband transmitter, it is desirable to eliminate all frequencies below 200 cycles. Most of these speech components do not contribute to intelligibility; moreover, their very high energy characteristics tend to overload the linear RF amplifiers of the transmitter. Once these useless speech components have been removed, the transmitter will then be able to concentrate most of its power capabilities on those portions of the speech spectrum essential to intelligibility. In actual performance, the removal of the lower frequencies will give a 3- to 6-db improvement in transmitter power. In order to obtain the same increase in performance when these low frequencies are transmitted, it would be necessary to double or quadruple the transmitter output power. Transmission of the low frequencies also makes the undesired sideband suppression more difficult.

AF BANDPASS FILTERS

The easiest way to eliminate the low frequencies in a speech amplifier is to reduce the values of the coupling capacitors between the plate and grid circuits of the various stages. The high frequencies may then be reduced by shunting them to ground through a small capacitor connected from grid to ground. When the associated plate and grid load resistors are also of the proper values, the combination of the R and C components will form an elementary audio-bandpass filter. The main difficulty with this method of shaping the audio response is that the load-resistor values required for proper filter action are not necessarily correct for the plates and grids. The result is usually a compromise, and the bandpass characteristics of the speech circuits will be somewhat less than ideal. While arrangements of this type are generally satisfactory as long as the skirt selectivity of the single-sideband filter is good, the design of a better R-C bandpass filter is not difficult.

The bandpass filter, as the name implies, is designed to pass all frequencies between two specified points in the audio spectrum. Frequencies higher and lower than those included within the bandpass are sharply attenuated. Let's assume we wish to design a filter that will pass all frequencies between 300 and 3,000 cycles, but attenuate all others. The graph in Fig. 6-3 shows the characteristic response of an audio filter suitable for use in the speech circuits of a single-sideband transmitter.

A bandpass filter may be composed of either of the two basic R-C filter networks shown in Fig. 6-4. In network A, X_C is smaller than R at high frequencies; hence, essentially the entire voltage input is delivered to the load. However, as the frequency becomes lower, X_C will equal and eventually become larger than R; and as X_C increases, the output voltage will become progressively lower. At the frequency where X_C is equal to R, the voltage drop across the resistor will be 3 db down from maximum. This is also considered to be the low frequency half-power (or 70% of maximum voltage) point. Frequencies lower than those at the −3-db point will be attenuated at the rate of approximately 6 db per octave.

90

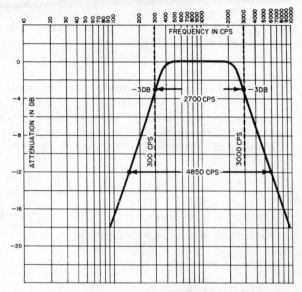

Fig. 6-3. Desirable AF response for speech amplifier.

In network B, capacitor C is essentially an infinite impedance at low frequencies and the output voltage is determined by the value of the resistor alone. As the frequency rises, the opposite now occurs—X_C becomes smaller than R. With each decrease in X_C, the output voltage becomes progressively lower. At the

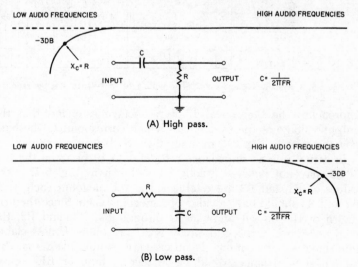

(A) High pass.

(B) Low pass.

Fig. 6-4. Basic R-C AF filter networks.

frequency where X_C is equal to R, the output voltage will be 3 db down from maximum. This is the high-frequency half-power (or 70% of maximum voltage) point. Once again, frequencies higher than those at the −3-db point will be attenuated at the rate of about 6 db per octave.

The attenuation rate of both networks can be increased by using a two-stage network and making the impedance of the output section greater than that of the input section. The response of such a two-stage network, utilizing an impedance step-up ratio of 1 to 10, is shown in Figs. 6-5 and 6-6. Note that the attenuation

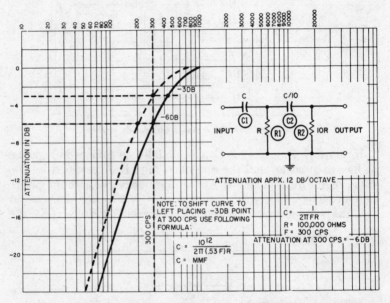

Fig. 6-5. Two-stage high-pass R-C filter with 1:10 impedance step-up ratio.

approaches the theoretical 12-db-per-octave rate and that the output voltage at the frequencies which correspond to the half-power points in Fig. 6-4 are now down 6 db from maximum.

In actual use, an impedance ratio of 1 to 10 between the two filters may not be very practical. As shown in Fig. 6-7, if the values of R1 and R3 are established at 0.1 megohm each, then R2 and R4 should have a value of 1 megohm each. Since the grid return of the output amplifier is through R4, R3, and R2, the total resistance in the grid circuit is 2.1 megohms. Unless elaborate shielding precautions are observed, it is quite likely that this high grid impedance would be subject to hum or RF pickup from other circuits. After numerous calculations and much ex-

92

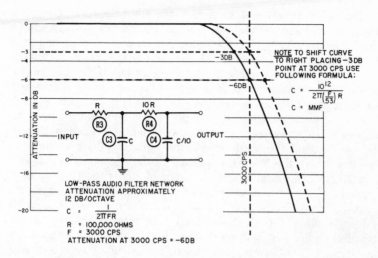

NOTE TO SHIFT CURVE TO RIGHT PLACING −3DB POINT AT 3000 CPS USE FOLLOWING FORMULA:

$$C = \frac{10^{12}}{2\pi \left(\frac{F}{53}\right) R}$$

C = MMF

LOW-PASS AUDIO FILTER NETWORK ATTENUATION APPROXIMATELY 12 DB/OCTAVE

$$C = \frac{1}{2\pi FR}$$

R = 100,000 OHMS
F = 3000 CPS
ATTENUATION AT 3000 CPS = −6DB

Fig. 6-6. Two-stage low-pass R-C filter with 1:10 impedance step-up ratio.

perimental work, it has been determined that an impedance step-up ratio of about one to three is a good compromise between theory and practical application. If we again select 0.1 megohm as the values for R1 and R3, then the values for R2 and R4 will be 0.3 megohm each. The total grid-return resistance of the output-amplifier stage will then be only 0.7 megohm. The attenuation rate, in the directions away from the bandpass will be about 10 db per octave.

In designing a bandpass filter, it must be remembered that the high-pass section will pass all frequencies higher than those of a given point in the spectrum and will attenuate all frequencies below this point. Conversely, the low-pass section will pass all frequencies lower than those of a given point and will attenuate all frequencies above this point. The two points of the audio spectrum generally selected for these frequency limits are 300 and 3,000 cycles.

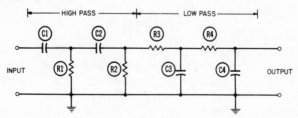

Fig. 6-7. Combination low- and high-pass sections forming a bandpass AF filter.

93

The usual practice is to design the filter in such a manner that the voltage at the filter output terminals will be down approximately 3 db at the 300- and 3,000-cycle points, compared with the maximum voltage value at the center of the bandpass It is desirable to attenuate the frequencies below 300 and above 3,000 cycles at a rate of at least 8 to 10 db per octave. A low-pass or high-pass filter composed of one capacitor and one resistor will have an attenuation of −3 db at the frequency where X_C equals R. In a two-stage filter, the attenuation in each stage will be −3 db, and the total attenuation will be −6 db at the frequency where the X_C of C1 is equal to the resistance of R1, and the X_C of C2 is equal to the resistance of R2. If the RF sideband filter has a rapid skirt-attenuation characteristic, the −6-db attenuation at 300 and 3,000 cycles in the audio circuit may be excessive since the sideband filter will also attenuate the recovered audio. If it is desired to maintain the −3-db attenuation at 300 and 3,000 cycles, and also to retain the 10-db-per-octave attenuation rate for frequencies outside the bandpass, it will be necessary to shift the filter attenuation curves toward the lower and higher frequencies, as shown in Figs. 6-5 and 6-6. A correction factor must now be inserted into the basic formula used for determining the values of capacitors.

The formula for calculating the values of C1 and C2 in the high-pass section becomes:

$$C = \frac{10^{12}}{2\pi\,(0.53f)\,R}$$

where,
C is the capacity in micromicrofarads,
R is the resistance in ohms,
0.53 is the correction factor required to shift the −3-db point,
π is 3.1416 (approx.)

The formula for calculating the values of capacitors C3 and C4 in the low-pass section is:

$$C = \frac{10^{12}}{2\pi\left(\dfrac{f}{0.53}\right)R}$$

The frequency (f) in the formula will be 300 cycles for the high-pass section and 3,000 cycles for the low-pass section. The 0.53 correction factor is a compromise between the calculated theoretical value and the average of data obtained by a number of actual measurements.

It is only necessary to calculate the values of C1 and C3 at their respective frequencies. Since the impedance step-up is one

94

to three, the capacitance of C2 will be one-third the calculated value of C1. Likewise, the value of C4 will equal one-third the calculated value of C3. If R1 and R3 are 0.1 megohm each, then R2 and R4 will each be 0.3 megohm.

In order to obtain proper performance from the filter, the input network should be fed from a relatively low-impedance source such as an AF cathode follower, and the output network must be fed into a high-impedance termination such as the grid of an amplifier tube. No resistance termination of the filter is necessary. Resistors R2, R3, and R4 form the grid return path of the output amplifier tube.

Capacitors C1, C2, C3, and C4, are silver mica types with a tolerance of 5%. Resistors R1, R2, R3, and R4, are 5% tolerance, low-noise 1-watt precision types. All R-C components of the

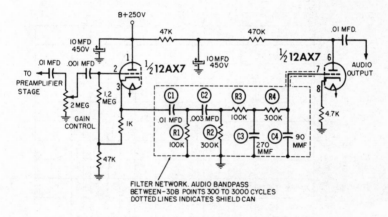

Fig. 6-8. Audio bandpass filter and 12AX7 circuitry.

filter should be mounted on a terminal board, which is then placed inside an aluminum case. The output lead from the junction of R4 and C4 should be loosely shielded up to the point where it connects to the grid terminal of the output amplifier. A complete circuit of a bandpass filter for the audio range from 300 to 3,000 cycles is shown in Fig. 6-8. One triode section of the 12AX7 is the cathode follower and the other is the output amplifier. The speech-amplifier gain control is placed in the grid circuit of the cathode-follower stage.

Burnell S-23197

Fig. 6-9 shows the electrical connections to the Burnell S-23197 bandpass audio filter. This unit has a flat frequency response from 300 to 3,000 cycles and a very rapid attenuation of all other

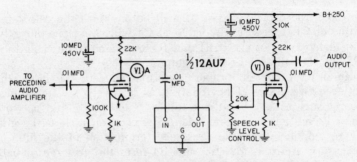

Fig. 6-9. Portion of speech-amplifier circuit, showing electrical connections to Burnell S-23197 audio filter.

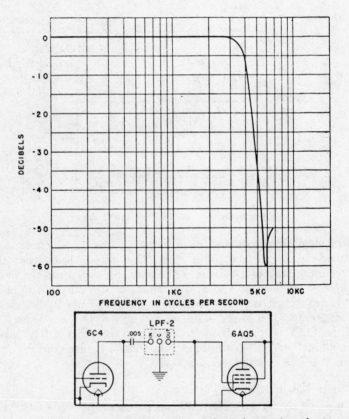

Fig. 6-10. Voltage-attenuation curve and electrical connections of Chicago Standard LPF-2.

frequencies. The necessary 20K-ohm termination of the filter is most conveniently made by using a 20K gain control as shown.

Chicago Standard LPF-1, 2

The electrical connections and frequency-response curve of the Chicago Standard LPF-2 are shown in Fig. 6-10. As the voltage attenuation curve shows, the high-frequency attenuation—beginning at 3,000 cycles—is very rapid. This filter is designed to operate

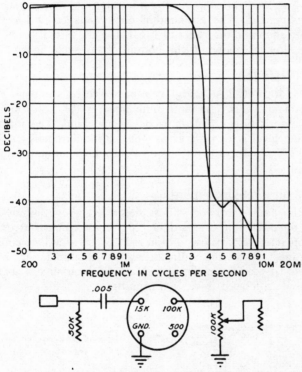

Fig. 6-11. Voltage-attenuation curve and electrical connections of Chicago Standard LPF-1.

out of a source impedance of 50K (plate of a 6C4, 6J5, or equivalent), into a 50K grid. A plate blocking capacitor must be used between the filter input and preceding audio-amplifier stage, since none is incorporated in the filter proper. The insertion loss of the LPF-2 is a low 0.8 db or so. If greater attenuation than that obtainable from a single section is desired or required, two sections can be cascaded. Attenuation of the low frequencies can be controlled by the use of a low-value coupling capacitor between the filter input and the plate of the preceding audio-amplifier tube.

97

The more economical LPF-1 operates out of a 15K source impedance (such as that presented by the plate of a single 6C5, 6J5, or triode-connected 6SJ7) into a 0.1 megohm grid. This filter also has a 500-ohm-impedance output terminal which might permit its use between a speech-amplifier and balanced modulator stage. Use of the filter would eliminate the need for a step-down audio transformer, such as T1 in Fig. 3-11. The plate blocking capacitor, which is required to prevent the DC from saturating the coils in the filter proper, can be selected for attenuation of the low frequencies. The attenuation characteristics of the LPF-1 filter are shown in the curve of Fig. 6-11. The circuit connections for the filter are shown at the bottom of the same figure.

Stancor C2340

The Stancor C-2340 audio bandpass filter has a bandpass of 200 to 3,000 cycles. The input impedance is 10K and the output impedance is either 500 ohms or 0.1 megohm. The maximum operating level is 10 volts across the output terminals. It should be possible to substitute this filter for step-down audio transformer T1 of Fig. 3-11.

Component Requirements

All the audio-frequency filters described above are designed to be operated out of relatively high-impedance sources. The low-impedance filter shown in Fig. 6-12 is very simple to construct and in most cases will require little or no shielding. This filter is used most generally in the speech-amplifier circuits of a phase-shift single-sideband amateur transmitter.

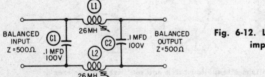

Fig. 6-12. Low-pass filter for low-impedance circuits.

Capacitors C1 and C2 are of a good-quality paper dielectric construction. The working volts rating should be at least 100 volts. The MIL-C-25A subminiature paper capacitors, such as the Sprague types KB104K and KC104K, series CP04, or equivalent, will be satisfactory. Their capacitance should be 0.1 mfd ±10%.

L1 and L2 are 26 mh each. The toroid inductor is preferred, although one with the specified value may be somewhat difficult to obtain. The toroids, particularly the variable-inductance types, are also fairly expensive. In most cases, satisfactory results can be obtained from 25-mh shielded iron-core RF chokes as a substitute for the toroids. The J. W. Miller type 857 RF choke has been used for L1 and L2 in several experimental filters. The inductances of these chokes are accurate to within 5%. The units are also enclosed in round aluminum shields 1¼ inches in diameter and 1⅛ inches high and fitted with two No. 6-32 spade bolts for easy assembly to the chassis. It is also possible for L1 and L2 to consist of the adjustable width controls designed for use in television-receiver sweep circuits. A suitable type is the J. W. Miller 6315 variable inductor. These coils are mounted through a single hole in the equipment chassis. The tuning slug must be adjusted for an inductance of 26 mh.

The most convenient method of adjusting the variable inductors to their proper values is shown in Fig. 6-13. An accurately cali-brated audio oscillator is required, along with an oscilloscope or audio vacuum-tube voltmeter. The 0.1-mfd capacitor and the inductance to be adjusted are connected in series across the

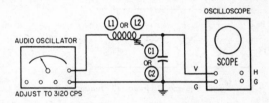

Fig. 6-13. Testing of L1 and L2 for 26 mh.

output terminals of the audio oscillator. The VTVM (or oscillo-scope vertical-amplifier input) is connected across the capacitor. The oscillator is now adjusted for an output frequency of 3,120 cycles, and the coil slug is adjusted for maximum indication on the VTVM or oscilloscope. If the coil has a reasonably high Q, the voltage increase across the capacitor at resonance will be quite pronounced. Each coil should be adjusted in the same manner. If several 0.1-mfd capacitors are available, a "matched pair" may be selected by substituting capacitors in the test circuit until two are found which give equal output at the same induct-ance adjustment. Always use the same capacitor for the adjust-ment of each coil. A filter of this type, using the specified values and adjusted as described, will have a characteristic impedance of approximately 500 ohms.

PRACTICAL SPEECH-AMPLIFIER DESIGN

As mentioned previously, practically no power is required from the speech-amplifier circuit of a single-sideband trans-

99

mitter. This means the audio-voltage requirements are also low. The most important factors to be considered in an amplifier are the frequency bandpass response and the amount of distortion contained in the speech signal at the output. Since the speech amplifier operates only at the middle AF range, the design procedure is very simple. In most cases, it will merely consist of selecting the proper tubes and components from the published charts and data sheets.

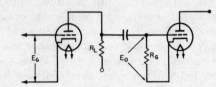

(A) Resistance-coupled triode amplifier circuit.

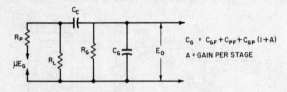

$$C_G = C_{GF} + C_{PF} + C_{GP}(1+A)$$

$$A = \text{GAIN PER STAGE}$$

(B) Equivalent circuit (all frequencies).

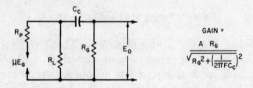

$$\text{GAIN} = \frac{A \cdot R_G}{\sqrt{R_G^2 + \left(\frac{1}{2\pi F C_C}\right)^2}}$$

(C) Equivalent circuit (low frequencies).

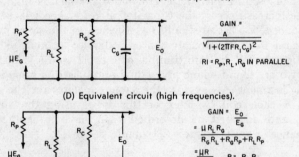

$$\text{GAIN} = \frac{A}{\sqrt{1 + (2\pi F R_1 C_G)^2}}$$

$$R1 = R_P, R_L, R_G \text{ IN PARALLEL}$$

(D) Equivalent circuit (high frequencies).

$$\text{GAIN} = \frac{E_O}{E_G}$$

$$= \frac{\mu R_L R_G}{R_G R_L + R_G R_P + R_L R_P}$$

$$= \frac{\mu R}{R_P + R}, \quad R = \frac{R_L R_G}{R_L + R_G},$$

$$\mu = \text{TRIODE AMPLIFICATION FACTOR}$$

(E) Equivalent circuit (medium frequencies).

Fig. 6-14. Resistance-coupled and equivalent circuits.

The voltage gain of an amplifier can be defined as the output signal voltage divided by the input signal voltage. In a practical amplifier using vacuum tubes, the voltage gain will always be less than the amplification factor (referred to by the symbol μ) of the tube. The amount of the gain lost is determined by the ratio of the load resistance to the internal plate resistance of the amplifier tube. As shown in Fig. 6-14A, the *effective load impedance* of the plate circuit consists of load resistor R_L, the next-stage grid resistor R_G, the capacitive reactance of coupling capacitor C_C, and the internal capacitances of the two tubes. The equivalent AC circuits for all low, high, and medium frequencies, are shown in Figs. 6-14B, C, D, and E, respectively. It is apparent that the load impedance, and consequently the output voltage between the grid and cathode of V2, will vary at the different audio frequencies. The effect of the capacitive reactances is such that the output voltage is lower at the extremely high and low frequencies. At the very low frequencies, the X_C of coupling capacitor C_C will be large, and the output voltage at the plate of V1 will divide across the coupling-capacitor reactance and grid resistor R_G. At the frequency where the reactance of the coupling capacitor is equal to the resistance of R_G, the voltage across R_G will be down by 3 db. As the frequency is decreased below this point, the voltage drop across the coupling capacitor will gradually increase and the voltage drops across the grid resistor will gradually decrease. This gradual voltage decrease across R_G, will be approximately 6 db per octave of frequency change at frequencies lower than those of the -3-db point. The voltage increase across the coupling capacitor will also occur at the same rate. If the voltages across the coupling capacitor and grid resistor (as the frequency is decreased below the -3-db point) are plotted against frequency, the shapes of the two curves will be identical but in opposite amplitude directions. When the two curves are added algebraically, the resultant will plot a straight line equal in amplitude to the output voltage at the plate of V1. As the frequency approaches zero (DC), the X_C of the coupling capacitor approaches an infinite impedance and no measurable voltage will appear across the grid resistor. When the frequency is increased (beginning at the frequencies slightly higher than the -3-db point) the voltage drop across the coupling capacitor will "flatten out" to a very low value, and most of the output voltage at the plate of V1 will appear across the grid resistor.

As the frequency increase is continued, however, the voltage across R_G will again gradually decrease. When the frequency has been increased to the point where the voltage across R_G has decreased by 3 db from maximum, the reactance of the shunt capacitance (tube internal capacitance, distributed capacitance, etc.) is now equal to the value of R_G. As the frequency is increased above the -3-db point, the voltage across R_G will decrease at about 6 db per octave of frequency change. At some high frequency, the output circuit will be effectively short-circuited by the shunt capacitance, and no measurable voltage will appear across the grid resistor.

Since these variations of output voltage are caused by the frequency-sensitive characteristics of coupling capacitor C_C and the shunt internal capacitances of the two tubes, it is obvious that we can control the frequency response of an audio amplifier by selecting certain values of coupling and shunt capacitances. The amplitude of the lower frequencies can be reduced by the use of a relatively low coupling capacitance, and the amplitude of the higher frequencies can be reduced by adding more shunt capacitance across R_G. When lumped constants are added to a circuit to control its frequency-response characteristic, the assembly of frequency-sensitive components is generally called a filter. An amplifier in which the frequency response is restricted or controlled is usually referred to as a bandpass amplifier.

From the mathematical point of view, the amplification at low frequencies, A_L, may be expressed as a fraction of the middle-frequency gain, A_M. The formula most commonly used for low-frequency gain calculations is:

$$A_L = \frac{A_M}{\sqrt{1 + \frac{1}{(2\pi f R C_C)^2}}}$$

where,

A_L is the low frequency gain,
A_M is the middle-frequency gain,
f is the frequency in cycles per second,
R is equal to $R_G + \frac{R_L R_P}{R_L + R_P}$
R_P is the tube plate resistance (internal),
R_L is the V1 plate load resistor,
R_G is the grid resistor of the following stage,
C_C is the capacitance of the coupling capacitor in farads.
π is 3.1416 (approx.)

Resistance Coupling

The low-frequency response of a speech amplifier can also be reduced by using a small capacitance across the cathode resistor. In circuits which use screen-grid tubes (such as the 6AU6),

102

the same effect can be obtained by the use of a low-value screen bypass capacitor. At low frequencies, the reactance of a cathode bypass capacitor will increase, and the resultant discriminative negative current feedback will reduce the gain of the amplifier stage. At medium and high frequencies, the reactance of the capacitor will be low and the stage gain will be normal. In the case of the screen-grid amplifier, the reactance of the screen bypass capacitor will increase at the low frequencies, and signal-voltage variations will appear in the screen circuit. The phase relationship of these voltage variations—with respect to the control-grid voltage variations—is such that the cathode-to-plate signal current will be reduced and the amplifier gain, at the frequencies where this condition occurs, will be attenuated. When no cathode bypass capacitor is used, as in the circuit of Fig. 6-15, the gain reduction of the amplifier stage (due to negative current feedback) will be constant over the normal frequency response of the circuit. The main reason for not using cathode bypass capacitors in this circuit is to reduce the inherent speech amplifier distortion by means of the negative current feedback.

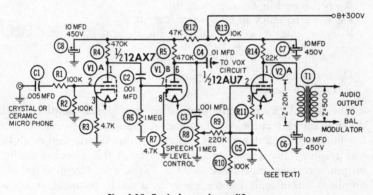

Fig. 6-15. Typical speech amplifier.

The high-frequency response of the speech amplifier is limited by the effect of the shunt capacitance, which includes the distributed capacitance of the leads, socket, and associated wiring, and the effective input capacitance of the amplifier tube. The latter is also affected by the amplification of the tube and will vary with the different types. The shunt capacitance will have the greatest effect at high frequencies when the combination of R_L and R_G (see Fig. 6-14D) has a large resistance. When this resistance is low, small changes in the shunt reactance will have very little effect on the total load value. In a circuit where an extended high-frequency response is desired (such

103

as that of a high-fidelity amplifier), the use of low values of plate and grid resistors, and tubes with low amplification factors and plate resistances, will usually extend the amplifier frequency limits well beyond the range of human hearing. In a speech amplifier designed for communications purposes, it is generally not desirable to extend the high-frequency response much beyond 5,000 cycles. The use of reasonably high resistances in the plate and grid circuits of high-gain amplifier tubes is common practice. In general, the effects of the circuit shunt capacitance on the frequency response of a speech amplifier is negligible. In the design of most circuits, it will be necessary to add to, rather than attempt to reduce, the shunt capacitance.

The high-frequency amplification of a resistance-coupled amplifier stage may be expressed as follows:

$$A_H = \frac{A_M}{\sqrt{1 + (2\pi f R_1 C_G)^2}}$$

where,

A_H is the high-frequency gain,
A_M is the middle-frequency gain,
f is the frequency in cycles per second,
R_1 is the parallel combination of R_P, R_L and R_G (Fig. 6-14D),
R_1 is equal to $\dfrac{R_P R_L R_G}{R_P R_L + R_P R_G + R_L R_G}$,
C_G is the effective input capacitance in farads.
π is 3.1416 (approx.).

The actual circuit configuration of the speech amplifier will depend on the audio voltage and impedance requirements of the balanced modulator. The majority of diode balanced modulators require only a few volts of audio from the speech-amplifier output across an impedance of 200 to 500 ohms. A typical speech-amplifier circuit suitable for use with a diode balanced modulator is shown in Fig. 6-15.

This speech amplifier is designed for use with either a crystal or ceramic microphone. The microphone element is isolated from the 12AX7 input-amplifier grid by .005-mfd capacitor C1. The two 100-K resistors, R1 and R2, present a high-impedance load to the microphone. The input-amplifier grid is connected to the junction of R1 and R2 to eliminate possible grid rectification of the transmitter RF signal voltages in this stage. When a high-power RF amplifier is included on the same chassis as the speech-amplifier circuitry, it is usually necessary to shield the audio-input leads to prevent RF signal pick-up. The presence of the RF signal voltage in the speech circuits will cause severe distortion in the transmitted signal. When this condition occurs, the audio signal recovered at the receiver will be rough and distorted. In most cases, the audio signal at the receiver will contain mysterious low-frequency growling noises in addition to the distortion. The most serious effect of RF pickup by the speech-amplifier circuits, however, is the generation of spurious products which may appear to be caused by some other section of the transmitter. In a number of instances, difficulty in obtaining adequate suppression of the undesired sideband was due to the presence of harmonic distortion in the speech amplifier. Unless the symptoms are recognized, the source of the trouble may be very difficult to locate, since the RF

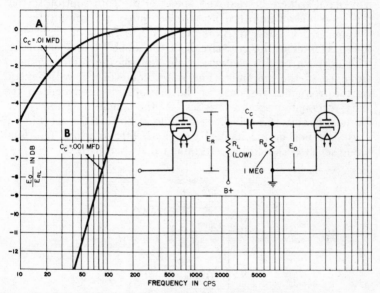

Fig. 6-16. Low-frequency characteristics of resistance-coupled amplifier.

feedback will occur only when an audio signal is present in the speech amplifier. The presence of only moderate distortion in the audio signal at the balanced modulator may cause spurious products to be generated and to be transmitted outside the operating channel.

The 12AX7 plate load resistors, R4 and R5, are .47 megohms each and cathode resistors R3 and R7 are 4700 ohms each. The cathodes are not bypassed in order to obtain the benefits of lower distortion produced by the negative current feedback, and the 12AU7 cathode is not bypassed for the same reason. Grid resistor R6 of V1B is one megohm. Interstage coupling capacitors C2 and C3 are .001 mfd each. A measured response curve

105

for the low-frequency transmission characteristics of a .001-mfd coupling capacitor, working into a 1-megohm grid resistor, is shown in Fig. 6-16. Another response curve, for a .01-mfd coupling capacitor working into the same value of grid load resistance, is shown for comparison. Even though the curves in Fig. 6-16 were obtained by using a low plate load resistance, the effect of the two .001-mfd capacitors, (C2 and C3 in Fig. 6-15) will be cumulative, and the low-frequency rolloff will be similar to that shown by curve B. The audio signal for operation of the automatic-control (VOX) circuits is taken directly from the plate of V1B through .01-mfd capacitor C4. It is necessary that this control signal voltage be removed ahead of the gain control, so that the speech-level adjustments will not affect its amplitude.

Capacitor C5 and resistors R9 and R10 form an elementary low-pass filter in the grid circuit of the 12AU7 output amplifier. The purpose of this network is to roll off the high-frequency response of the amplifier. The exact value of C5 will depend on the frequency response of the microphone used and on the skirt attenuation characteristics of the single-sideband filter. In most circuits, C5 will have a value of 56 to 120 mmf when a crystal lattice or mechanical sideband filter is used. The final value selected should be determined by experiment.

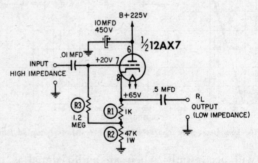

Fig. 6-17. Practical audio cathode-follower output.

Audio-output transformer T1 is a miniature plate-to-line unit. The primary impedance is 20K, and the secondary impedance is either 200 or 500 ohms. Notice that the plate current of the 12AU7 does not pass through the transformer primary winding, but is returned to B+ through 22K plate load resistor R12. Although most plate-to-line transformers will pass the 12AU7 plate current without core saturation, the audio-waveform distortion is perceptibly less when the arrangement in Fig. 6-15 is used. The audio signal appearing in the primary circuit is returned to ground through 10-mfd electrolytic capacitor C6.

106

The plate circuits of the three tubes are decoupled from the power supply by C7-C8, and R12-R13.

The speech amplifier circuit described can be used in either a filter or phase-shift type of single-sideband generator. In a phase-shift generator circuit, impedance step-down transformer T1 must be used in order to obtain the balanced audio voltage required by the differential phase-shift network. If the speech amplifier is to be used with a filter type of single-sideband generator, transformer T1 may be omitted, and the audio voltage fed to the balanced modulator by a cathode follower. A typical audio-signal cathode-follower output circuit is shown in Fig. 6-17.

Cathode Follower

The cathode follower is basically a power-output stage, since the voltage gain is always less than 1. The input signal is applied between the tube control grid and ground. The plate is at ground potential with respect to the input and output

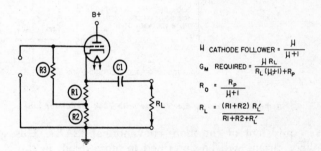

Fig. 6-18. Design of cathode follower.

signal voltages, and the output signal appears across cathode load resistor R1. All the voltage across R1 is fed back to the input circuit, constituting 100% negative voltage feedback. As a result, the output impedance of the circuit is very low. Also, the range of usable load impedance values is much greater than for the more conventional triode amplifier circuits. The cathode follower has a wide frequency range, and very low distortion and phase-shift characteristics. The input and output signals are of the same phase relationship. The voltage "gain" of the cathode follower will depend on the type of tube and on the value of load impedance R_L. When the load impedance is only a few hundred ohms, the voltage gain will be about 0.5. Above 10,000 ohms, the voltage gain may be as much as 0.9. However, it will never equal unity, or 1.0. The design equations given in

107

Fig. 6-18 will apply to both AF and RF cathode-follower output circuits.

The simple speech-amplifier circuit shown in Fig. 6-19 is designed for use with the RCA "7360" beam-deflection-tube balanced modulator. The peak-to-peak audio signal required for full beam deflection is approximately 2.8 volts. Since the input impedance to the deflection electrodes is relatively high, no matching transformer will be required. A 7025 tube is the low-

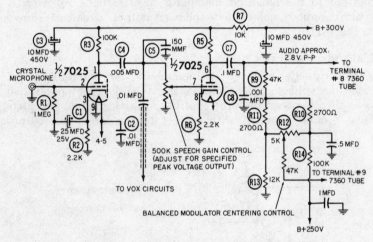

Fig. 6-19. Speech amplifier for use with 7360 modulator tube.

noise equivalent of the more conventional 12AX7. This speech amplifier circuit will be described in more detail in the chapter on single-sideband generators.

COMMERCIAL SPEECH-AMPLIFIER CIRCUITS

The speech-amplifier circuits described here are found in single-sideband transmitters manufactured by Collins, Hammarlund, and Johnson. These transmitters are used in both commercial and amateur communications services and are considered examples of good engineering design.

Collins 32S-1

The simplified schematic in Fig. 6-20 shows the speech-amplifier circuit for the Collins 32S-1 single-sideband transmitter. The triode section of a 6U8A (V1A) serves as the input audio amplifier, and the pentode section as the second audio

108

amplifier. The triode section of another 6U8A (V2A) is used as a cathode-follower low-impedance output stage, and the pentode section is the crystal-controlled carrier generator described in a preceding chapter. The speech amplifier is designed for use with a high-impedance microphone. When a low-impedance microphone is used, it will be necessary to incorporate a suitable matching transformer between the microphone and the high-impedance input circuit.

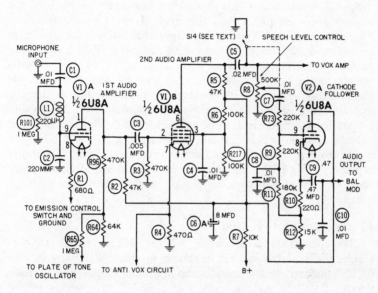

Fig. 6-20. Collins 32S-1 speech amplifier.

The microphone element is isolated from the input audio amplifier grid by .01-mfd capacitor C1. The purpose of RF choke L1 is to prevent pickup and rectification of the transmitter RF voltages in the grid circuit. Capacitor C2, connected from terminal 9 to ground, bypasses any RF voltages passed by L1. The 220-mmf capacitor, C2, also is used to roll off the amplifier response at the higher audio frequencies. In order to obtain distortion reduction from the negative current feedback, the 680-ohm cathode resistor R1, is not bypassed. During tuning of the transmitter RF circuits, or during operation on CW telegraphy, the cathode circuit of the speech input-amplifier is opened by the switch.

Notice that R5 (the plate load resistor for the V1B pentode section) is comparatively low in value. The 6U8A screen is fed from a DC voltage divider which consists of the two 0.1 megohm

109

resistors, R6 and R117. Screen bypass capacitor C4 is .01 mfd, a much lower value than usual in conventional pentode audio amplifiers. The purpose of such a low value is to introduce degenerative feedback action in this stage and thereby reduce the amplifier response at the lower audio frequencies. Cathode resistor R4 is not bypassed, and the resultant negative current feedback is used to reduce distortion in the pentode amplifier stage.

Speech-level control R8 is inserted between the plate of the second audio amplifier and the grid of the cathode follower. The rotor arm of R8 is isolated from the cathode-follower grid by .01-mfd capacitor C7 and 220K resistor R73. Switch S14 closes when the speech-level control is rotated to its maximum counterclockwise position. The purpose of S14 is to disable the speech-amplifier circuit during transmitter tune-up or standby periods. The cathode-follower plate is maintained at AF ground potential by 8-mfd electrolytic capacitor C6A. The audio-output voltage appears across cathode load resistors R10 and R12, and is fed to the balanced modulator through 0.47-mfd coupling capacitor C9. R10 (220 ohms) is the cathode-follower bias resistor, although it appears as part of the output load-resistor circuit.

Hammarlund HX-500

The speech-amplifier circuit of the Hammarlund HX-500 single-sideband transmitter is shown in simplified form in Fig. 6-21. The first and second audio-amplifier stages use a dual-triode 12AX7 tube. One section of a 6CM7 tube serves as the audio-output amplifier. The audio circuit, while very simple, is somewhat different from the speech-amplifier circuits described.

The speech circuits of the HX-500 are designed for use with a high-impedance crystal or ceramic microphone. The high-frequency response of the amplifier is modified by an unusual input-circuit arrangement. The 47K resistor (R31) and 100-mmf capacitor C44 are connected in series across the microphone input jack, with the capacitor in the grounded side. Input coupling capacitor C45 is connected from the junction of R31 and C44 to the control grid of V5A. For all practical purposes, C44 is effectively in shunt with the high resistance of R32 (the 4.7-megohm grid load resistor in the input-amplifier circuit). Rolloff of the higher audio frequencies will occur at a rapid rate. The 12AX7 input-amplifier section has its cathode connected to ground, so that this stage operates with contact potential bias only. The V5A plate load resistor, R33, is 220K ohms.

110

The AF response is further modified by .001-mfd interstage coupling capacitor C47 and by the following-stage grid-circuit network composed of the three 1-megohm resistors R34, R37, and R41; and .02-mfd capacitor C48. The over-all AF response of the speech amplifier is such that when it is combined with the single-sideband filter-attenuation characteristic, the audio frequencies most useful for maximum intelligibility and power output will be transmitted. The 3.9K cathode resistor, R35, provides bias voltage and negative current feedback for the

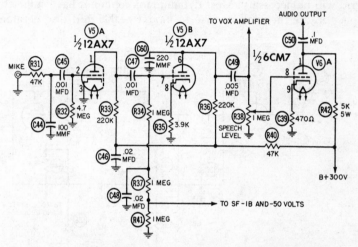

Fig. 6-21. Hammarlund HX-500 speech amplifier.

V5B second audio amplifier. The .005-mfd coupling capacitor, C49 is connected from the plate of V5B to the top of the speech-level control. The audio-signal voltage for operation of the VOX (automatic-control) circuits is taken from the top of the speech-level control, and the audio voltage developed across 5K load resistor R42, in the plate circuit of V6A, is applied to the balanced modulator through 0.1-mfd coupling capacitor C50. The output impedance of the 6CM7 triode, V6A, is relatively low.

Johnson *Invader*

The Johnson *Invader* speech-amplifier circuit, shown in Fig. 6-22 is quite simple and conventional in most respects. The first and second audio-amplifier stages comprise a 12AT7 dual-triode. The cathode of the 12AT7 section used for the input amplifier (V5A) is connected to ground. Since C62 is directly in shunt with the high resistance of R35, rolloff of the higher audio frequencies will occur at a rapid rate. A 4.7K resistor, R34, is in

111

series with the inner conductor of the microphone cable and the 12AT7 input-amplifier grid. The combination of resistor R34 and capacitor C62 forms an RF filter to prevent pickup and rectification of the transmitter RF voltages by the V5A grid.

The *Invader* speech amplifier is designed for use with crystal or ceramic high-impedance types of communications microphones, and the microphone is not isolated from the 12AT7 input-amplifier grid. If a dynamic microphone is used, DC isolation of the microphone secondary winding from the input-amplifier grid will be necessary. Most dynamic microphones have sufficient space inside the shell or case to mount a .005-mfd disc ceramic

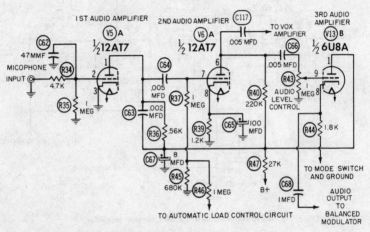

Fig. 6-22. Johnson INVADER speech amplifier.

blocking capacitor. The capacitor is connected in series with the inner conductor of the microphone cable, at the point where the cable connects to the matching-transformer secondary. Without the blocking capacitor, the comparatively low DC resistance of the transformer secondary winding will drain away the contact potential bias at the input-amplifier grid.

The audio-signal voltage at the plate of V5A is, for all practical purposes, fed to a capacitance voltage divider. The total resistance in the grid circuit of the second audio amplifier, V6A, is 1.68 megohms. The resultant network—which consists of C63 and C64, and resistors R36, R37, and R45—will modify both the high- and low-frequency responses of the speech-amplifier circuit.

SPEECH-AMPLIFIER SUMMARY

It should now be apparent that the communications effectiveness of any type of single-sideband transmitter will depend to

112

a great extent on the proper design of the speech amplifier. The two most important factors involved in the design of single-sideband speech circuits are the limitation of the amplifier frequency response and the reduction of distortion in the audio-frequency output signal. The speech-amplifier frequency response should be limited to a bandpass of the frequencies between 300 and 3,000 cycles; all frequencies below and above these limits should be rapidly attenuated. The exact design of the speech-amplifier and audio-bandpass filter circuits will depend on the method of sideband selection (phase shift or filter systems). In single-sideband transmitters which use the filter method of sideband selection, the speech-amplifier and audio-bandpass circuitry is relatively simple, since the sideband filter will usually suppress the undesired speech frequencies. In most filter-type transmitters, the audio-frequency response is shaped by a careful selection of circuit component values. In phase-shift transmittters, the speech-amplifier circuitry is generally much more complex. Here it is important to suppress any AF components which fall beyond the effective range of the AF differential phase-shift network. Most AF phase-shift networks of the communications type (such as the Barker and Williamson Type 2Q4, Model 350), are designed to function within the range of 300 to 3,000 cycles with a phase differential of 90°. The network performance below 300 and above 3,000 cycles will deteriorate rapidly. Unless the speech-amplifier AF response is limited to the effective range of the network, severe distortion and spurious signal products will be generated. The suppression of the undesired sideband will also be very low.

The principal reason for reducing the distortion content of the speech-amplifier audio-output signal is to prevent the generation of spurious signal products in the balanced modulator. This precaution is especially important in the design of speech amplifiers to be used with phase-shift transmitter. In most of these transmitters, the amplifier circuits which follow the balanced modulators have relatively poor selectivity. The filter type of single-sideband generator will usually discriminate against spurious signal products which fall outside its normal bandpass response. In either type of transmitter, the presence of distortion in the audio signal will usually reduce the intelligibility and increase the bandwidth of the transmitted signal. It is good engineering practice to keep to a minimum any distortion or other factors which tend to deteriorate the desired emission characteristics of the transmitter.

Chapter 7

Single-Sideband Generators

In a single-sideband system, the circuits most closely associated with the development of the signal are usually grouped together as a single section of the over-all design. This section is generally referred to as the *single-sideband generator*. It is obvious that the generator is the heart of any single-sideband transmitter since, with the two exceptions of amplitude and frequency, none of the other transmitter circuits will affect the characteristics of the generated signal.

The essential circuits required to form a single-sideband generator are a carrier generator, balanced modulator, and audio amplifier, as well as some means of suppressing the undesired sideband. All of these circuits have been covered individually and in detail in the preceding chapters. Now their combination, in the form of the sideband generator, will be considered. The relatively simple filter type of single-sideband generator will be discussed first, with the more complex phase-shift generator left until later in the chapter.

BASIC GENERATORS

The block diagrams in Figs. 7-1A and B show the essential circuits of a simple single-sideband (SSB) generator of either the filter or phase-shift type. In both methods the audio input signal must be amplified and shaped before it is applied to the balanced modulator circuit. Sideband generation is accomplished by using the audio signal to vary the amplitude of the carrier in the balanced modulator. In the filter method, the desired sideband is selected from the modulator output by means of the sideband filter. The carrier wave is suppressed by the balanced modulator and the high degree of skirt selectivity in the sideband filter. In the phase-shift method, the desired sideband is selected by controlling the phase of the RF and audio voltages applied to a pair of balanced modulators.

114

The carrier wave is suppressed in the circuit of the balanced modulators. In either case, a "genuine" sideband signal appears at the output of the sideband generator and, except for amplitude and frequency, is an exact replica of the signal applied to the antenna by the final RF amplifier.

The amount of audio amplification required will depend on the input-signal requirements of the balanced modulator. It is customary to adjust the level of the RF carrier voltage applied to the balanced modulator so that it is between 10 and 30 volts. In order to keep distortion products to a minimum, the audio signal at the modulator must be less than 1 volt. In general, the average diode balanced modulator requires an audio signal of 0.1 to 1.0 volt at impedances of 200 to 500 ohms. The audio-output signal from a microphone or a telephone line is usually several hundred times lower than the audio-voltage level required by the modulator. For most efficient utilization of the transmitter RF amplifier, the applied driving signal should be as close to maximum as possible without exceeding the overload level, and must not exhibit excessively wide amplitude excursions. In most commercial SSB transmitters, the driving signal is automatically adjusted to the level where maximum output is obtained with the maximum input signal. The wide amplitude excursions of the driving signal are either compressed or clipped so that they do not appear in the emitted signal. With the exception of the Johnson *Invader* and the Central Electronics 100-V, most of the low-power amateur SSB transmitters use neither audio compression nor clipping. The transmitters designed for amateur service generally depend on ALC circuitry to raise the average transmitted power level.

The two speech amplifiers shown in Figs. 7-1A and B may be similar in all respects. When they are properly designed, the bandpass will be restricted and the distortion characteristics reduced to minimum. Also, they may contain compressor or clipper circuits to limit the voice-signal peak excursions and raise the average power level of the emitted signal. The audio-output signals from both speech amplifiers will have similar characteristics.

As we leave the speech-amplifier output circuits, however, the two sideband generator systems become entirely different. In the phase-shift generator (Fig. 7-1B), the speech-amplifier audio-output signal is applied to an audio phase-shift network, which separates it into two audio signals 90° out of phase, over the frequency range from 300 to 3,000 cycles. The two audio signals are then applied to two balanced modulators. The carrier oscillator signal is also separated into two components 90° out

115

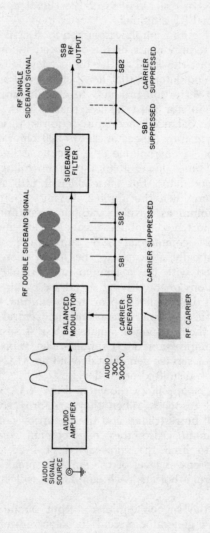

(A) Filter type.

Fig. 7-1. Block diagram of a

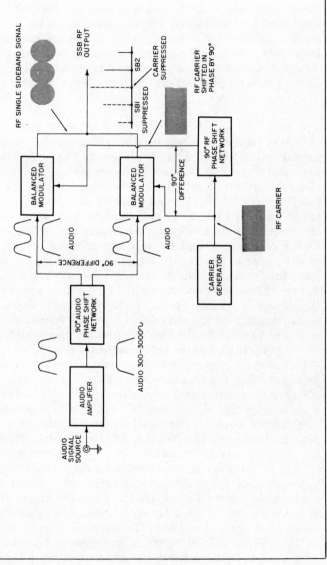

RF SINGLE SIDEBAND SIGNAL

SSB RF OUTPUT

SB2

CARRIER SUPPRESSED

SB1 SUPPRESSED

RF CARRIER SHIFTED IN PHASE BY 90°

90° RF PHASE SHIFT NETWORK

BALANCED MODULATOR

BALANCED MODULATOR

90° DIFFERENCE

RF CARRIER

AUDIO

AUDIO

90° DIFFERENCE

CARRIER GENERATOR

90° AUDIO PHASE SHIFT NETWORK

AUDIO 300-3000∿

AUDIO AMPLIFIER

AUDIO SIGNAL SOURCE

(B) Phase shift type.

basic single-sideband generator.

117

of phase, which are also applied to the two balanced modulators. The RF signal from the common output circuit of the two balanced modulators will consist of a single sideband only; the carrier and one sideband will be suppressed.

In the filter generator shown in Fig. 7-1A, the audio-output signal and carrier RF signal are both applied directly to a single balanced modulator. The RF signal in the balanced modulator output circuit will consist of a pair of sidebands only because the carrier will be suppressed in the balanced modulator. An additional 20 db or so of carrier suppression will be obtained in the sideband filter, where sideband selection takes place.

FILTER METHOD

A very simple filter generator, designed for use with a mechanical sideband filter, is shown in Fig. 7-2. The carrier generator uses a miniature 6AU6 pentode in the series-tuned Colpitts circuit. Oscillator tank inductance L1 is a high-Q ferrite rod antenna coil. The 35-mmf variable capacitor, C1, is used to adjust the carrier frequency to the proper position on the slope of the mechanical-filter response. Ordinarily, C1 is set at half of its full capacitance, and the coil slug adjusted for a frequency at the center of the filter bandpass. By increasing or decreasing the capacitance of C1, the carrier frequency may be placed at the −20-db point on either slope of the filter response. When the carrier is placed on the higher-frequency slope, the RF signal output from the mechanical filter will consist of the lower sideband. Conversely, the filter will pass the upper sideband when the carrier is placed on the lower-frequency slope.

In order to keep the carrier-generator section as simple as possible, a 6C4 triode is used as an RF phase inverter to supply a balanced carrier signal to the modulator. The 3- to 30-mmf trimmer capacitor, C7, across 6C4 cathode load resistor R6, is adjusted for equal carrier-signal voltages at the phase-inverter plate and cathode. The 50K-pot, R8, is the carrier-balance control. Carrier balance is carried out by alternate adjustments of C7 and R8 for minimum carrier-signal voltage at the filter output terminals. Generally, the carrier-balance adjustments are most easily made when C1 is adjusted to place the carrier frequency in the center of the filter bandpass. After the balancing adjustments have been completed, the carrier frequency is returned to the −20-db position on the filter response. The two 15K resistors, R9 and R10, improve the impedance match between the diode balanced modulator and mechanical filter. The two trimmer capacitors, C10 and C11, are used to resonate the input and

118

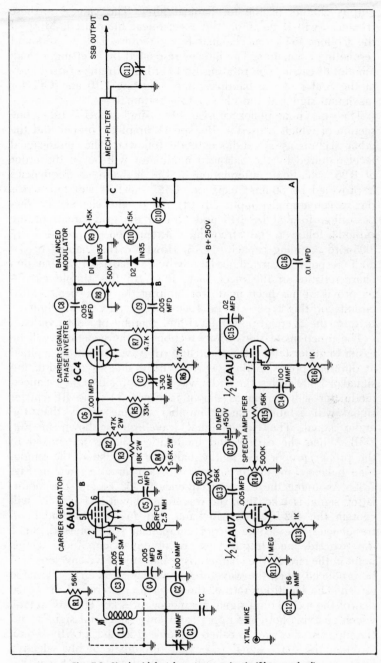

Fig. 7-2. Single-sideband generator circuit (filter method).

119

output circuits of the mechanical filter. The values of these trimmers will depend on the mechanical filter used. Most of the Collins 455-kc mechanical filters require 110- to 130-mmf resonating capacitors. The filter is resonated by inserting a small amount of carrier (by rotating R8 to either extreme of its range) at the center of the bandpass and adjusting C10 and C11 for maximum signal at the filter output terminals.

The speech amplifier consists of a single 12AU7 tube, one section of which is used as the speech amplifier proper and the other section as an audio cathode follower. The audio-signal level required by the balanced modulator will be on the order of 0.25 volt. Some attenuation of the high audio frequencies is provided by 56-mmf capacitor C12, which is shunted across the speech-amplifier input circuit, and by the elementary low-pass filter formed by R15 and C14 in the grid circuit of the cathode follower. Low-frequency attenuation is provided by .005-mfd coupling capacitor C13. However, the shaping of the audio response is carried out largely by the sharp skirt-attenuation characteristics of the mechanical filter. In this simple circuit, no provision has been made for limiting the voice peaks. Most circuits of this type will be followed by ALC peak limiters, to raise the average power level and thereby prevent overload.

The functions of the various sections of the generator will be easier to understand if the audio and RF waveforms are examined at different points in the system. With a sine-wave modulating signal of 1,000 cycles, the audio waveform applied to the balanced modulator will appear as shown in Fig. 7-3A. The RF carrier signal will exhibit a larger number of sine waves than the audio signal. The carrier-signal waveform is shown in Fig. 7-3B. When the carrier and modulation signals are mixed in the proper proportions in the balanced modulator, the single-tone balanced-modulator output will appear as shown in Fig. 7-3C. Assuming the carrier frequency is 453 kc and the modulating signal is 1 kc, then the waveform shown in Fig. 7-3C will contain the 452-kc lower-sideband and 454-kc upper-sideband frequencies; the 453-kc carrier component is suppressed. Since the two sideband frequencies are of equal amplitude at this point in the circuit, the characteristic half-sine wave envelope will be produced when the waveform is displayed on an oscilloscope screen. The repetition rate of the envelope pattern will be twice that of the modulating signal frequency, or 2 kc. This RF signal, which contains both the upper- and lower-sideband signals and the suppressed carrier, is called a double-sideband, (DSB) signal.

When the DSB signal is passed through a highly selective filter, one of the sidebands will be passed and the other atten-

120

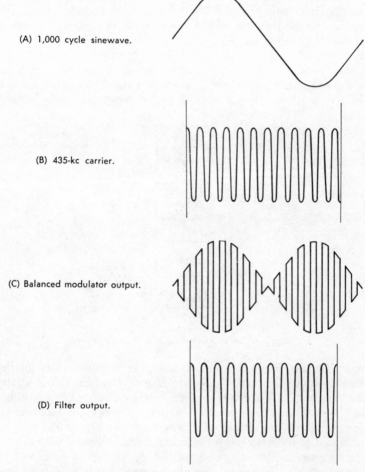

(A) 1,000 cycle sinewave.

(B) 435-kc carrier.

(C) Balanced modulator output.

(D) Filter output.

Fig. 7-3. Audio and RF waveforms appearing at various points in the generator of Fig. 7-2.

uated. As shown in Fig. 7-3D, the SSB passed by the filter will be a pure sine wave when the audio-modulation signal consists of a single tone. The frequency of the single-sideband signal at the filter output terminals will be equal to the carrier frequency plus or minus (depending on which sideband is passed) the modulating frequency. The single-sideband signal at the filter output can be applied to a frequency-converter stage and heterodyned to the operating frequency. Its amplitude may be increased to any desired practical level by amplifying it in a linear RF power amplifier. At the receiver, the incoming signal can only be de-

121

modulated by mixing it with another independent oscillator signal having the same frequency as the original carrier signal suppressed in the balanced modulator of the transmitter. The output signal obtained from the receiver demodulator circuit will be a facsimile of the original 1-kc modulating tone.

Many commercial and amateur generators have provision for reinserting the carrier component into the SSB signal after it has passed through the filter. Fig. 7-4 shows a simple method

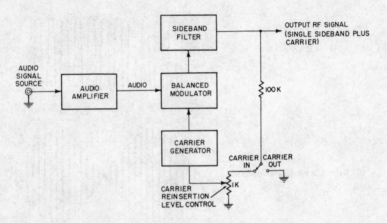

Fig. 7-4. Carrier reinsertion in a filter generator.

of doing this. Since the reinserted carrier signal must be of the proper amplitude with respect to that of the SSB signal at the filter output, the carrier amplitude is usually made adjustable as shown. When the reinserted carrier and single-sideband signal are equal in amplitude, the waveform in Fig. 7-5A will be obtained at the filter output terminals. The sideband with carrier signal can be heterodyned to the operating frequency and amplified to any desired practical power level, in exactly the same manner as a sideband without carrier.

Notice that the waveforms in Fig. 7-3C and 7-5A are both similar in appearance. However, their frequency components are not the same in value. Those of the waveform at the balanced modulator output are 452 and 454 kc when the modulating tone is 1 kc. The frequency components of the sideband with carrier are 453 and 454 kc, or 453 and 452 kc—depending on whether the upper or lower sideband is passed. (The audio modulating tone is assumed to be 1 kc in both instances.)

When the reinserted carrier is below the level of the single-tone single-sideband signal, the waveform in Fig. 7-5B will be viewed on an oscilloscope. This is the waveform of the signal

122

from a commercial SSB transmitter with a pilot carrier system. The same waveform will be transmitted by an amateur transmitter which has carrier leakage around the sideband filter.

When *two* separate audio tones are combined and applied simultaneously to the balanced modulator, one of the sidebands will be suppressed by the filter. The resultant *two-tone* sideband signal at the filter output terminals, viewed on an oscilloscope, is shown in Fig. 7-6A. Notice that the two-tone single-

(A) Carrier and tone equal in amplitude.

(B) Carrier amplitude less than tone.

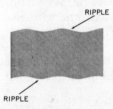

(C) Signal with small amount of reinserted carrier.

Fig. 7-5. Single-sideband waveforms with single tone modulation and reinserted carrier.

sideband signal is quite similar in appearance to the single-tone double-sideband signal in Fig. 7-3C and the SSB with carrier in Fig. 7-5A. However, the two-tone single-sideband signal contains an entirely different set of frequency components from those of the other two waveforms. Assuming a 453-kc carrier frequency, when the two-tone audio-modulation signal consists of equal amplitude 1,000- and 2,000-cycle sinewave tones, the RF signal at the filter output terminals will contain either the 451- and 452-kc or 454- and 455-kc frequencies (depending on which sideband is passed).

The two-tone single-sideband waveform shown in Fig. 7-6A will be obtained only when the carrier component is suppressed to a very low value. When a small amount of carrier signal is inserted into the two-tone signal, the presence of the carrier component will be indicated by a sine-wave ripple on the two-tone waveform, as shown in Fig. 7-6B.

123

(A) Two-tone modulated signal.

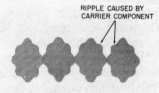

RIPPLE CAUSED BY
CARRIER COMPONENT

(B) Insertion of small carrier component.

Fig. 7-6. Single-sideband waveforms, two tones (1,000 and 2,000 cycles).

The generation of the two-tone single-sideband waveform will be more clearly understood from Fig. 7-7. The two signal-component vectors, designated E1 and E2, represent the 1,000- and 2,000-cycle audio-modulation tones, respectively. When E1 and E2 are 180° out of phase as in Fig. 7-7 at A, the envelope will have zero amplitude. When they are exactly in phase as in B, the envelope amplitude will be maximum. Moreover, the same type of waveform is produced, whether they are adding in a positive or negative direction. This is a characteristic of the suppressed-carrier waveform. It will be interesting to compare the vector diagram of the two-tone SSB suppressed-carrier waveform with that of the amplitude-modulation waveform in Fig. 2-4.

Analysis of the waveforms produced in the single-sideband generator is of great importance in more clearly understanding the principles upon which the system is based. The waveforms

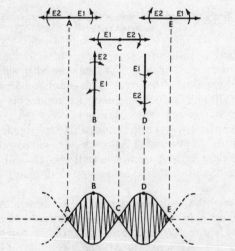

Fig. 7-7. Vector analysis of two-tone single-sideband waveform.

124

are also useful for test and measurement purposes. The two-tone SSB envelope is of special significance, since virtually all power and distortion specifications in a system are made with reference to the two-tone transmission conditions. Power measurements and waveform analysis will be treated in more detail in a later chapter.

The filter generator shown in Fig. 7-8 was designed to provide a study of the characteristics of the RCA 7360 beam-deflection tube when used as a balanced modulator. A technical description of this sideband generator will be of interest, since the 7360 tube is found in both commercial and amateur transmitters at the present time. The photographs in Figs. 7-9, 7-10, and 7-11 will aid the amateur to construct a very simple yet effective transmitter.

The generator proper consists of three tubes and their associated circuitry. The speech amplifier uses a 7025 dual-triode, which is the low-noise version of the 12AX7 ordinarily employed in high-fidelity audio amplifiers. The input circuit is designed for use with a crystal communications microphone. The two 2,200-ohm cathode bias resistors, R2 and R6, are not bypassed in order to obtain distortion reduction by negative current feedback. The .005-mfd coupling capacitor C4 and 150-mmf shunt capacitor C5 form an elementary bandpass audio filter. With the communications microphone, no further shaping of the speech-amplifier audio response is necessary. The 7025 plate load resistors, R3 and R5, are 0.1 megohm each. Speech signal-level control R4 is in the grid circuit of the 7025 output amplifier section and the audio-signal voltage for the VOX circuits is taken from the top of R4, through .01-mfd capacitor C43. The audio voltage required from the speech-amplifier output circuit for full deflection of the 7360 electron beam is about 3 volts peak-to-peak. The high-frequency speech-signal components in the audio-output circuit are bypassed to ground by C8. This .001-mfd capacitor is also the RF bypass for the 7360 deflection electrode.

The audio-signal voltage is applied to deflection electrode 1 of the 7360. Deflection electrode 2 (socket terminal 9) is bypassed to ground by 0.1-mfd capacitor C16. The rather elaborate resistor network (R9, R10, R11, R13, R14, and R19) in the deflection circuit permits the application of approximately +25 volts of bias voltage on the deflection electrodes for beam-centering purposes. The 5,000-ohm pot, R12, is the carrier balance control. It allows the deflection voltage to be regulated so that the electron beam will be centered between the two plates when no audio signal is present. Initially, R12 is adjusted, with no

125

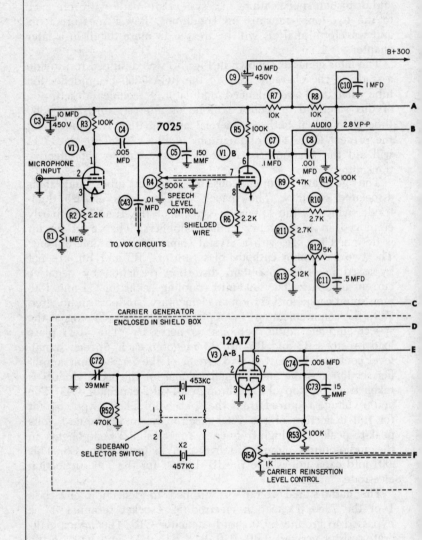

Fig. 7-8. Filter generator

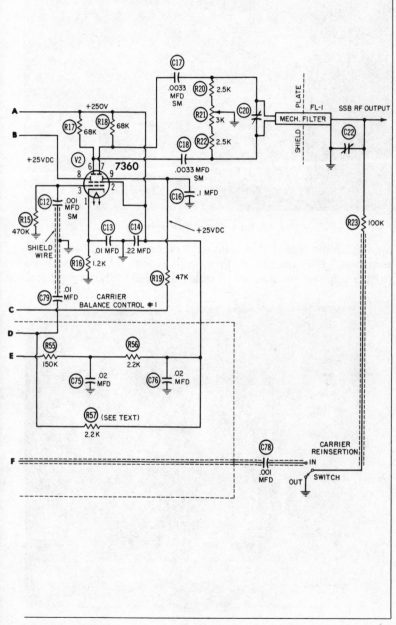

using RCA 7360 tube.

Fig. 7-9. Front view of filter generator.

applied audio signal, for minimum carrier at the filter output terminals. The control is then sealed with *glyptol*, and no further adjustment is required unless the 7360 tube is replaced.

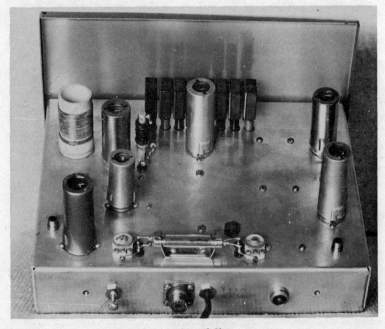

Fig. 7-10. Rear view of filter generator.

Since this generator was intended strictly as an experimental unit, the carrier generator was built onto a separate chassis. However, the carrier generator can be included as a part of the sideband-generator proper, if desired—provided the necessary isolation and shielding precautions are taken, to prevent leakage of the carrier signal into the circuits which follow the filter. As shown in Fig. 7-8, a 12AT7 dual triode is utilized as the crystal-controlled carrier generator. One section serves as a modified Pierce low-frequency crystal oscillator, and the second section as an isolation amplifier for

Fig. 7-11. Bottom view of filter generator. Note shield plate between input and output filter terminals.

the relatively weak crystal-oscillator signal. The carrier RF signal measures about 15 volts peak-to-peak at the amplifier-section plate. Losses in the shielded output cable reduce this voltage to the required 10 volts at grid 1 (socket terminal 3) of the 7360. The carrier-signal voltage may be increased by replacing R57 (2,200 ohms) with an 8,200-ohm unit. The carrier signal for reinsertion into the single-sideband signal at the filter output terminals is removed from the 12AT7 amplifier cathode circuit. The level of the reinserted carrier is adjusted by 1,000-ohm potentiometer R54.

The SSB filter used in this generator is a Collins Type F455Y-40. This particular mechanical filter has a 4.38-kc bandpass between the two −20-db attenuation points. Although the filter functions satisfactorily, the proper bandpass for speech transmission is from 2.7 to 3.1 kc. The circuit constants for the preferred filter are shown in Fig. 7-8. The two crystal frequencies required to position the carrier at the −20-db points on the filter skirt are specified by the manufacturer for the individual filter. In the filter shown in the photograph, the −20-db points are located at 452.73 and 457.11 kc. The closest FT-241-A surplus-crystal frequencies are 452.777 kc (channel 326) and 456.9444 kc (channel 329). These frequencies are satisfactory for experimental work but for good speech quality the carrier frequency should not deviate from the −20-db frequencies by more than 50 cycles.

The first step in the alignment of the sideband-generator circuits is to resonate the filter to the center of its bandpass response. If a variable-frequency carrier-signal generator is available, it is adjusted to a frequency halfway between the frequencies of the −20-db points on the filter skirt. Carrier-balance control R12 is rotated to one of its extreme positions, and plate-circuit balance control R21 to approximately the center of its range. Speech-level control R4 is rotated to its "off" position so that no audio signal of any kind is applied to the 7360 deflection electrode. The carrier-signal level at the 7360 control grid (socket terminal 3) should be approximately 10 volts peak-to-peak, measured on an RF VTVM or oscilloscope. Always use an RF isolation probe when measuring the carrier and sideband RF voltages.

With a carrier signal of the proper frequency and amplitude applied to the control grid of the 7360 balanced modulator, connect the RF VTVM or oscilloscope vertical input, through a suitable isolation probe, to the output terminals of the single-sideband filter. The carrier-signal level at the filter output should be sufficient to give an indication on the VTVM or oscilloscope. Adjust variable capacitance trimmers C20 and C22 for maximum carrier-signal indication. Once the two trimmers have been peaked, seal the adjustments with a drop of *polystyrene* cement.

The next step is the carrier-suppression adjustments. The carrier frequency and amplitude remain the same, as specified above. Adjust the VTVM or oscilloscope sensitivity so that a fairly large indication of the carrier voltage is obtained. Carrier-balance control R12 is carefully adjusted for minimum carrier-signal indication on the VTVM or oscilloscope. Quadrature balance control R21 is now adjusted for minimum carrier indi-

130

cation. The two balance-control adjustments interact to some extent; thus, it will be necessary to alternately adjust them to obtain the lowest possible carrier level at the filter output terminals. When the two controls are properly adjusted, the carrier level should be at least 50 db down from the maximum indication. Another 20 db of carrier suppression will be obtained when the carrier frequency is returned to its proper position on the filter slope.

With the carrier frequency at one of the −20-db points on the filter response, apply a sine-wave signal of about 1,000 cycles to the input jack of the speech amplifier. Then rotate speech-level control R4 to approximately three-fourths of its maximum position, and adjust the audio input-signal level so that about 3 volts peak-to-peak is applied to the 7360 deflection electrode. The carrier level at the balanced modulator control grid should be checked and, if necessary, adjusted to 10 volts peak-to-peak. We are now ready to observe the circuit waveforms on the oscilloscope screen.

After all the preliminary adjustments discussed above have been carried out and the carrier frequency is at the proper position on the filter response, the single-sideband signal at the filter output terminals should appear as a pure sine-wave carrier of constant amplitude. The waveform observed on the oscilloscope screen should look like Fig. 7-3D. Any ripple or other variations in the signal amplitude will indicate the presence of the carrier, undesired sideband, or spurious-product signals from the balanced modulator and speech amplifier. As speech-amplifier level control R4 is varied, there should be no change in the signal waveform other than an increase or decrease in amplitude.

Carrier reinsertion control R54 is now slowly advanced to the point where a perceptible ripple appears at the top and bottom of the signal. As the level of the reinserted carrier is increased to that of the signal, the waveform shown in Fig. 7-5A will be observed. If the reinserted carrier has a lower amplitude than the signal, the waveform may look like Fig. 7-5B.

It should be understood that the waveform at Fig. 7-5A will be obtained only when the levels of the sideband signal at the filter output and the reinserted carrier signal are equal. When the reinserted carrier level is higher, either it can be reduced or the level of the SSB signal increased (by turning up the speech-amplifier gain), until the proper waveform is obtained. When making tests or measurements, it is important to keep the audio signal at the balanced-modulator deflection electrode below the level where spurious products begin to be generated. The reinserted-carrier level is then adjusted for the proper waveform.

The frequency response of the generator is determined by applying a number of audio frequencies to the speech-amplifier input and plotting the amplitudes of the sideband signal voltages at the filter output terminals. The sideband-signal levels may be measured with an RF VTVM or an oscilloscope, and the readings should be plotted in decibels. The audio signal at the speech-amplifier input must be kept at a constant level as the measurements are made at 100-cycle intervals over the frequency range from 100 to 4,000 cycles. The filter response is determined by holding the audio signal at the 7360 deflection electrode constant at 2.8 volts peak-to-peak and measuring the sideband voltage developed at the filter output terminals. The speech-amplifier frequency response is determined by maintaining a constant-level audio signal at the amplifier input and measuring the audio voltage at the deflection electrode of the balanced modulator tube.

The two basic generators described in the preceding pages are relatively simple. The main purpose in presenting their circuits is to make you more familiar with the basic principles involved in the generation of the single-sideband signal. The waveforms shown will be the same in amateur or commercial SSB equipment. As might be expected, however, most commercial generators are much more complex. The trend in the commercial design field is toward closely integrated transmitting and receiving equipment. Since it is extremely difficult to describe commercial generators without referring to the action of the associated circuitry, this type of equipment will be covered in detail in the chapter on low-power transmitters.

PHASE-SHIFT METHOD

The various circuits that make up the phase-shift generator have been individually described. We shall now discuss the design of a simple phase-shift sideband generator and explain its circuit adjustments.

Fig. 7-12 shows the speech amplifier, low-pass audio filter, and audio phase-shift network circuits of a generator. The carrier-generator and RF phase-shift circuits, and the double balanced modulator circuit, are shown in Fig. 7-13. The complete phase-shift sideband-generator circuit is formed by combining the circuits of Figs. 7-12 and 7-13. The component values indicated on the schematics will be correct for a generator operating in the vicinity of 9 mc.

The speech amplifier for a phase-shift generator is usually more critical in design than the audio circuits of the filter generator. Being highly selective, the filter will remove most of the spurious signal products which fall outside its bandpass response; it will also tend to shape the audio response of the transmitter for best intelligibility. The tuned circuits which follow the balanced modulators in the phase-shift transmitter have much poorer selectivity than the filter. As a result, any spurious products generated in the speech-amplifier or balanced modulator circuits will be passed on to the power-amplifier stages and appear in the emitted signal. It is especially important that the frequency response of the speech amplifier be of the proper shape, since the audio phase-shift networks will only maintain the required 90° phase difference over the range from 300 to 3,000 cycles. It is also essential that any inherent distortion be reduced to the lowest possible degree before the audio signal is applied to the phase-shift network. The audio amplifiers which follow the network not only must be free from distortion, but must not introduce any additional phase shift into the audio signals applied to the balanced modulators. Unless these precautions are observed, proper suppression of the undesired sideband will be virtually impossible.

The speech amplifier shown in Fig. 7-12 is designed to pass the frequencies between 300 and 3,000 cycles. The first and second audio amplifiers are a dual-triode 12AT7, and the third audio amplifier is one section of a 12AU7. C1 serves primarily as an RF filter, but also attenuates the very high speech frequencies. Negative current feedback is used in all three audio-amplifier stages in order to reduce signal distortion. The two .005-mfd capacitors C2 and C3, and resistors R5 and R6, form a high-pass AF filter network for rapid attenuation of frequencies below 300 cycles. A similar network—consisting of C4, C5, R9, and R10—couples the second and third audio-amplifier stages together. Transformer T1 couples the audio signal from the plate of the 12AU7 third audio amplifier to the balanced low-impedance, low-pass filter network. The latter is designed to attenuate all audio frequencies higher than 3,000 cycles. Transformer T1 is a miniature plate-to-line type with a primary impedance of 20K and a secondary impedance of 500 ohms. The DC plate current of the 12AU7 is returned to B+ through the 22K load resistor R12. (A small amount of distortion would be introduced into the audio signal if the 12AU7 DC plate return were completed through the T1 primary.)

The balanced low-pass audio filter is designed for an input and output impedance of 500 ohms, and inductances L1 and L2

133

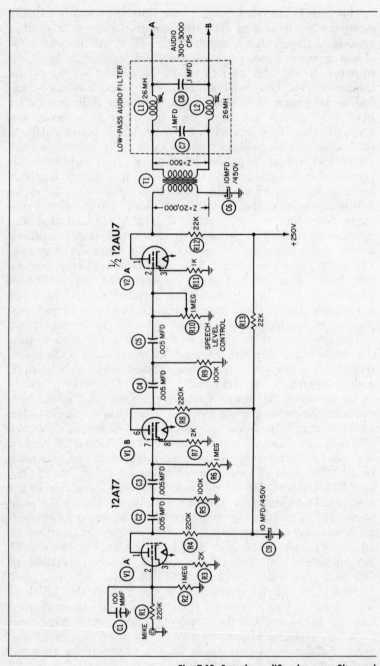

Fig. 7-12. Speech amplifier, low-pass filter and

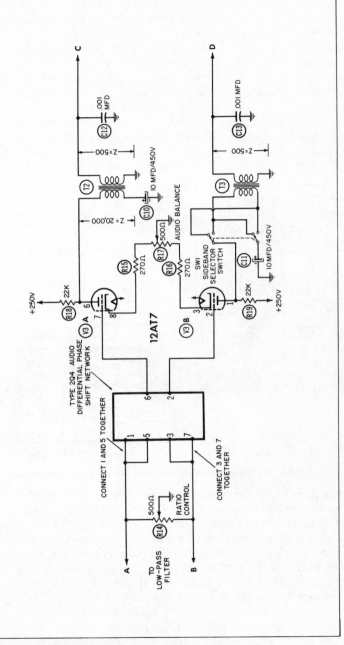

audio phase shift circuits of a phase-shift generator.

are adjusted to 26 mh each, as shown in Fig. 6-13. Filter output terminals A and B connect to the outside terminals of R 14 and the input terminals of the B & W Type 2Q4 audio phase-shift network, as shown in Fig. 7-12. The 500-ohm pot R14 is the "ratio" control (sometimes called the audio phasing control) of the audio phase-shift network. Normally it is adjusted to provide equal-amplitude audio-signal voltages at the output terminals (6 and 2) of the audio phase-shift network.

The audio-signal voltages at the control grids of audio amplifiers V3A and V3B should be equal in amplitude but 90° out of phase. The 500-ohm audio balance control, R17, is adjusted for equal audio-signal levels across the secondary windings of

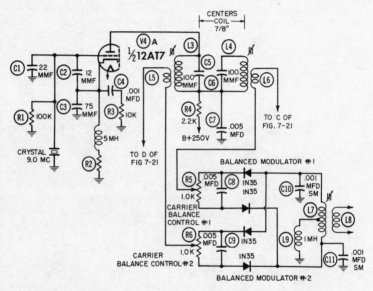

Fig. 7-13. Double balanced modulator and phase-shift generator.

T2 and T3. To prevent the possibility of phase shift and distortion being introduced into the two audio-output signals, the DC plate currents of V3A and V3B are returned to B+ through 22K plate load resistors R18 and R19. The upper or lower sideband is selected by reversing the connections between the plate of V3B and T3 primary. The two 90° displaced audio signals from terminals C and D are fed, through RF coil link windings L6 and L5, to the balanced modulators. The two .001-mfd RF bypass capacitors, C12 and C13, prevent the carrier-signal voltage from reaching the audio-amplifier circuits.

The crystal-controlled carrier generator is designed to operate at frequencies in the vicinity of 9 mc. The function of RF phase-shift network L3-L4 is to divide the carrier-generator signal into two separate RF signal components that must be approximately equal in amplitude and *precisely* 90° out of phase. In Fig. 7-13, the tuning core of L3 is adjusted to a slightly higher frequency, and L4 is adjusted to a slightly lower frequency, than that of the crystal. Each coil consists of twenty-two turns of No. 22 enameled copper wire closely wound onto a National XR-50 form. The forms are mounted with their centers spaced ⅞ inch apart. Link windings L5 and L6 consist of four turns of plastic-covered hookup wire wound over the "cold" ends of L3 and L4. To insure stable RF phasing adjustments, the coil windings should be drawn tightly on the forms. The tuned winding and the link of each coil is then coated with low-loss coil cement. The use of locknuts on the slug adjustment screws will assure that the phasing adjustments will remain fixed longer.

The two RF signals from link coils L5 and L6 are now applied to the rotors of R5 and R6, as shown in Fig. 7-13. The balanced output circuit, which consists of L7, C10 and C11, is resonated to the carrier frequency.

Alignment

The phase-shift single-sideband generator is considered somewhat more difficult to properly adjust than either of the filter generators previously described. In order to forestall vague and unusual conditions during adjustment, it is advisable to make some preliminary measurements in the circuit. The test instruments required for the adjustment and tests are an audio oscillator capable of good sine-wave output over the frequency range from 100 to 5,000 cycles, an oscilloscope, a VTVM, and a selectable-sideband communications receiver. The audio oscillator should include a built-in audio VTVM or other output-level indicating device, so that the same-amplitude audio signal will be applied to the speech-amplifier input at all frequencies. The gain of the speech amplifier should be adjusted to what is considered a normal value for the microphone to be used, and then left alone during adjustments on the generator circuits. The output attenuator of the audio oscillator is then used to prevent overloading of the speech-amplifier input stage. Such overload conditions must be guarded against, since erroneous readings will be obtained from a distorted audio test signal.

The first measurement is of the speech-amplifier frequency response, and the most convenient point to do this is at the input terminals of the audio phase-shift network. (The network should be removed from its socket during this test.) Audio ratio control R14 is adjusted for equal voltages at the 1-5 and

137

3-7 terminals of the phase-shift network socket. The VTVM test leads are then connected to socket terminals 1-5 and 3-7, as shown in Fig. 7-14. Beginning at 100 cycles, measure and record the VTVM readings (in decibels) obtained at 100-cycle intervals, up to 4,000 cycles. The output signal from the audio oscillator must be maintained constant at all test points. The vacuum-tube voltmeter readings are then plotted, on a db scale, against frequency.

The speech-amplifier response should be down at least 6 to 12 db at 300 and 3,000 cyclss, with rapid attenuation below and above these two frequencies. If there is insufficient attenuation of the low and high frequencies, the cause must be determined and corrected before any other measurements or adjustments are

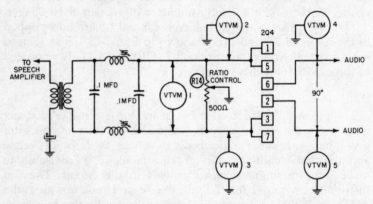

Fig. 7-14. Test points.

made. Low-frequency attenuation can be increased by using smaller values for C2, C3, C4, C5, R5, and R9. The low-pass filter components (L1, L2, C7, and C8) should be checked, as shown in Fig. 6-13. It is very important that the frequencies above 3,000 cycles be sharply attenuated, since the 90° differential between the output signals from the audio phase-shift network will deteriorate rapidly in this region.

After establishing that the frequency response of the speech amplifier is correct, replace the audio phase-shift network in its socket. Now adjust audio ratio control R14 for a signal-level ratio of precisely 2 to 7 at the input terminals of the audio phase-shift network. In the B & W Type 2Q4 network, the lower audio voltage should appear on terminals 3 and 7, which are connected together at the socket. The proper ratio is most easily obtained by adjusting the audio-signal level and R14 until 2 volts is indicated at terminals 3 and 7, and 7 volts at

138

terminals 1 and 5. Voltage measurements are made from each pair of terminals to ground. It may be necessary to reduce the level of the audio signal at the audio-oscillator output terminals before proceeding to the next adjustment.

The next step is to measure the levels (with respect to ground) of the audio signals at terminals 2 and 6 of the audio phase-shift network. The two voltages should be equal. If not, lightly touch up the adjustment of R14. Always recheck the ratios of the network input voltages after any adjustment of R14. If necessary, adjust R14 for the best compromise between the 2-to-7 input-voltage ratio and the equal output voltages.

All preliminary adjustments of the audio circuit are made with a test-signal frequency of 1,000 cycles when the B and W Type 2Q4 network is used. The Central Electronics Type PS-1 network requires a test frequency of 1,225 cycles. For other networks, refer to the manufacturer's instructions.

The VTVM is now connected alternately to terminals C and D, and the audio-signal voltages across the secondaries of T2 and T3 are measured. Adjust audio balance control R17 until the T2 and T3 secondary voltages are equal. The audio balance adjustment is ordinarily made at a frequency of 1,000 cycles. However, it is good practice to compare the levels of the two voltages at 100-cycle intervals over the range from 300 to 3,000 cycles.

At this point, the audio signal is removed and the carrier applied to the balanced modulators. If an RF demodulator probe is available, the VTVM may be used as an indicator for preliminary adjustments of the carrier generator and balanced modulator. Connect the VTVM (with RF probe) to the movable arm of carrier-balance potentiometer R6, and adjust L3 for maximum indication on the meter. Now detune L3 toward the high-frequency side of resonance, until the meter reads approximately 70% of maximum. Connect the VTVM to the movable arm of R5, and peak L4 for maximum indication. Detune L4 in the low-frequency direction, until the meter reads 70% of maximum. The RF voltage levels at the center terminals of R5 and R6 should be approximately equal.

Now rotate carrier balance controls R5 and R6 to either extreme. Connect the RF probe of the VTVM from one terminal of output link coil L8 to ground. Adjust the tuning core of L7 for maximum indication on the meter, and alternately adjust R5 and R6 for minimum indication. The nulls should appear near the center of the potentiometer ranges and be well defined. The two adjustments will interact, so a number of alternate adjustments will be required before the lowest possible indication is obtained.

The preliminary audio and RF adjustments have now been completed. Final adjustments on the phase-shift sideband generator will be made with an audio oscillator and an oscilloscope. Fig. 7-15 shows the proper method. The oscilloscope should be a high-frequency type, which will pass the 9-mc sideband signal through its vertical amplifier. Otherwise, an RF amplifier will be necessary between the balanced-modulator output circuit and the vertical-deflection plates of the oscilloscope. Most final adjustments of the sideband generator will be made after the remainder of the transmitter circuits have been wired and are operating. If the power-amplifier stages are working, it is

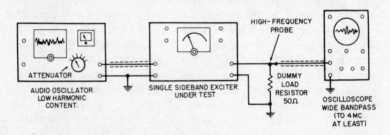

Fig. 7-15. Use of audio oscillator and oscilloscope for adjustment of phase-shift single-sideband generator.

advisable to make the final adjustments with the transmitter output circuits tuned to one of the amateur frequency bands. This will permit use of the sideband receiver for checking some of the adjustments. The RF output circuit of the transmitter should be terminated in a resistance dummy load, as shown in Fig. 7-15.

When a pure audio tone is applied to the speech amplifier of a perfectly designed and adjusted SSB generator or transmitter, the RF output signal will also be a pure tone. The waveform will appear on the oscilloscope screen as a succession of constant-amplitude sine-wave RF cycles. When the oscilloscope sweep rate is adjusted to a few hundred cycles, the RF signal will appear as a horizontal band across the screen, as shown in Fig. 7-16A. The top and bottom edges should be perfectly straight lines. Any traces of ripple indicate the presence of undesirable components in the signal.

Several typical oscilloscope RF patterns are depicted in Fig. 7-16. The pattern in Fig. 7-16A shows the desired sideband component when the modulating tone is a pure sine wave and the carrier and undesired sideband components are suppressed. In Fig. 7-16B, the presence of desired sideband is shown, along
140

with incomplete suppression of the undesired sideband and complete suppression of the carrier component. The width of the ripples should be observed; when the audio test signal is a pure 1,000-cycle sine wave, the ripple frequency will be 2,000 cycles, as shown. The pattern in Fig. 7-16C shows the presence of the desired sideband, plus incomplete suppression of the carrier and undesired sideband. Notice the two sets of ripple patterns. The wider (1 kc) pattern is due to the presence of the carrier signal. The narrow or (2 kc) pattern is caused by the undesired sideband component, shown alone in Fig. 7-16B.

(A) Properly adjusted generator (no ripple).

(B) Incomplete suppression of undesired sideband, 2-kc ripple.

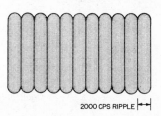

2000 CPS RIPPLE |←→|

(C) Incomplete suppression of carrier and undesired sideband, 1-kc ripple.

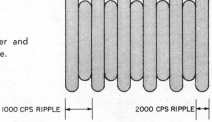

1000 CPS RIPPLE |←——→| 2000 CPS RIPPLE |←→|

Fig. 7-16. Single-sideband RF signal at generator output.

The patterns should be studied, preferably on the oscilloscope screen, until you can readily identify each ripple component. These oscilloscope waveform patterns are the key to the adjustments required in the sideband-generator circuit.

During the preceding discussions, it was emphasized that the audio signal applied to the balanced modulators must be as free from distortion as possible. If distortion occurs, either in the audio oscillator itself or in the speech-amplifier circuit,

141

AF harmonics will be generated and will appear as spurious components in the RF output signal. In phase-shift generators, the third harmonic of the 1,000-cycle test signal can be especially troublesome during undesired-sideband-suppression adjustments. As shown in Fig. 7-17, the RF signal produced by the third harmonic of the 1,000-cycle audio tone will appear 3,000 cycles away from the carrier frequency in the spectrum. The frequency difference between the desired-sideband component signal and spurious third-harmonic signal will be 2,000 cycles, and so will the frequency difference between the desired and undesired

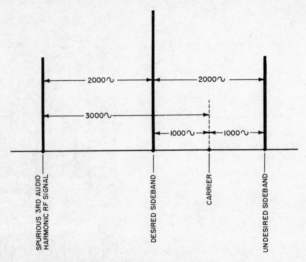

Fig. 7-17. Audio third-harmonic RF signal.

sidebands. Since the oscilloscope will show *all* the signal components present in the transmitter RF output, it is possible that the spurious RF signal caused by the audio harmonic, and the undesired-sideband component signal, will be out of phase and appear to cancel each other on the oscilloscope screen. This condition is more likely to occur when the level of the audio test signal at the speech-amplifier input is excessively high. As a result, the oscilloscope will present a false indication of the undesired sideband suppression.

The selectable-sideband communications receiver offers the most practical and convenient means of checking the transmitter signal for spurious components caused by audio harmonics. It is also valuable for checking the carrier and undesired-sideband suppression.

When the transmitter RF output circuit is terminated in a resistive dummy load, it will be necessary to short-circuit the

142

receiver antenna and ground terminals to prevent overloading the input RF-amplifier circuit during the tests. The receiver should be adjusted for a bandpass of 500 cycles or even narrower. The beat-frequency oscillator must be turned on and properly adjusted. Remove the audio signal from the speech amplifier of the transmitter, and accurately tune the receiver to zero-beat with the transmitter carrier. In most cases, there will be sufficient residual carrier in the signal to provide an indication on the receiver. If not, additional carrier signal can be obtained by adjusting either R5 or R6 from its null position. When the carrier has been identified and tuned to zero-beat on the receiver dial, readjust carrier-balance controls R5 and R6 for minimum indication on the receiver signal-level meter. Note the point on the receiver dial where zero-beat with the carrier signal occurs.

Apply the 1,000-cycle audio-modulation tone to the speech-amplifier input of the transmitter. Tune the receiver 1,000 cycles higher than the carrier frequency. Assuming that the phasing of the RF carrier signals at the balanced modulators is at least approximately correct, and that sideband-selector switch SW1 is in the proper position to transmit an upper-sideband signal, a strong unmodulated signal should appear on the receiver. Accurately tune the receiver for maximum signal indication, and note the meter reading obtained. Now tune the receiver 1,000 cycles lower than the carrier frequency. Another strong unmodulated signal should appear. This is the lower and, in this case, undesired sideband signal. It is quite likely that the signal levels of the two sidebands may be approximately equal at this time. When the modulating tone is a pure sine wave, the only signals which should appear in the transmitter output are the carrier and the two sidebands; any others are spurious. If the spurious signals occur at multiples of the modulation frequency, they are caused by AF harmonics. The source of the audio distortion may be in either the speech amplifier or audio oscillator. The majority of simple homemade audio oscillators have a high percentage of distortion. The best audio signal generator for single-sideband work is the type designed for testing high-fidelity audio amplifiers. Most of these generators have feedback circuits, which reduce the inherent distortion of the signal to a very low value.

If only the carrier and two sideband signals are present, you can proceed with the sideband-generator adjustments. It is best to obtain a visual indication with the oscilloscope, and then use the receiver to verify the information displayed on the screen.

Suppression of the carrier and undesired sideband can be approximated by measuring the amplitude of ripple component A

143

and comparing it with the over-all pattern amplitude of B, as shown in Fig. 7-18. The decibel values for several ratios of A to B are given in the accompanying table and are a fair approximation of the carrier and sideband suppression. It will be apparent, however, that accurate measurements of suppression values greater than 30 db are extremely difficult because of the smallness of ripple component A. The final critical adjustments are made by observing the signal level on the "S" meter of the receiver.

The preliminary oscilloscope pattern will very likely be similar to Fig. 7-16C. The carrier component must be suppressed before the sideband-suppression adjustments can be completed. The two carrier-balance controls, R5 and R6, are now alternately

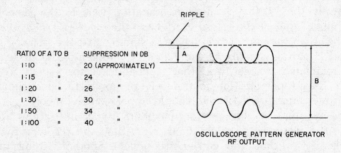

RATIO OF A TO B		SUPPRESSION IN DB	
1:10	=	20 (APPROXIMATELY)	
1:15	=	24	"
1:20	=	26	"
1:30	=	30	"
1:50	=	34	"
1:100	=	40	"

RIPPLE

OSCILLOSCOPE PATTERN GENERATOR RF OUTPUT

Fig. 7-18. Carrier and sideband suppression ratios.

adjusted to produce the pattern Fig. 7-16B. At this time, the carrier suppression should also be checked on the receiver. It may be necessary to readjust the carrier-balance controls from time to time during alignment.

After obtaining the pattern in Fig. 7-16B, alternately adjust the tuning slug of L4 the (RF phase adjustment) and audio balance control R17 for minimum ripple. When the RF phase and audio balance adjustments are correct, the pattern of Fig. 7-16A should be seen.

The sideband selector switch SW1 is now rotated to the opposite sideband position. If all adjustments are correct, the oscilloscope pattern should not change. In most cases, however, the RF phase and audio balance controls will require additional readjustment.

At this time, the relative amplitudes of the two sideband signals should be checked with the receiver. Place the transmitter sideband-selector switch in position 1, tune the receiver for maximum "S"-meter indication on the upper-sideband signal, and note the reading. Now tune the receiver to the lower-sideband

144

signal and again note the maximum "S"-meter reading. One of the sidebands should have a considerably higher signal level. Adjust the coupling between transmitter and receiver so that the stronger signal gives a level indication of exactly "S-9" when the receiver is tuned for the maximum reading. The weaker signal may then read, say, "S-5." Since the receiver is calibrated in 6-db steps, this would indicate that the weaker signal is 24 db below the stronger signal. With the receiver tuned to the weaker signal, very carefully adjust audio balance control R17 and the L4 slug for minimum signal indication. Tune to the stronger sideband signal and note whether its level changes. If so, readjust ratio control R14 *very carefully* on both the weak and strong sideband signals. The objective is to find the adjustment of R14 which will further reduce the level of the weaker sideband signal without affecting the level of the stronger signal.

The transmitter sideband-selector switch is now placed in position 2, and the levels of the two sideband signals observed on the receiver "S" meter. The sideband signal which was the stronger with the selector switch in position 1 should now be the weaker, and vice versa. The weaker signal in either switch position is the undesired sideband. In general, the RF phase, audio balance control, and ratio control are alternately adjusted for best suppression of the undesired sideband. The receiver is then tuned to the carrier frequency, and carrier-balance controls R5 and R6 alternately readjusted for minimum "S"-meter indication. All final adjustments are extremely critical, so handle them lightly.

It should be possible to suppress at least 30 db of undesired sideband without difficulty. In most cases, the suppression of one of the undesired sidebands will be slightly better than the other and the carrier suppression should be 40 db or better.

Chapter 8

Balanced Mixers
and Converters

The single-sideband signal is rarely if ever generated at the transmitted frequency. Instead, it is customary to generate the signal at some fixed frequency—usually in the low-frequency portion of the radio-frequency spectrum—and at a very low power level. This relatively weak signal is then heterodyned, through one or more translator stages, to the transmission frequency. Here the weak sideband signal is amplified to the desired power level in a system of linear RF amplifiers. The main concern is to translate the single-sideband waveform into the transmission frequency without changing its signal component. The frequency-converter circuits must be very carefully designed so that they do not add distortion or other spurious products to the signal. These special converter stages are generally referred to as "balanced" mixers and converters.

In order to understand why balanced mixers are necessary, let us review the operation of a typical mixer in the ordinary broadcast-band receiver. As shown in Fig. 8-1, the tuned RF

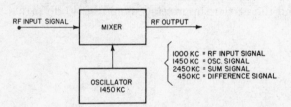

Fig. 8-1. Radio-receiver mixer circuit.

circuits of the receiver are adjusted to receive a 1,000-kc RF signal. This signal is then amplified and applied to the grid of the mixer tube, along with RF signal voltage from a local oscillator operating on a frequency of 1450 kc. It is common knowledge that the two RF signals will mix in the electron stream of the tube and produce the 450-kc IF in the mixer

146

plate circuit. What is *not* so commonly known is that other signals are present in the mixer plate circuit.

During our discussion of balanced modulators we learned that AF and RF signals, when mixed in a suitable device, will produce sum and difference frequencies which are different from either of the original signals. Likewise, when two RF signals are mixed, sum and difference RF signals are also produced. In the balanced modulator circuits, the original RF signal (carrier) was very carefully suppressed by circuit design and balancing adjustments. The audio signal did not appear in the output circuit because no low-frequency load was provided. However, when two RF signals are applied to a mixing device, the common output load impedance may be sufficiently high that all signals will appear with considerable amplitude.

In the mixer plate circuit, the signals which appear are the 1,000-kc RF carrier, 1450-kc local-oscillator, 450-kc difference-frequency, and 2450-kc sum-frequency signals, plus the harmonic frequencies of the 1000 and 1450-kc signals. With the exception of the 450-kc IF signal, the other frequencies in the plate circuit of the mixer are usually ignored, since they do not appear in the bandpass response of the IF amplifier. In a radio receiver, the mixer circuit is usually converting a high RF to a lower RF. In a single-sideband transmitter, however, the mixer circuit is almost always converting a low RF to a higher RF. The signal and conversion oscillator-frequency harmonics may mix under certain conditions to produce spurious signals within the bandpass of the RF amplifier stages which follow the mixer circuit. These undesired signal products may not only interfere with adjacent channels, but may also deteriorate the transmitter's own emitted signal. Usually, in the mixer plate circuit there are several undesired products greater in amplitude than the desired signal, and several with a lower amplitude. All of these products in the plate circuit—with the exception of the desired sum or difference signals—should be eliminated.

The circuit design engineer minimizes the spurious signal problem by (1) an intelligent selection of the signal and oscillator frequencies, (2) an experimental selection of mixer tubes, and (3) the use of special mixer-stage circuitry in which certain undesired products in the mixer plate circuit are suppressed. The selectivity of the tuned circuits which follow the mixer must be such that spurious signals outside the desired bandpass range will be rejected. In some transmitter designs, high-Q rejection traps are used to eliminate certain spurious signals which might be radiated at unauthorized frequencies. The problems involved in elimination of the various spurious-signal components becomes very complex in equipment which must be operated over a wide frequency range.

The block diagrams shown in Figs. 8-2A and B will illustrate some of the spurious-signal problems involved in the design of a practical transmitter. The block diagram at Fig. 8-2A shows

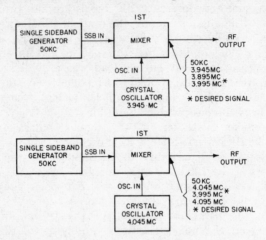

(A) Single-conversion circuits.

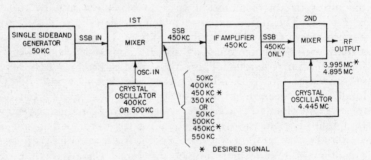

(B) Double conversion circuit.

Fig. 8-2. Conversion circuits of a single-sideband transmitter.

a sideband signal, generated at a carrier of 50 kc, being converted to an operating frequency within the 80-meter amateur band. Assume that we wish to operate on a frequency of 3.995 mc—which is well inside the legal band-frequency limits. In order to place the 50-kc sideband signal at 3.995 mc, we must mix the sideband signal with the output from an oscillator operating on a frequency of either 3.945 or 4.045 mc. When the 50-kc sideband signal is mixed with the 3.945-mc oscillator signal, the signals

148

appearing in the mixer plate circuit are 50 kc, 3.945 mc, the difference frequency at 3.895 mc, and the desired sum frequency at 3.995 mc. Harmonics of the input signals will also be present, but for purposes of this discussion they will be ignored.

When the 50-kc sideband signal is mixed with 4.045-mc oscillator signal, the signals appearing in the mixer plate circuit again are 50 kc, 4.045 mc, the desired difference frequency signal at 3.995 mc, and the sum frequency signal at 4.095 mc. And we again ignore the harmonics of the input signals.

All signals—except 3.995 mc are spurious. In any practical transmitter (using this particular scheme of frequency conversion), highly selective tuned circuits would be necessary to attenuate the undesired sum or difference sideband signals (±100 kc from the carrier). The oscillator signal which appears in the mixer plate circuit is separated from the operating frequency by only 50 kc. In most cases, the oscillator signal is greater in amplitude than that employed in ordinary receiver applications and rejection of this signal by tuned circuits in the mixer plate circuitry would require too high a degree of selectivity to be practicable. In this case, the solution is to use a double conversion system.

DOUBLE CONVERSION

A practical double-conversion system is illustrated in Fig. 8-2B. The sideband signal generated at 50 kc is mixed with the oscillator signal. The frequencies which appear in the mixer plate circuit will then be the two input signals and the usual sum and difference frequencies. As an example, when the injected oscillator signal is 400 kc, the mixer signals will include the 50-kc sideband signal, the 400-kc oscillator signal, the sum frequency of 450 kc, and the difference frequency of 350 kc. When the oscillator signal is 500 kc, the frequencies appearing at the mixer plate will be 50, 500, 550 and 450 kc. In both examples, all frequencies except the 450-kc signal are spurious.

Notice that the amount of frequency separation between the desired and undesired signals is the same as in Fig. 8-2A. However, because of the better selectivity obtainable in the tuned circuits at 450 kc, attenuation of the various spurious signals— except possibly the oscillator signal at the mixer plate will not be difficult. Since the oscillator signal is usually quite strong and is also close in frequency to the desired signal, it is generally suppressed by a balanced mixer arrangement.

The double-conversion system of Fig. 8-2B can also be used for sideband selection (upper or lower) in the transmitted signal. In the previous discussions on sideband selection, it was pointed

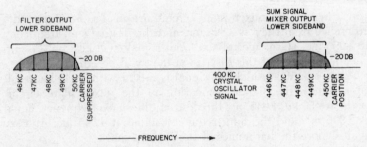

Fig. 8-3. Sum frequency at mixer output.

out that when the carrier was placed at the −20-db attenuation point on the high-frequency slope of a symmetrical filter, the filter would pass the lower sideband. Likewise, when the carrier was placed at the same attenuation point on the low-frequency slope, the upper sideband would be passed. While this condition is true for HF symmetrical bandpass filters, many low-frequency toroidal filters do not have a symmetrical bandpass characteristic. A good example of a nonsymmetrical bandpass single-sideband filter is the Burnell S-15000, the characteristic response of which is shown in Fig. 4-1. This particular filter is designed for a 50-kc carrier and passes the lower sideband, down to approximately 46.5 kc.

When the lower sideband from the filter is mixed with the 400-kc oscillator signal (as shown in Fig. 8-2B), the 50-kc carrier will add to the oscillator signal; and the new sum frequency will then appear at 450 kc. Let's assume that the filter passes a sideband consisting of 49-, 48-, and 47-kc signals (Fig. 8-3); then the sideband frequencies at the mixer plate will be 449, 448, and 447 kc. Since they are lower than the 450-kc carrier, the desired signal in the mixer circuit will be a still lower sideband.

When the lower sideband from the filter is mixed with the 500-kc oscillator signal, the signal at the mixer plate will be

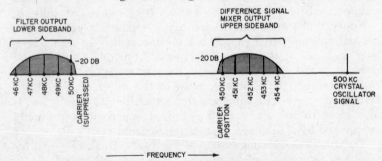

Fig. 8-4. Difference frequency at mixer output.

150

the difference frequency. Subtracting the 50-kc carrier from the 500-kc oscillator signal gives the new difference frequency, also 450 kc. In the same manner the 49-kc filter signal, subtracted from the 500-kc signal, will appear at 451 kc, the 48-kc signal will appear at 452 kc and the 47-kc signal will appear at 453 kc, as shown in Fig. 8-4. Since the sideband frequencies are now higher than the 450-kc carrier, the desired signal at the mixer plate is an upper-sideband signal.

TRIODE BALANCED MIXERS

Any of the balanced modulators described can be used for frequency conversion. The diode mixer, however, is rarely used at high frequencies because of its internal losses and the expense of the special diodes themselves. Current practice is to use vacuum tubes for RF mixers and frequency converters, because of their conversion gain, low cost, and relative freedom from spurious signal products. Because of its low noise characteristic, the triode is the tube most widely used as a balanced mixer.

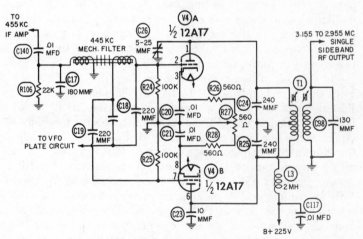

Fig. 8-5. Balanced first mixer of the Collins 32S-1.

Fig. 8-5 shows the balanced first mixer of a single-sideband transmitter. The tube in this circuit is a 12AT7 dual-triode. Not shown is a 6DC6 pentode 455-kc amplifier between the balanced modulator and sideband filter. The resonant input circuit of the filter is tuned to 455 kc and connected, in an unbalanced configuration, into the plate circuit of the 6DC6. The double-sideband signal applied to the filter input terminals is approximately 100 millivolts.

151

The resonant output circuit of the filter is arranged in a balanced, or push-pull, configuration. The output signal is applied to the control grids of a 12AT7 mixer. The sideband signal at the 12AT7 grids will have the usual 180°, or push-pull, phase relationship. The two plates of the mixer are also connected in a push-pull, or balanced, output. It is important to understand, however, that the resonant output is in push-pull *only for the single-sideband RF signal* at the mixer plates; the mixer output is *not* tuned to the input frequency.

If you examine the mixer input circuit of Fig. 8-5, you will notice that C18 and C19 are connected in series across the output winding of the filter. The center junction of these capacitors is *not* returned to ground—as is customary in push-pull resonant circuitry—but to the plate circuit of the 6AU6 oscillator. Since an equal amount of oscillator signal will be applied to each grid, the grids are effectively connected in parallel. From your study of balanced modulators, you learned that when two grids are driven in parallel and the plates are connected in push-pull, the applied signal will be balanced out, or "suppressed," in the output circuit. In Fig. 8-5, the oscillator components cancel in the primary of T1 and therefore do not appear in the secondary. The sideband signal appears, however, because it is applied in push-pull to the two grids and is removed in push-pull from the two plates.

The 12AT7 cathodes are bypassed for RF by C20 and C21. Each triode section is biased by its own 560-ohm cathode resistor, R26 and R28. Both are returned to the outside terminals of the 500-ohm balance pot, R27, the main purpose of which is to equalize the bias applied to each grid. R27 normally is adjusted for minimum oscillator signal across the secondary winding of T1. In addition to R27, two capacitors are used for RF balancing purposes. C23 (10 mmf) is connected from the plate of V4B to ground, and 5- to 25-mmf variable trimmer C26 is connected from the plate of V4A to ground. The adjustments of R27 and C26 will interact to some extent, so a number of alternate adjustments may be necessary before satisfactory suppression of the oscillator signal can be obtained.

Fig. 8-6 shows a 12AT7 balanced mixer circuit, which was used in some of the older sideband transmitters. The two signals are mixed in the cathode circuit. The oscillator signal is suppressed in the output circuit because it is fed out of phase (with respect to the applied RF) to the mixer plate (Pin 1) through trimmer C1. C1 normally is adjusted for minimum oscillator signal across the secondary of T1. The main advantage of this mixer is that no push-pull input or output circuitry is

152

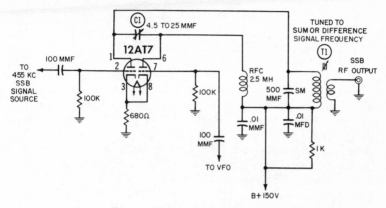

Fig. 8-6. Dual-triode balanced mixer.

required. For optimum mixer performance, the conversion oscillator signal should have at least 15 to 20 times the amplitude of the sideband input signal. The mixer circuit of Fig. 8-5 will generally give superior performance, compared with the circuit of Fig. 8-6.

PENTODE MIXERS

The Hammarlund HX-500 single-sideband transmitter makes extensive use of pentode mixer circuitry. Fig. 8-7 shows the

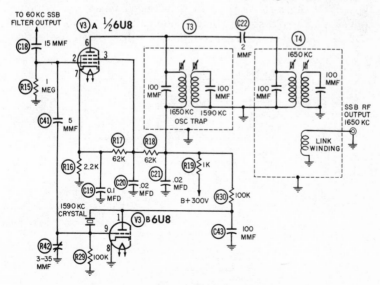

Fig. 8-7. First mixer of the Hammarlund HX-500.

153

first mixer of the HX-500. The 6U8 triode section acts as a crystal-controlled conversion oscillator, the signal of which is injected into the control grid of the pentode section.

The sideband signal in this transmitter is generated and filtered at a carrier of 60 kc, after which it is applied to the 6U8 pentode and mixed with the 1590-kc oscillator signal. The desired sideband then appears in the plate circuit at 1650 kc. This is the *sum* signal, obtained by adding the 60-kc sideband frequencies to the 1590-kc oscillator frequency. The difference-frequency signal appears at 1530 kc and is rejected by the relatively high-Q tuned circuits of output transformer T4. Notice that a relatively small amount of signal is fed, through C22, into the primary of T4 from the plate of V3A. Both T3 and T4 are individually shielded, and there is no magnetic coupling between the windings of the two sets of tuned circuits. A high-Q trap, closely coupled to the tuned plate coil of T3, is tuned to the oscillator frequency in order to absorb or "trap out" the oscillator signal which appears in the mixer plate circuit. The HX-500 first mixer circuit is not balanced in any sense of the word, but is a good example of how undesired signal components can be removed by selective tuned circuits.

BEAM-DEFLECTION TUBE MIXER

In addition to being an excellent balanced modulator, the RCA 7360 can also be used as a balanced mixer or frequency converter. Fig. 8-8 shows the recommended circuit for the 7360 when employed as a balanced mixer with separate excitation.

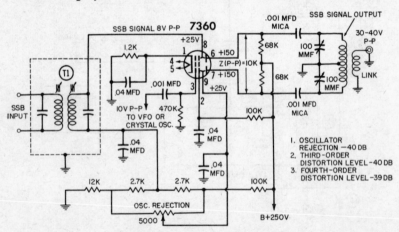

Fig. 8-8. RCA 7360 used as a balanced RF mixer.

Unlike the output, the input sideband and oscillator signals are unbalanced to ground. In a balanced mixer, the tube is very similar in action to the balanced modulator described previously.

The DC applied to each plate should be 150 volts, and the accelerator (grid 2) voltage should be approximately 175 volts. The required maximum RF deflection voltage is approximately 8 volts, peak-to-peak, and the peak-to-peak oscillator signal at grid No. 1 should be about 10 volts. The sideband signal may be applied to either deflection electrode, provided of course that the other electrode is RF bypassed to ground. The RF output will be on the order of 40 volts when the tube is operated under the specified conditions. The oscillator signal in the tuned output circuit will be about −40 db with respect to the single-sideband output voltage. The third- and fourth-order distortion will be approximately −40 and −39 db, respectively, with reference to the sideband output voltage.

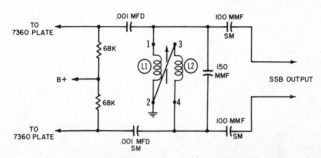

Fig. 8-9. Details of bifilar output coil for 7360 balanced mixer.

The balanced output circuit may be tuned with a two section variable capacitor as shown in Fig. 8-8, or by a bifilar-wound, slug-tuned coil as in Fig. 8-9. A bifilar output coil for 14 mc will consist of 10 turns of No. 18 enameled copper wire wound onto a National XR-50 form. A value of resonating capacitor should be selected that allows the tuned circuit to resonate at 14 megacycles with the tuning slug positioned at the center of its adjustment range. In either case, the output tuned circuit should have a reasonably high Q.

When used in either a balanced modulator or balanced mixer application, the 7360 should be mounted as far as possible from all devices producing extraneous magnetic fields (such as power transformers, filter chokes, and tube heater wiring). A standard metal shield is recommended on the 7360 for both balanced modulator and balanced mixer service. All components and wiring associated with the plates and deflection electrodes should be

155

laid out symmetrically on the chassis. These precautions are especially important in balanced mixer applications, since only slight differences in stray circuit capacitance can unbalance the output circuit. In addition, all components of a balanced mixer stage should be rigidly mounted.

Chapter 9

Low Power Single-Sideband Transmitters

In the preceding chapters the basic circuitry of the single-sideband transmitter was discussed in detail. This chapter is devoted to the design objectives and principles of several commercial SSB transmitters, in order to illustrate current good engineering and design practice. The emphasis will be placed on basic principles and approaches rather than on precise circuit details. While all schematics shown here are accurate, keep in mind that all communications equipment is subject to minor changes from time to time. Consequently, readers who desire more information on specific pieces of equipment should refer to the manuals and other literature published by the particular manufacturer. When any of your communications equipment requires service, always follow the instructions in the manufacturer's service manual.

COLLINS 32S-3

The Collins 32S-3 is a good example of current engineering design. The 32S-3 is a single-sideband (SSB) or CW, 175-watt, amateur transmitter covering the 80-, 40-, 20-, 15-, and 10-meter bands. The transmitter uses filter-type sideband generation and heterodyne exciter principles. A crystal-controlled BFO, crystal-controlled high-frequency oscillator, and highly stable VFO form a double-conversion circuit. The low-frequency IF is 455 kc, and the high-frequency IF is a 200-kc wide bandpass circuit. The 32S-3 may be connected in transceiver service with any of the Collins 75S series receivers. Fig. 9-1 shows the front panel and operating controls, and Fig. 9-2 illustrates the general arrangement of the circuits.

Microphone or phone-patch input is connected to the grid of first audio amplifier V1A, amplified, and coupled to the grid of second audio amplifier V1B. Output from V1B is coupled to the

157

grid of cathode follower V2A across the microphone gain control. Output from the cathode follower is fed to the balanced modulator. In "tune," "lock key," and "CW" positions of the emission switch, output from tone oscillator V11B is fed to the grid of the second audio amplifier. Amplified tone-oscillator signal is taken from the plate of V1B and applied to the grid of VOX amplifier V14A and CW sidetone jack J19.

Fig. 9-1. Front view of Collins 32-S3 transmitter.

Audio output from the cathode of V2A is fed to the junction of CR3 and CR4. In USB and LSB positions of the emission switch, the BFO voltage is fed to the junction of C187A and C187B. In "tune," "lock key," and "CW" positions of the emission switch, the BFO voltage bypasses the balanced modulator, IF amplifier, and mechanical filter and is fed directly to one of the first-mixer cathodes. An output signal from the balanced modulator, consisting of both upper and lower sidebands, is coupled through IF transformer T2 to the grid of IF amplifier V3. The amplified double-sideband signal from the V3 plate is fed to the mechanical filter, FL1. The passband of FL1 is centered at 455 kc.

The mechanical filter will pass either the upper or lower sideband, depending on the sideband polarity selected when the emission switch connects BFO crystal Y12 or Y13. The single-sideband output from FL1 is connected to the grids of the first balanced mixer in push-pull.

While the 455-kc single-sideband signal is fed to the first balanced mixer grids in push-pull, the VFO signal is applied to the grids in parallel and the mixer plates are connected in push-

158

pull. As a result of this circuit arrangement, the mixer cancels the VFO signal energy in the plate circuit and translates the 455-kc single-sideband signal to a 2.955- to 3.155-mc single-sideband carrier signal. This signal is at the bandpass IF frequency. The coupling network between the plates of the first mixer and the grid of the second balanced mixer is broadbanded to provide a uniform response to the bandpass intermediate

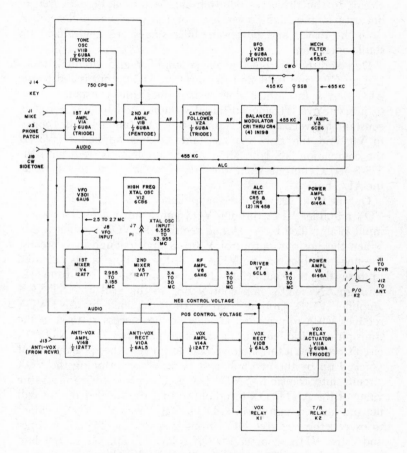

Fig. 9-2. Block diagram of 32-S3 transmitter.

frequency. The bandpass IF signal is fed to one of the grids of the second balanced mixer, and the high-frequency injection signal from crystal oscillator V12 is fed to the signal input cathode and to the other grid. This arrangement cancels the high-frequency injection-signal energy within the mixer and translates the bandpass IF signal to the desired operating band.

159

The slug-tuned circuits coupling V5 to V6, V6 to V7, and V7 to the power amplifier are ganged to the exciter tuning control. The signal is amplified by the RF amplifier, V6, and the driver, V7, to drive power amplifiers V8 and V9. The RF output from the parallel power amplifiers is tuned by a pi-network and applied to the antenna through the contacts of transmit-receive relay K2. Negative RF feedback from the power-amplifier plate circuit to the driver cathode circuit permits a high degree of linearity at the high-power level of the power-amplifier tubes. Both the driver and power-amplifier stages are neutralized for stable operation.

Detected audio from the power-amplifier grid circuit is rectified by CR5 and CR6, and the negative DC output is fed to the ALC bus. A fast-attack slow-release dual time constant is used to prevent over-driving on initial syllables and to hold the gain constant between words. The fast-time-constant ALC is applied to V6, and the slow-time-constant ALC is applied to V3. If the companion 30S-1 or 30L-1 power amplifier is used with the 32S-3, ALC output from the 30S-1 or 30L-1 is fed back to the ALC bus.

Output from second audio amplifier V1B is fed to the grid of VOX amplifier V14A through VOX gain control R74. This audio input is amplified by V14A and rectified by VOX rectifier V10B. When the positive output of V10B is high enough to overcome the negative bias on the V11A grid, the VOX relay is actuated to turn the transmitter on. Receiver output is fed from J13 through ANTIVOX gain control R85 to the grid of ANTIVOX amplifier V14B. Output from V14B is rectified by ANTIVOX rectifier V10A to provide the negative bias necessary to keep the transmitter disabled during receive periods. The ANTIVOX circuit provides a threshold voltage to prevent the speaker output (picked up by the microphone circuits) from tripping the VOX circuits into transmit. ANTIVOX gain control R85 adjusts the value of the ANTIVOX threshold so that the speaker output will not produce enough positive DC voltage from the VOX rectifier to exceed the negative DC output from the ANTIVOX rectifier and cause V11A to actuate VOX relay K1. Speech energy into the microphone will cause the positive VOX voltage to overcome the negative ANTIVOX voltage and produce the desired action of K1. The contacts of relay K1 control relay K2, the key line, the power amplifier and driver screens, the receiver muting circuits, the oscillator plate voltages, and the high-voltage relay in the DC supply.

The microphone gain control is a dual potentiometer, one section of which controls the audio gain during SSB operation.

160

The other section is a cathode potentiometer which controls the gain of RF amplifier V6 during CW operation.

The tone oscillator is used for VOX-circuit actuation and sidetone generation during CW operation. It consists of an RC phase-shift type of oscillator operating at approximately 750 cps. Its output signal is amplified by the second audio amplifier, which then supplies the sidetone output and also activates the VOX circuitry to provide CW break-in. In "tune" and "lock key," the oscillator is used in conjunction with the second audio amplifier to give sidetone output. The oscillator is turned on when the emission switch section SC8 is placed in the "tune," "lock key," or CW position.

The BFO is crystal controlled at either 453.650 or 456.350 kc, depending on whether Y12 or Y13 is selected by the emission switch. These crystal frequencies are matched to the passband of mechanical filter FL1 so that the carrier frequency is placed approximately 20 db down on the skirts of the filter response. This 20-db carrier suppression is in addition to the 30-db suppression provided by the balanced modulator.

The VFO uses fixed capacitors, a permeability-tuned variable inductor, and fixed inductors to provide the tuning range of 2.5 to 2.7 mc. The frequency-determining network is composed of capacitors C301, C302, C303, and C305, and inductors L301, L302, and L303. Capacitor C303 is paralleled by trimmer capacitor C308 and diode CR301 connected in series. A DC bias voltage is applied to the diode through an RF isolation resistor, R303. When LSB transmission is selected, negative bias is applied to CR301 which switches C308 out of the circuit. Selection of USB emission applies positive bias to CR301 and causes it to conduct, which switches C308 into the circuit. Proper adjustment of C308 shifts the VFO output frequency by an amount equal to the frequency separation of the two BFO crystals. This allows selection of either sideband without changing the suppressed-carrier frequency of the exciter RF output.

The high-frequency crystal oscillator, V12, is crystal-controlled by one of the 13 crystals selected by bandswitch S11. The RF output from the high-frequency crystal oscillator is fed to the second mixer. This frequency is always 3.155 mc higher than the lower edge of the desired transmit band. This high-frequency injection signal is the crystal fundamental frequency for all desired output signals below 12 mc; but for operating frequencies higher than 12 mc, the crystal frequency is doubled in the plate circuit of the oscillator.

Grid-block type keying is used for CW operation in the 32S-3. With the key up, a negative voltage is applied to the grids

161

of the second audio amplifier and the second mixer. This prevents the amplified tone-oscillator output from actuating the VOX circuitry and also cuts off the second mixer. The keying time constant of the second audio amplifier is fast attack and slow release—with R127 and C115 determining the fast attack, and R125 and C115 determining the slow release. The keying time constant of the second mixer is slow attack and slow release, with the slow attack determined by R123, R124, and C81. R123, R124, C81, and C115 determine the slow-release time. When keying takes place, the second audio amplifier and therefore the VOX circuitry are actuated before the second mixer. The release times of the second audio amplifier and second mixer are approximately the same. The VOX time-constant control adjusts the release time of the VOX circuitry to permit fast on-off keying.

The variable resistor, R123, provides a choice between the extremes of "hard" and "soft" keying. Capacitor C115 largely determines the release time of the "break." An additional effect is that the larger this capacitor is, the greater is the "lag" introduced, which is characterized by the bell-like type of keying well known to CW operators. The values of C115 and R123 have been chosen to produce generally acceptable keying. While it is not suggested that the value of C115 should be changed, if the operator desires more of the bell-like characteristic, a slightly larger value will produce the effect. The additional "lag," however, will reduce the maximum speed at which the 32S-3 may be satisfactorily keyed.

THE HAMMARLUND HX-500

The Hammarlund HX-500 single-sideband transmitter covers the 80-, 40-, 20-, 15-, and 10-meter amateur bands. The desired operating frequency is selected by means of an eight-position rotary bandswitch. Four of the bandswitch positions provide complete frequency coverage of the 10-meter band. The VFO covers a frequency range of 500 kc in any one of the eight bandswitch positions. The VFO "slide-rule" scale is calibrated to an accuracy of 200 cycles or better. One rotation of the tuning knob covers 20 kc on the illuminated drum dial.

The HX-500 is capable of transmitting either an upper- or lower-sideband, or a suppressed-carrier double-sideband CW, MF or FSK signal. The power output is 70 to 100 watts, except on double-sideband (with carrier) AM, which is 17 to 25 watts. The carrier suppression on both upper- and lower-sideband transmission is better than −50 db, and the unwanted-sideband rejection is greater than −50 db. Spurious signals generated within the unit are suppressed to a level of −50 db or more, and the inter-modulation-distortion products have been suppressed beyond the −30-db level.

The linear power-amplifier (final) tank circuit uses a pi-network to match the 6146 plates to the 50-ohm transmission line. The network also tends to suppress any output-stage RF harmonics which might interfere with television reception. The logarithmic carrier-level indicator provides a very simple means of tuning and continuously monitoring the transmitter. As shown in Fig. 9-4, all controls required for tuning and operating the transmitter have been grouped on the front panel for maximum operating convenience.

Fig. 9-4. Hammarlund HX-500 transmitter.

Fig. 9-5 (see foldout section) shows the HX-500 circuit, and a simplified block diagram appears in Fig. 9-6. The technical description which follows can be most easily understood by referring to both the schematic and the block diagram. Since the HX-500 speech-amplifier circuitry and the carrier generator were described in previous chapters, a detailed description of these sections will not be included. Instead, the description will begin with the balanced modulator and sideband filter sections.

Circuit Analysis

The sideband generator section of the HX-500 (Fig. 9-7) is designed as a complete electrical and mechanical subassembly.

163

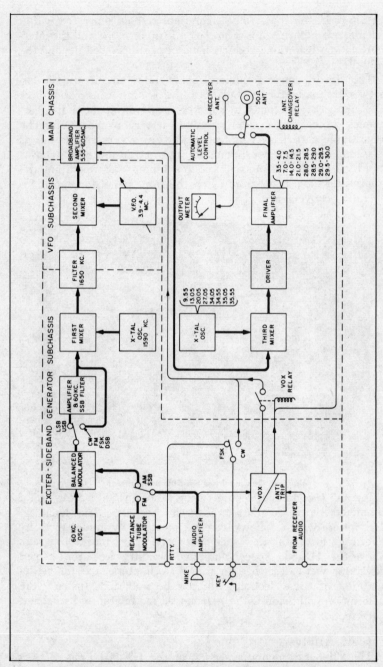

Fig. 9-6. Block diagram of Hammarlund HX-500.

That includes the 60-kc generator, speech amplifier, balanced modulator, and the 60-kc amplifier and sideband filter. Also included are the first mixer, the 1590-kc oscillator, a reactance-tube modulator for FM and FSK transmission, and the VOX relay circuitry.

As shown in Fig. 9-5, signal voltage from the microphone is applied to the speech-amplifier input through a front-panel microphone connector. It is then amplified by means of a three-stage resistance-coupled amplifier, which consists of both sections of the 12AX7 (V5A and V5B), and one section of the 6CM7 (V6A). The amplifier response is limited to frequencies below 300 cycles by using appropriate values of coupling capacitors. This limited frequency response helps to improve the unwanted sideband rejection in the sideband filter, and also prevents distortion due to overloading of the amplifier circuits by high-energy, low-frequency peaks. The main audio output signal is applied either to the balanced modulator for AM (double-sideband) and single-

Fig. 9-7. HX-500 sideband-generator subassembly.

sideband operation, or to the reactance-tube modulator for FM operation. When the transmitter is operated on CW or FSK, the audio amplifier is out of the circuit. A portion of the audio signal is routed to the VOX circuits for automatically controlled voice-operated relay operation.

The carrier generator operates at 60 kc, using a 6AU6 pentode tube (V1) in an electron-coupled Hartley oscillator circuit. The

165

low LC ratio of the oscillator tank circuit, and the low frequency used for the carrier signal, provide a degree of frequency stability usually obtained in a crystal-controlled oscillator only. The use of a self-controlled oscillator permits its frequency to be varied (modulated) for FM and FSK transmission. This is accomplished by the reactance-tube modulator connected in parallel with the oscillator tank circuit. The temperature stability of the 60-kc oscillator is improved by use of a special ferrite tuning core in tank coil L1.

The carrier-generator signal is coupled to the diode modulator by transformer, T1, the secondary of which is bifilar wound in order to supply the necessary balanced carrier signal to the modulator. Diodes CR1 and CR2 are employed as the modulator elements because of their good linearity and very high front-to-back conduction ratio. The operation of this balanced modulator in producing a double-sideband suppressed carrier is similar to that of the diode modulators described previously. When the modulator is unbalanced by disconnecting one of the diodes, a conventional AM signal will be produced.

The low carrier frequency permits the use of a highly efficient and unique tuned filter circuit for removing the undesired sideband and properly shaping the high side of the desired sideband. The first group of filters (Fig. 9-5) consists of L3, L4, and L5 working into the 6EW6 pentode amplifier tube, V2. The output signal from V2 is applied to a second filter group composed of L6, L7, L8, and L9. The amplification obtained in the 6EW6 compensates for the insertion loss of the two filter sections, and the amplifier circuitry provides the isolation required for optimum performance.

As shown in Fig. 9-7, each tuned circuit of the over-all filter is individually shielded. Coupling between the tuned circuits is made through small fixed capacitors; the values selected are such that some circuits are overcoupled and others are undercoupled. The over-all effect is to produce a filter with adequate bandpass and the sharp cutoff characteristics required for single-sideband operation. To further improve the skirt selectivity of the filter, a bifilar "T" trap rejection filter (T2 and Z1 in Fig. 9-5) is inserted between the 6EW6 plate and the input to the second group of tuned circuits. This trap is adjusted for maximum rejection of the undesired sideband at 250 cycles away from the carrier frequency.

The filter is factory-aligned to pass the upper sideband of the 60-kc suppressed carrier. When passage of the lower sideband is desired instead, a small amount of closely controlled fixed capacitance is added to each bandpass tuned circuit in order to lower the resonant frequency. In this manner, the passband is

166

located symmetrically below the carrier frequency instead of above it. During CW, FM, FSK, or AM, the 60-kc amplifier and sideband filter are bypassed and the signal is applied directly to the first mixer stage.

In the first mixer stage, a 6U8 dual-purpose pentode triode combines the function of both mixer and oscillator. The pentode section (V3A) acts as the mixer and the triode section (V3B) is used as a 1590-kc crystal-controlled oscillator. The resultant beat signal from the mixer is applied to the input of a 1650-kc filter for still further shaping of the signal passband characteristics.

The oscillator plate voltage is regulated at 150 volts to insure good frequency stability. A special 1590-kc trap, which is part of the output filter, prevents the oscillator signal from being passed on the following stages. The two sections of the 1,650-kc filter located on the exciter chassis are joined to the third section on the VFO chassis by a low-capacitance, shielded polyethylene cable. The output of this filter is applied to the grid of the second mixer.

The sideband signal at the grid of V9A is mixed with the signal from the VFO (V9B), which is tunable over the frequency range from 3.9 to 4.4 mc. The second mixer and oscillator stages are assembled on a separate subchassis to provide good mechanical and electrical isolation. This modified Colpitts oscillator has a low LC ratio; it uses a special ceramic coil form and a high-stability tuning capacitor. The circuit is also temperature-compensated to minimize frequency drift during warm-up.

The output signal from the second mixer may be at any frequency from 5.55 to 6.05 mc, depending on the VFO frequency. The output signal is then applied to filter sections T7, T8, and T9, which are resonated in the 5.55 to 6.05-mc bandpass region. T7 and T8 are located on the VFO subchassis and T9 is on the main chassis. The signal is coupled from T8 to T9 by a low-impedance, low-capacitance polyethylene cable. From the center tap of bifilar transformer T7 there are two wave traps, which comprise the Z2 subassembly and are connected to ground. These traps are tuned to 5.5 and 6.15 mc so that they effectively eliminate the possibility of spurious radiation at or close to these frequencies.

Since the single-sideband signal may be anywhere within 5.55 to 6.05 mc, a broadband RF amplifier must follow. The RF amplifier consists of 6CB6 pentodes V10 and V11, and bandpass transformers T9, T10, and T11. The 6CB6's are used chiefly because of their excellent linearity and wide frequency-handling capabilities. Normally they are biased at a high −50 volts so that in the receive or standby modes, the signal does not pass beyond this stage. When the telegraph-key or VOX relay contacts are closed during transmission, this high negative bias is removed. The amplifier then amplifies the signal in the normal manner. The grids of the two amplifiers are returned to the transmitter ALC voltage source.

After the signal has been amplified, it is applied to the control grid of the 6EW6 third mixer. Notice that the secondary of T11 is not connected directly to the 6EW6 grid. Instead, the signal is coupled to the grid through 10-mmf capacitor C110. The purpose of this arrangement is to prevent the third-mixer grid resistor, R110, from loading the T11 tuned circuits. The sideband signal, which is in the 5.55- to 6.05-mc frequency range when applied to the 6EW6, is mixed with a signal from crystal-controlled oscillator V13. The oscillator frequency is selected so that, when the two signals are mixed, the resultant signal at the 6EW6 plate will be at the desired operating frequency (3.5 to 30 mc, depending on the crystal frequency and the position of the band-selector switch). In the HX-500 frequency-conversion scheme, the sidebands are reversed, with respect to the front-panel knob indication, up to the input of the third mixer. The desired signal from the third mixer is the difference frequency between the two input signals. It is here that the sidebands are again reversed to correspond to the front-panel knob indication. The use of separate oscillator and mixer tubes provides a high degree of electrical isolation and frequency stability. When not transmitting, the 6EW6 third mixer is also biased at −50 volts to provide additional protection against undesired radiation of RF energy.

In Fig. 9-5, the signal from the third mixer plate is applied to the 12BY7 amplifier driver. The purpose in selecting the 12BY7 high-gain amplifier is to obtain sufficient RF voltage swing (about 50 to 60 peak volts) to drive the final output stage to full power capability. The operation of the 12BY7 as a class-A amplifier is also quite linear. Since the power-amplifier output stage is operated class AB_1, no grid current is drawn under normal operating conditions and thus the 12BY7 need not supply any RF driving power. The driver stage operates as a high-gain RF voltage amplifier only.

The final linear power amplifier is two 6146 pentodes connected in parallel. These provide a nominal PEP power output of 100 watts on either upper- or lower-sideband transmission; 100 watts on CW, FM, and FSK, plus maximum linearity and minimum distortion. The power output on AM (double sideband) is 25 watts.

The power amplifier is neutralized on the highest-frequency portion of the 10-meter band by 15-mmf adjustable capacitor C149 in order to maintain its performance over the entire range of operating frequencies. RF choke, L34, in the grid circuit of the 6146's, provides the proper input impedance, as well as serving as a grid return for the negative bias supply voltage. RF chokes L27 and L28, and the 100-ohm, two-watt resistors R120 and R121, act as low-Q parasitic suppressors. R119 and R122, in series with the 6146 screens, also suppress parasitic oscillations.

The RF output signal is applied to a pi-network which includes L31 and appropriate values of tank capacitance. Taps on L31 are selected, by the band-selector switch, to provide optimum load impedance for the frequency band in use. The output impedance is fixed at 50 ohms, thus eliminating an impedance mismatch between the transmitter output and a standard 50-ohm antenna systems. With other impedances, a simple external antenna coupler may be used. The antenna changeover relay is also included in the transmitter.

A portion of the RF output signal is also applied to the cathode of 6AL5 ALC rectifier V17B. It is then rectified to provide a negative control voltage, which is applied to the two 6CB6 bandpass amplifier tubes, V10 and V11. This control voltage varies directly with changes in the output signal. The net result is to control, or limit, the gain of the bandpass amplifier so that subsequent stages (particularly the final amplifier) will not be overdriven.

The 50K pot, R124, acts as a voltage divider across the ALC rectifier and thereby permits the threshold level to be varied according to individual operating requirements. This arrangement delays the action of the ALC rectifier until the output from the final amplifier is relatively high. In this manner, the transmitter is able to operate with normal gain characteristics under average signal conditions. When the predetermined level of output signal is exceeded, the automatic level-control circuit will then respond very rapidly and keep the output at a safe value.

During transmission, a portion of the audio signal from second audio amplifier V5B is fed, through .005-mfd capacitor C49, to VOX sensitivity control R43. The rotor of R43 is connected to the grid of the 6CM7 VOX amplifier, V6B. This amplified VOX signal is then applied to the plate of the 6AL5 VOX diode rectifier, V7A. The V7A cathode circuit contains a 0.1-mfd fixed capacitor and two resistors—R47 is 1 megohm, and R48 is adjustable from zero to 5 megohms. These three form a time-constant network to control the release time delay in the operation of VOX relay K1 and antenna changeover relay K2. The time constant, which responds to the difference in characteristics of different human voices, is ordinarily one to two seconds, so that the transmitter will not go off the air during the pause between words in a sentence. The attack time will be very fast because the voltage developed across C52 will decay rapidly during the normal pauses between sentences. A fast attack time is required to prevent the first syllable of the first word spoken into the microphone from being clipped. When the positive control voltage developed at the cathode of V7A is applied to the grid of V8B (the 6U8 relay control tube), its plate current will increase and actuate the VOX and antenna change-over relays.

Audio signal voltage from the receiver is applied, through 1-megohm pot R53, to the grid of the 6U8 pentode "antitrip" amplifier, V8A. The amplified signal is then applied to the cathode of the 6AL5 "antitrip" diode rectifier, V7B. Notice that the two plates of the 6AL5 are connected together through 0.47-megohm resistor R62. The rectified audio signal from the receiver will produce a negative voltage drop across time-constant network C52-R47-R48. During reception, this negative voltage will appear at the control grid of V8B and cut off the plate current, to prevent actuation of the VOX and antenna changeover relays. When someone speaks into the microphone, the positive voltage developed across the time-constant network will be greater than the negative voltage developed by the receiver audio signal. The net positive voltage applied to the 6U8 grid will increase the plate current sufficiently to actuate the two relays. With proper adjustment of both the VOX and "antitrip" sensitivity controls, a condition of balance will be obtained which will provide correct VOX operation and at the same time prevent the station's own receiver from actuating the relays.

The output indicating meter provides a means for measuring the relative RF output of the transmitter in all modes of transmission. The scale is semilogarithmically calibrated from 0 to −60 db.

The metering circuit uses a 1N34A crystal diode, CR3, and a special HD6164 silicon diode, CR4, in such a manner that the scale calibration of the output meter will agree with the output level of the signal from the final amplifier. The 1N34A diode establishes the basic reference voltage for operation of the meter, but the characteristics of the HD6164 silicon diode do not allow the latter to conduct appreciably until the 1N34 output reaches a predetermined voltage. At this point (about 0.6 volt or higher), the silicon diode will conduct so heavily that the meter circuit is in effect swamped. As a result, the rapid rise of the pointer will be slowed and allow the meter to give a much more accurate indication of relative output. A sensitivity control on the front panel permits the meter indication to be varied according to specific requirements.

The power supply is located on the main chassis of the HX-500 transmitter. The 12AX4GTB high-voltage rectifiers, V18 and V19, supply 780 volts DC for the 6164 amplifier plates. The 6CA4 low-voltage rectifier, V20, supplies 350, 300, and 215 volts DC, and 150 volts DC regulated, for the other tubes in the transmitter. The 6AL5 bias rectifier, V17A, supplies two bias voltages of −50 and −100 volts.

The two low-power transmitters just described are good examples of the use of low-frequency filter circuitry for removal of the undesired sideband. The circuits of different manufacturers' equipment will vary, but in general the power output, signal shaping, carrier and undesired sideband suppression, VOX operation, and other features will have similar specifications. The number of frequency conversions, and the frequencies involved in the intermediate stages, will be determined largely by the carrier and sideband frequencies of the balanced modulator and filter sections. The Hammarlund transmitter generates the sideband signal at a carrier frequency of 60 kc, and further shapes it at the various levels during conversion to the operating frequency. The Collins transmitter generates the sideband signal in the 455-kc region, where practically all shaping takes place in the mechanical filter. The Hammarlund HX-500 system, on the other hand, requires one additional frequency-conversion stage because of the low frequency at which the signal is generated.

HALLICRAFTERS HT-46 TRANSMITTER

The Hallicrafters HT-46 transmitter, shown in Fig. 9-8, is an example of a different type of transmitter design. It generates the single-sideband signal at approximately 9 megacycles. Fig. 9-9, the block diagram, shows the signal path and frequency-conversion scheme employed. As shown in Fig. 9-10, a single 6HF5 tube is used as a linear RF power amplifier. The PEP RF power output is specified as 70 to 100 watts, which is adequate either for low-power operation directly into the antenna or as a driver for a higher-power linear RF amplifier. The HT-46 may be operated as an independent SSB or CW transmitter with any communications receiver, or it may be used with the companion SX-146 receiver as a transceiver combination.

The HT-46 utilizes a solid-state (diode) type of modulator followed by a selective filter for generation of the sideband signal. Single-frequency conversion is used to translate the 9-mc sideband signal to the operating frequency. The heterodyning signal is generated by the VFO directly on the 80- and 20-meter bands and indirectly by premixing with the heterodyne crystal oscillator for the remaining bands. For "slave" or transceiver operation with the SX-146 receiver, the premixed injection

171

voltages *from the receiver* are substituted for the transmitter's premixer stages. The carrier oscillator frequencies for the two units are matched within cycles to provide equal receive and transmit frequencies.

The carriers for the upper- and lower-sideband signals are generated in tube V2B at nominal frequencies of 8998.7 kc and 9001.5 kc. These are the frequencies at the 25 db down (-25 db) points on the skirts of the six-pole crystal filter which is centered at 9000 kc. The 8998.7-kc carrier, when modulated by the diode modulator, CR1 and CR2, produces an upper-sideband suppressed-carrier signal at 9000 kc. Conversely, the 9001.5-kc carrier, when modulated, produces a lower sideband at 9000 kc. The modulator is driven at audio frequency by the two triode

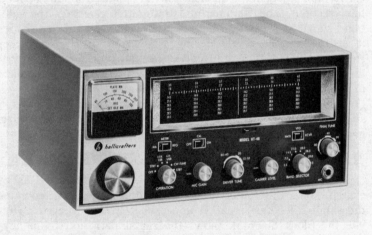

Fig. 9-8. Hallicrafters Model HT-46 transmitter.

stages of tube V1 and cathode follower V2A. Audio for VOX adapter unit HA-16 is taken from the plate of the first audio amplifier ahead of the microphone gain control.

The upper or lower sideband signal at 9000 kc is amplified by tube V3A and coupled to signal mixer tube V4, where the information signal is translated to the operating frequency.

To translate the 9000-kc information signal to the operating frequency, a heterodyne-frequency signal is generated within the transmitter by tubes V7 (VFO) and V8 (heterodyne crystal oscillator-mixer), or for "slave" operation it is taken from the SX-146 receiver through heterodyne mixer tube V8B working as an RF amplifier stage. The plate circuit of the heterodyne mixer (V8B) is coupled to the signal mixer grid through bandpass transformers T2, T3, and T4 on 40, 15, and 10 meters. On 80

172

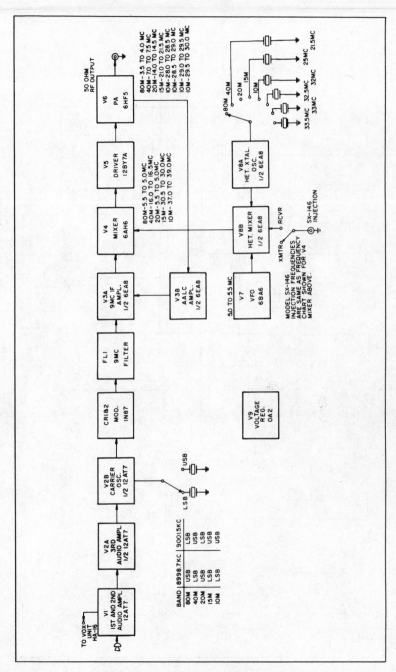

Fig. 9-9. HT-46 transmitter block diagram.

173

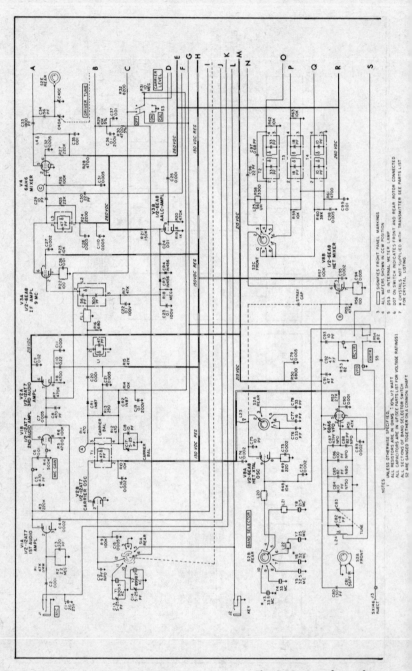

Fig. 9-10. Complete schem

174

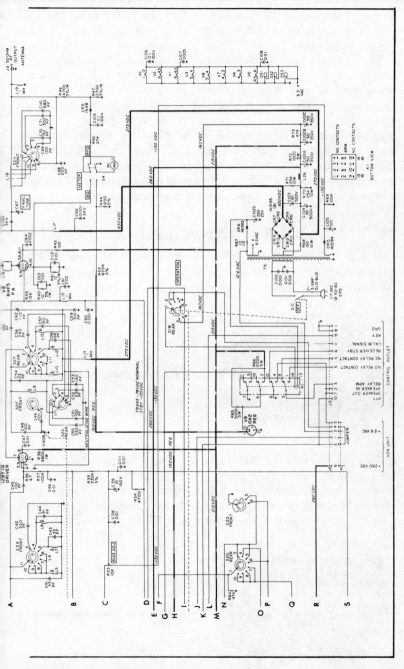

atic of HT-46 transmitter.

and 20 meters, in order to accommodate the VFO tuning range, the coupling is made through a broadly tuned 5- to 5.5-mc resonant circuit.

The desired mixer product resulting from the 9000-kc information signal and the tunable-heterodyne CW signal at the signal mixer grid is amplified by driver stage tube V5 and power amplifier V6. The amplified signal is coupled to the antenna transmission line with a pi-network that is preadjusted to properly load the final amplifier when a 50-ohm antenna load is connected to the output terminal. The mixer- and driver-stage coils are gang tuned on each band by the driver tuning control on the front panel. The final stage pi-network tank capacitor is adjusted from the front panel by the final tuning control.

R. L. DRAKE T-4 AND T-4X EQUIPMENT

The R. L. Drake Models T-4 *Reciter* (Fig. 9-11) and T-4X transmitter (Fig. 9-12) offer selectable single-sideband, semi break-in CW and controlled-carrier AM transmission with capa-

Fig. 9-11. Drake T-4 "Reciter."

bilities for covering the 160- through 10-meter amateur bands as well as many other frequencies such as MARS, etc. The T-4 unit is called a *Reciter* since it is designed to be used with the Drake Model R-4 or R-4A receiver for transceiving on the frequency to which the receiver is tuned. The T-4X is a complete

Fig. 9-12. Drake T-4X transmitter.

transmitter which may be used for transceiving with the R-4 or R-4A receivers or for independent receive-transmit usage. A front-panel switch on the T-4X selects between transceiving with the T-4X VFO, the receiver, or independent frequency control. The T-4 may be crystal controlled in the transmit mode for novice, MARS, DX, or net operation. Both units have a CW sidetone oscillator, automatic transmit-receive switching on CW, transmitting AGC to prevent flat topping, plate meter (relative output indicator), *two* crystal lattice filters for sideband selection, receiver muting, receiver antenna switching, and VOX and PTT (push-to-talk) on AM and SSB, all built-in for optimum operating convenience.

Both units provide 200 watts PEP input on AM and SSB and 200 watts input on CW for plenty of "punch" when run "barefoot" and more than ample drive for most grounded-grid linears.

The signal transmitted from the T-4 or T-4X is the result of mixing three separate oscillators and the audio signals from the microphone in the case of AM or SSB. Most of the following explanation applies equally to both the T-4 and T-4X. Any difference between the two units will be noted.

The signal on single sideband begins in a crystal-controlled oscillator, V1A, which oscillates at 5645 kc on all bands. The oscillator output is fed to a balanced modulator consisting of four diodes and a carrier balance control. The audio signal from the microphone is amplified by V9. The speech gain control, R84, is placed in the grid circuit of the second half of this tube. Two different audio outputs are taken from V9B. The low-impedance output from the cathode is applied to the balanced modulator for SSB operation. High-impedance output is taken from the plate of V9B and applied to the grid of V11 for screen modulation on AM.

The high-impedance audio signal is also fed to VOX amplifier V10A through VOX-adjust control R89. The output from V10A is rectified to produce a positive DC voltage which is applied to the grid of relay control tube V10B, causing it to conduct and close the transmit relay. Audio voltage from the receiver reaches the transmitter through the ANTIVOX cable and is rectified by D9. The resulting negative voltage is applied to the grid of V10B, so that audio-signal voltage resulting from speaker sounds picked up by the microphone will not cause the transmit relay to close. For push-to-talk operation, the negative bias on V9B is shorted to ground. This causes the tube to conduct and close the relay. The relay will be held closed until the push-to-talk button is released.

Returning to the balanced modulator, the audio and 5645-kc RF inputs combine to produce a double-sideband suppressed-

177

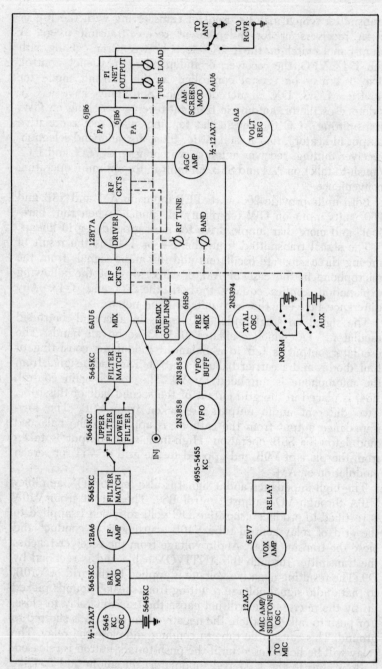

Fig. 9-13. Block diagram of the Drake T-4X transmitter.

178

carrier output. The DSB signal is amplified through V2 and, after impedance transformation in T2, is applied to either the upper or lower crystal filter, where the undesired sideband is filtered out. The resulting SSB signal is fed through T3 to the mixer stage, V3.

The second input signal for mixer V3 is supplied by the premixer stage, but its origin is different in the T-4X and the T-4. In the T-4X the permeability-tuned VFO (Q2) is controlled by the main tuning dial and oscillates on frequencies from 4955 to 5455 kc. RF output from the VFO is applied to the premixer

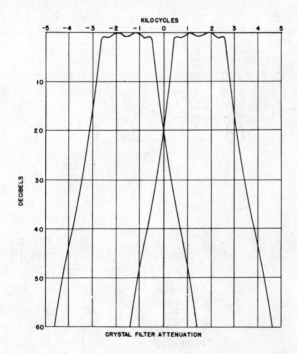

Fig. 9-14. Crystal sideband filter characteristics of T-4 and T-4X transmitters.

through buffer stage Q1. Another transistor oscillator, Q3, is crystal controlled and is operated at frequencies 11.1 mc above the low edge of the band in use. In the premixer stage, V8, the output of the high-frequency crystal oscillator and the VFO are combined and the difference frequency is taken from the plate, through T4 and T5, and fed to mixer V3. At mixer V3, the 5645-kc single-sideband signal and the high-frequency injection signal from T5 are applied to the same grid. The plate circuit of this tube is tuned by T6 to the difference of the two input signals.

179

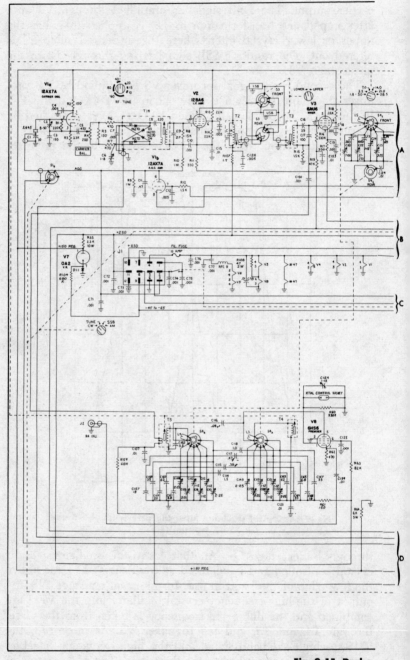

Fig. 9-15. Drake

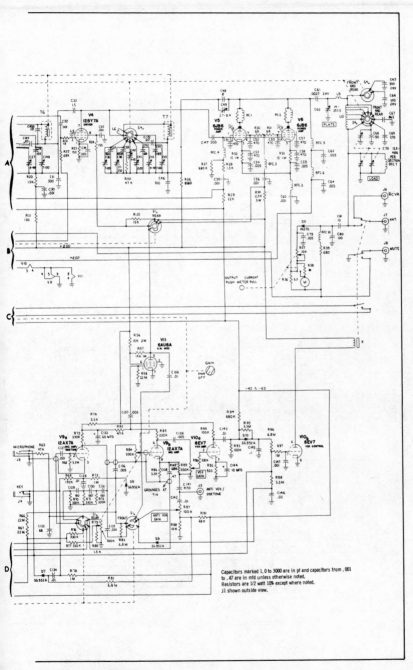

Model T-4 "Reciter."

Capacitors marked 1, 0 to 3000 are in pf and capacitors from .001 to .47 are in mfd unless otherwise noted.
Resistors are 1/2 watt 10% except where noted.
J1 shown outside view.

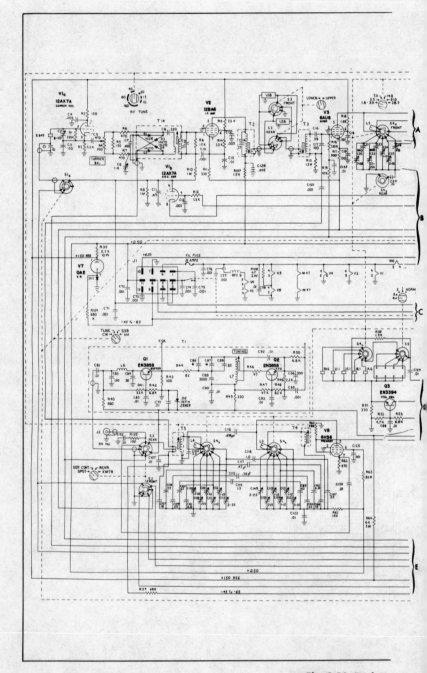

Fig. 9-16. Drake

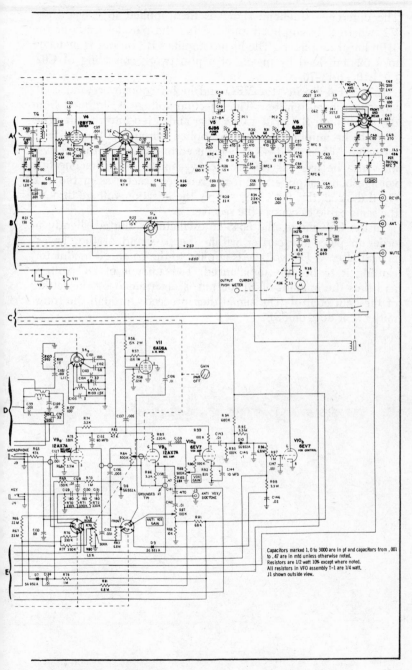

Model T-4X transmitter.

Capacitors marked 1, 0 to 3000 are in pf and capacitors from .001 to .47 are in mfd unless otherwise noted.
Resistors are 1/2 watt 10% except where noted.
All resistors in VFO assembly T-1 are 1/4 watt.
J1 shown outside view.

The difference sideband signal is then applied to driver stage V4, where it is amplified and fed to the parallel grids of the 6JB6 linear amplifiers. The linear-amplifier RF output is matched to a 52-ohm load by means of a pi-network consisting of C62, L9, L10, and C70.

In the T-4 *Reciter* the VFO and high-frequency crystal oscillator have been omitted. The injection voltage is supplied from the companion R-4 or R-4A receiver and is fed into the premixer stage to be amplified and then applied, through T4 and T5, to mixer V3. When the T-4X is being used to transceive, the receiver may also be used as the frequency control, with the injection voltage being supplied from the receiver exactly as in the T-4. Or, if desired, the T-4X may supply the injection voltage through the same cable to control the receiver.

In the CW mode, the 5645-kc oscillator is shifted slightly in order to place the carrier within the passband of the "lower" crystal filter. A DC voltage is applied to the balanced modulator, causing it to become unbalanced. The amount of DC voltage and thus the amount of RF output is determined by the setting of the gain control. The signal then proceeds through the transmitter as it does on SSB.

Chapter 10

Linear RF Power Amplifiers

The RF power amplifier of the single-sideband transmitter receives a relatively low-power signal from the exciter. The function of the power amplifier is to increase the power level of the single-sideband signal without changing its other characteristics. In an ideal amplifier, the signal from the output circuit will be an amplified replica of the input signal. An amplifier capable of performing this function is called a linear power amplifier.

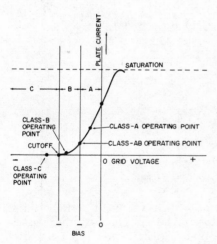

Fig. 10-1. Graph of classification system for RF power amplifier operation.

Although RF power amplifiers may involve a variety of circuit arrangements and operating conditions, it is convenient to define the operation of the amplifier tube in terms of the relationship between the grid voltage and plate current, with all other electrode voltages held constant. The system of classification based on this relationship is illustrated in Fig. 10-1. In this classification system, the transfer or mutual charac-

185

teristics of the tube is divided into three regions. The *A* region represents the linear portion of the transfer characteristic. The *B* region is in the immediate vicinity of plate-current cutoff and the *C* region lies beyond plate-current cutoff.

AMPLIFIER CLASSES

When the operating point of an RF amplifier is centered in region *A*, the tube can respond to both the positive and the negative excursions of the grid voltage. A tube operated in this manner is called a class-A amplifier and has a continuous plate-current flow over the full 360° of the RF cycle. As

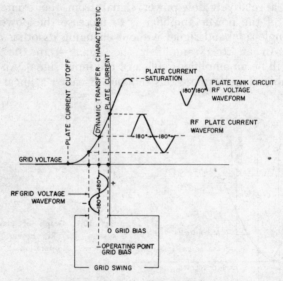

Fig. 10-2. Graph of class-A RF-amplifier operation.

shown in Fig. 10-2, the operation is over a small portion of the plate-current range of the tube. The efficiency of the class-A amplifier (in the conversion of DC plate power input into RF power output) is very low. As a result, this class of amplifier is used principally as a voltage amplifier for small signals, where very low waveform distortion is required. An example of the use of class-A RF amplifiers is in the RF or IF circuits of a communications receiver, or in the low-level voltage-amplifier stages of a single-sideband transmitter.

The class-B RF amplifier is biased in such a manner that its operating point is in the vicinity of plate-current cutoff. The true class-B amplifier will respond to only the positive ex-

186

cursions of the grid voltage. Plate current flows for approximately 180° of the RF cycle, as shown in Fig. 10-3. Amplifiers in which the plate-current flow is appreciably more than 180° but less than 360° are called class-AB amplifiers. In practical application, the distinction between class-B and class-AB is somewhat arbitrary, since both actually operate over more than 180° but less than 360° of each cycle of AC grid voltage. Both class-AB and class-B operation are used in the high-power linear RF amplifiers of commercial single-sideband transmitters. Operating at a relatively high efficiency, these amplifiers produce maximum output power with low dis-

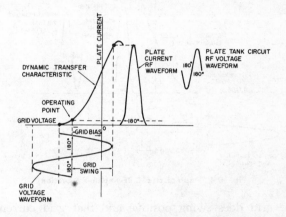

Fig. 10-3. Graph of class-B RF-amplifier operation.

tortion. The actual plate efficiency will depend on the particular tube used and on the selected operating conditions. However, plate efficiencies in the range of 50 to 70% are readily obtainable. The efficiency of the class-B amplifier is slightly higher than that of the class-AB amplifier. The class-AB amplifier draws appreciably more static (idling) plate current than the class-B. The general trend in commercial application, however, is toward class-AB operation because of certain advantages which will be explained later.

The class-C amplifier, as shown in Fig. 10-4, is biased in such a manner that its operating point is well beyond plate-current cutoff. The tube will respond to only those portions of the alternating grid-voltage cycle which are positive with respect to the cutoff point. Plate current flows for approximately 120° of the RF cycle. The class-C amplifier requires a high-level driving signal. Since the output waveform is not a replica of the input signal, the class-C is not a linear amplifier. Although very efficient in converting DC plate power into RF power output, the class-C is not suitable for use in single-sideband transmitters.

It is common practice to add a suffix number to the class designator of the amplifier, to indicate whether or not the tube is operated in the positive grid region over a portion of the grid-voltage cycle. As an example, class-AB$_1$ indicates that the grid never swings positive and that no grid current is drawn during any portion of the grid-voltage cycle. Class-AB$_2$ indicates

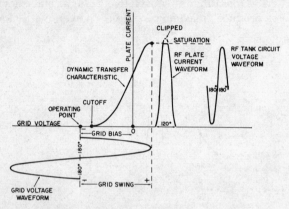

Fig. 10-4. Graph of class-C RF-amplifier operation.

that the grid does swing positive and that grid current flows during a portion of the grid-voltage cycle. Suffix numbers are usually omitted in the class designators for class-A and class-C amplifiers.

TYPES OF TUBES

In tube terminology, terms such as "diode," "triode," "tetrode," and "pentode" describe the number of electrodes directly associated with the emission, control, and collection of electrons. In transmitting tubes, the element associated with the emission is usually called the "filament," even though the tube may actually contain a cathode and heater. The term "grid" is usually applied to the control element to which the input signal is applied, no matter whether the tube is a triode, tetrode, or pentode. The screen grid in either a tetrode or a pentode is usually called the "screen," and the most common term for the pentode suppressor grid is simply "suppressor." The collection electrode is usually called the "plate," although the term "anode" is also in common usage. The currents and potentials associated

188

with the tube electrodes are generally referred to as current and voltage, such as grid current or grid voltage. The term "bias" means that a voltage is applied to one or more *control* electrodes such as the grid or cathode; it is not used for referring to the voltages applied to the screen or suppressor grids.

Until a few years ago, the triode was the only type of tube available for use in medium- and high-power linear RF power amplifiers. During the past few years, however, much effort has been directed toward the development and improvement of tetrode and pentode power transmitting tubes. The tetrodes, which include a screen grid between their control grid and plate, are widely used as linear RF power amplifiers in both amateur and commercial single-sideband transmitters. The screen grid provides an accelerating potential to the electron stream. It also provides an electrostatic shield between the control grid and plate. In most power tetrodes used for single-sideband transmission, the control and screen grids are designed to provide a beaming action to the electron stream. In this manner, the DC screen current is reduced and the action of the control grid is improved. Power pentodes designed for operating levels of 1,000 watts or less generally include an additional electrode between the screen grid and the plate. This additional element may be in the form of a grid (in which case it is called a suppressor), or a pair of beam-forming plates. The purpose of either one is to improve the plate characteristic when the plate voltage swings in the region of or below the DC screen voltage.

Triode power tubes offer the advantages of simplicity and low cost. They are also generally available in sizes suitable for use at any power level. However, triodes have a number of serious disadvantages. In the first place, they usually require a large amount of driving power and there is a considerable amount of capacitive coupling from the plate to the grid. This plate-to-grid capacitance must be accurately neutralized when the triode is used in linear RF power-amplifier applications. In general, the only triodes suitable for this are the low- and medium-*mu* types. In order for the full power-amplification capabilities of the tube to be obtained, a large grid-voltage swing will be required.

Many of the serious disadvantages of linear amplifier operation with a conventional triode can be eliminated, however, by the use of degenerative linear-amplifier circuits. The widest use for degenerative linear amplifiers is in circuits where the control grid is at RF ground potential and the driving (input) signal is applied to the tube cathode. The triodes most generally used in this configuration are medium-*mu* types such as the PL-6569

189

and PL-6580, which are designed especially for grounded-grid RF-amplifier service. These tubes contain an effective shield structure as a part of the design, and no neutralization is required in ordinary grounded-grid applications.

In tetrode and pentode power amplifiers, the screen grid forms an electrostatic shield between the plate and control grid. Although usually operated at a DC potential of a few hundred volts the screen grid is bypassed to ground for RF voltages. The electrostatic shielding effect of the screen acts to reduce the plate-to-grid capacitance to as little as one-one hundredth that of a triode of similar power capabilities. For best high-gain linear performance, however, neutralization

Fig. 10-5. 4CX-1000A and 4-1000A transmitting tubes.

of the small residual plate-to-grid capacitance is still required, because of the high gain of tetrode and pentode tubes. This high-gain characteristic is an advantage when a tetrode or pentode is used as a linear amplifier, because a high power output can be obtained from relatively little drive.

At present, high power amplifiers use tetrodes. The pentode is somewhat more complex and expensive, and may require more circuitry and voltages for the suppressor grid. While these disadvantages are usually of no great importance in power levels of 1,000 watts or less, they could create serious design problems above this level. One important advantage of the pentode tube at low-power levels is its ability to provide good linearity with relatively low plate and screen voltages.

The demand for compact high-power transmitters for both the VHF and UHF ranges has resulted in many improvements in the design of transmitting tubes. The power-amplifier tubes designed for VHF or UHF operation will generally offer improved performance over the 3- to 30-mc range. A typical example of the tube improvements carried out over the past few years can be obtained by a comparison of the 4-1000A and the 4CX-1000A tubes, which are in the same power class. The compact design of the 4CX-1000A, as shown in Fig. 10-5, results in short (hence, low-inductance)terminal lead lengths, better screening, closer element spacing and improved heat radiation. The 4CX-1000A is also capable of improved linear-amplifier performance at much lower plate voltages than those required for the 4-1000A. The ceramic instead of glass construction permits the tube envelope to be operated at higher temperatures without damage to the terminal seals. The ceramic sealed tube is also more rugged than its glass counterpart. Ceramic tubes such as the Eimac 4CX-5000A are capable of power outputs in the vicinity of 10,000 watts. Similar tubes are available which will deliver outputs of 500 kilowatts or more. At the present time, considerable research and development are also being carried out in the field of water-cooled high-power transmitting tubes suitable for use in linear RF power amplifiers.

BASIC CIRCUITS

The triode or tetrode power amplifiers used in single-sideband transmitters are generally operated class AB_1 or AB_2. The circuit configuration is usually quite conventional, the signal being injected into either the grid or cathode circuit. However, for optimum linearity with a given tube and circuit, the design considerations can become extremely stringent. The operating point on the tube transfer characteristic must be very carefully selected, often with respect to the characteristics of the individual tube. The neutralization must be as perfect as possible. The operating grid bias, and the screen plate volages, must be correct for the particular tube. These voltages must be maintained within close tolerances of their proper values under all operating conditions. The input and output impedances also must be held as constant as possible. To further improve the performance of the linear amplifier, degeneration may be necessary in the amplifier circuit. In many of today's single-sideband transmitters, RF feedback circuitry is used extensively to improve the performance of the linear amplifiers.

Triode Types

Fig. 10-6 shows a typical grounded-cathode linear RF amplifier using a triode. The input and output circuits are both tuned to the operating frequency. The large plate-to-grid interelectrode capacitance is neutralized by capacitor C_n. Swamping resistor R, across the grid tuned circuit, maintains a constant input impedance and also contributes to the stability of the amplifier.

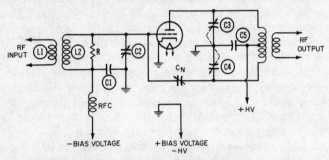

Fig. 10-6. Schematic of grounded-cathode linear RF power-amplifier.

When a linear amplifier is operated class AB_2, the grid will draw current during the positive portion of the grid-voltage cycle but not during the negative portion. Over the period of one RF cycle, the grid will present a very high impedance to the driving signal during the 180° when no grid current is drawn, and a very low impedance during the remaining 180° when the grid current flows. When a fairly low swamping resistance is added, the varying grid impedance represents only a small portion of the total grid load; thus the load impedance presented to the driving signal will be relatively constant. This resistance further improves the amplifier stability by offering a low impedance to ground for the regenerative-feedback effects caused by the tube plate-to-grid capacitance.

Fig. 10-7 shows a typical triode grounded-grid RF power-amplifier circuit. The control grid is at ground potential for the RF signal, and the driving-signal voltage is applied to the cathode. When the triode is operated in this manner, the control grid becomes an effective electrostatic shield between the plate and cathode. As a result, neutralization will seldom be required. Although the class-AB_2 grounded-grid amplifier will draw grid current over 180° of the input cycle, no swamping resistors are necessary because the feedthrough power forms an effective

192

load across the input circuit. One of the disadvantages of the circuit is the relatively large driving power required to obtain a reasonably high output. Power gains of 6 to 10 can usually be realized from a practical grounded-grid linear RF amplifier. This means that an amplifier with an RF power output from 600 to 1,000 watts will require a driving-power source of approximately 100 watts. However, most of the driving power is not lost, since it feeds through the stage and reappears in the plate circuit. The grounded-grid (or cathode-driven) linear ampli-

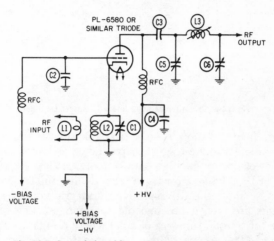

Fig. 10-7. Grounded-grid linear RF power-amplifier circuit.

fier is most useful for increasing the power level of an existing single-sideband transmitter. An amplifier of this type, using a PL-6580 or similar triode, will permit the amateur station to operate at the maximum legal power limit. The linear amplifier stage can then be driven to full power output by any of the popular 100-watt single-sideband transmitters.

Tetrode Types

The tetrode can be used in either a grid- or cathode-driven (grounded-grid linear RF power-amplifier circuit. In the grid-driven circuit shown in Fig. 10-8, the tube is normally operated class-AB$_1$. In general, the design considerations for tetrode amplifiers are similar to those for the triodes previously described. If the tetrode is driven into the grid-current region during operation, swamping of the tuned grid circuit will be required in order to present a constant input impedance. Neutralization will also be required, particularly if the tetrode amplifier is to be operated over a wide frequency range.

193

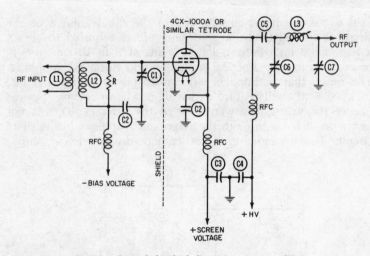

Fig. 10-8. Grounded-cathode linear RF power amplifier.

However, neutralization of a tetrode is simpler than for the triode, since its plate-to-grid capacitance is very small. The tetrode, because of its high gain characteristics, requires only a small RF driving power to realize its full power-output capabilities. Since the driving-power and grid-voltage-swing requirements are low, it has become common practice to operate a number of tetrode tubes in parallel where a high output power is required. The screen voltage required for optimum linearity and best efficiency is generally quite critical. It is customary to use voltage-regulated power supplies for both the grid bias and screen voltages.

When a 50-to 100-watt driving signal is available, it is possible to substitute a fixed resistor for the tuned input circuit of the tetrode or pentode. This type of input is called a "passive" grid

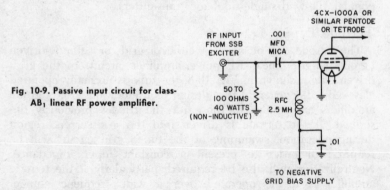

Fig. 10-9. Passive input circuit for class-AB₁ linear RF power amplifier.

194

circuit. Fig. 10-9 shows such a circuit, suitable for use with the Eimac 4CX-1000A tube. The value and power rating of the resistor will depend on the amount of driving signal available. As an example, when 100-watt single-sideband transmitter is used as the exciter, the resistor should be about 50 ohms at a power rating of 40 to 50 watts. A suitable resistor can be constructed by connecting *twenty* 1,000-ohm, 2-watt carbon resistors in parallel. This combination will give 50 ohms at a 40-watt power rating. The peak grid voltage required for the 4CX-1000A is 60 volts across the 50-ohm resistance. The PEP dissipation of the resistor, during voice operation, will be 72 watts. The average power dissipation, however, will be low. If the signal is a constant tone such as an audio test signal, the power rating of the carbon-resistor assembly may be exceeded. Such tests should be of short duration, or a resistor assembly with a higher-power dissipation rating used. However, the 50-ohm value is more desirable, since it properly terminates the exciter coaxial output cable in its characteristic impedance.

PRACTICAL DESIGN

The design of a practical linear RF power amplifier will depend on the output desired and the amount of driving power available. During the past few years, it has become customary for the amateur to purchase a commercial single-sideband transmitter, with about 100 watts' PEP output, and use it as a low-power transmitter for a short period of time. Later he adds a linear RF power amplifier to bring the transmitted power level up to the maximum legal limit of the amateur service. Under FCC regulations, the maximum legal limit of power input for the tube or tubes supplying RF power to the antenna system of an amateur station is 1,000 watts. (Input power is determined by multiplying the final plate voltage and the plate current, or DC input power in watts = $E_p I_p$.)

In a single-sideband transmitter where the final-amplifier plate current varies from the low static to a relatively high dynamic value during operation, the FCC has added some specifications. When the amplifier has been adjusted to prevent the generation of excessive sidebands, the legal input power to the final stage of a voice-operated single-sideband transmitter is equal to the plate voltage times plate current, as indicated on a plate-current meter which has a time constant not in excess of 0.25 second. In the special case of the cathode-driven (grounded-grid) linear amplifier, the permissible power input to the final amplifier plate circuit is 1,000 watts, less the feedthrough driving power from the exciter. For example, if the RF driving power applied to the cathode of a grounded-grid linear amplifier is 50 watts, then the DC input power to the amplifier plate must not exceed 950 watts as indicated by the plate-voltage and -current meters. As a matter of fact, the peak input power of a voice-operated linear amplifier may be on the order of several kilowatts when adjusted for a legal input of 1 kilowatt. Current engineering practice is to rate linear amplifiers in terms of PEP output in watts. Single-sideband linear amplifiers are commonly rated between 2,000 and 3,000 watts PEP output for voice transmission when the DC input power is 1,000 watts.

The majority of modern amplifiers will be relatively simple in design, since most of the essential data is supplied by the tube manufacturer, who usually lists the maximum ratings for the specific tube and recommends a set of typical operating values. (The recommended and the actual operating conditions are generally quite close together when the amplifier is adjusted for optimum performance.) In actual practice, about the only job left is to design the input and output tank circuits.

As shown in Fig. 10-3, the class-AB and -B amplifiers are assumed to have a conduction angle of 180°. The RF plate-current waveform is essentially half of a sine-wave pulse. The design of the amplifier plate-tank circuit must be such that these pulses will be converted into full sine-wave voltage across the tank circuit. This RF voltage waveform should be an amplified replica of the applied grid-voltage waveform. It is obvious that the design of the RF tank circuits will greatly determine the efficiency and distortion characteristics of the linear-amplifier stage.

It will be necessary to determine the plate-load resistance of the tube before the tank-circuit parameters can be calculated. In most cases, any tube used in linear RF amplifier service at power levels of 300 watts or less can also be designed to work as an AF power amplifier. Types 6146 and 813 "beam power" tetrodes and types 811-A and 805 triodes are good examples. When the RF amplifier operates at a few hundred watts or less, the audio tubes will give excellent performance. In this case the audio ratings give a close enough approximation of the RF performance characteristics, and much of the mathematical computation which would otherwise be required can thus be eliminated. The audio-amplifier data is also applicable to tubes used as single, parallel, or push-pull linear RF power amplifiers. The 6146 tetrode provides an example of linear RF power-amplifier design from published audio-amplifier data. The use of two 6146 tubes in a push-pull RF linear amplifier operated class-AB$_1$ will be discussed first.

The 6146 Amplifier

Table 10-1 shows the typical operating conditions for the 6146 in both class-AB_1 and -AB_2 push-pull audio-amplifier service. Notice that the class-AB_2 produces approximately 10 watts more signal power output than the AB_1 does. However, since in class-AB_2 operation the grids will draw current over a portion of the grid-voltage cycle, swamping of the tuned input circuit will be required. Class-AB_2 operation will also

Table 10-1.

Operating conditions for Class-AB_1 and AB_2 6146s in linear RF amplifier service.

Electrodes	Potentials	
	AB_1	AB_2
Plate Voltage	750 VDC	750 VDC
Grid Voltage*	—50 VDC	—45 VDC
Screen Voltage	200 VDC	165 VDC
Zero-Signal DC Plate Current	57 ma	35 ma
Zero-Signal Screen Current	1 ma	0.6 ma
Single-Tone DC Plate Current	227 ma	240 ma
Single-Tone DC Screen Current	27.5 ma	21 ma
Single-Tone Signal Grid Voltage (Peak)**	100 VAC	101 VAC
Effective Load***	8000 Ω	8000 Ω
Maximum Signal Driving Power	0	30 mw
Single-Tone Plate Power Output	120 watts	130 watts

Notes:

* Adjust DC grid voltage to give stated DC plate current.

** Signal grid voltage shown is peak AF (grid-to-grid) for two tubes in push-pull circuit configuration. The peak RF voltage requirements for the two grids in push-pull will be approximately the same. When the two tubes are used in parallel, the peak grid voltage required will be one-half the push-pull value.

*** Effective load value shown is correct for either AF or RF when the two tubes are used in push-pull. When the tubes are connected in parallel, effective load will be one-forth the push-pull value.

require more RF driving power because of the grid-current flow and the losses in the swamping resistor. An additional disadvantage of class-AB_2 operation is that the tuned input circuit must be very carefully designed so that the L/C ratio is correct for the grid conditions encountered.

The class-AB_1 amplifier is not permitted to draw grid current over any portion of the RF grid-voltage cycle. Since no power is dissipated in the grid circuit, the only concern is whether the peak voltage supplied to the grids is sufficient to produce maximum signal power output. No swamping resistor is necessary across the tuned input circuit.

197

The effective load (plate-to-plate) resistance is given as 8,000 ohms for both class-AB_1 and AB_2 push-pull operation. The plate-to-plate load resistance value which will invariably be given in the tube AF amplifier data, can be used in the calculation of the tank-circuit parameters for a push-pull linear RF amplifier operated under similar plate-, screen-, and grid-voltage conditions. When a single tube is used in linear RF service, the proper plate load resistance will be one-half that of the push-pull

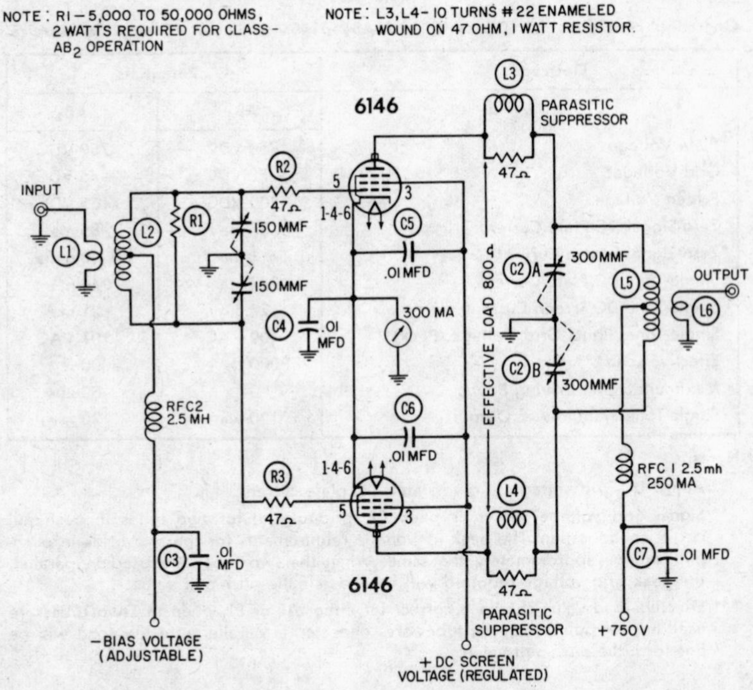

Fig. 10-10. Push-pull 6146 tubes used in class-AB_1 or class AB_2.

value; when the two tubes are operated in parallel, the resistance will be one-fourth. One 6146 tube, operated class AB_1, will require a plate load of 4,000 ohms, as given in Table 10-1. If two 6146 tubes are operated in parallel (as shown in Fig. 10-10) under the same voltage conditions, the proper plate load will be 2,000 ohms. Determination of the plate load value is important since it is also used to determine the L and C values of the plate tank circuit.

It has been determined that a loaded plate tank Q of 12 to 15 is most suitable for optimum linear RF amplifier performance. The Q of the plate circuit must be sufficient to convert the RF plate-current pulses to sine-wave RF voltage waveforms across the resonant tank circuit. If the plate circuit Q is too low, the RF voltage waveform will be distorted and the amplifier will operate at a low plate efficiency. The reactance (X_C) of the plate-circuit tank capacitor will be equal to R_L/Q. At resonance, the tank-circuit capacitive reactance (X_C) and inductive reactance (X_L) are equal, so the common reactance figure obtained from the expression, $R_L/Q = X$, can be used to calculate the required L and C values. If a loaded plate tank Q of 12 is desired, the X_C value will be equal to R_L/Q, or $8,000/12 = 666$ ohms (approximately). The exact values of the tank-circuit capacitance and inductance may be calculated as follows:

$$C = \frac{10^6}{6.28 \times F \times X_C}$$

$$L = \frac{X_L}{6.28 \times F}$$

where,
F is the frequency in megacycles,
X_C is the capacitive reactance value obtained from R_L/Q,
X_L is the inductive reactance value obtained from R_L/Q,
C is the capacitance in micromicrofarads,
L is the inductance in microhenrys.

In actual practice, the frequency selected for the design calculations is usually the highest operating frequency in a given band. For example, in designing an amplifier for use on the 75-meter band, a frequency of 4 mc will be selected. After the L and C values have been calculated, a tank capacitor with a maximum capacitance slightly higher than the calculated value will permit operation over the entire band of frequencies.

For example, assuming an operating frequency of 4 megacycles, and substituting this numerical value for F in the formula, the exact value of the tank-circuit capacitance will be:

$$C = \frac{10^6}{6.28 \times 4.0 \times 666} = 59.8 \text{ mmf (approximately)}$$

The exact value of the tank-circuit inductance for the operating frequency of 4 megacycles will be:

$$L = \frac{666}{6.28 \times 4.0} = 26.5 \text{ microhenrys (approximately)}$$

The values of L and C required to present the proper plate load to the amplifier on the other amateur bands may be similarly calculated.

199

The design of a push-pull linear RF power amplifier operated class-AB_1 is somewhat academic, since this configuration is rarely used in modern design practice. Fig. 10-11 shows a more practical circuit arrangement, for a low-power RF amplifier using a pair of 6146 tubes operated in parallel. The plate tank circuit consists of a pi-network that matches a transmission line of relatively low characteristic impedance (50 or 75 ohms) to the tube plates, which must "see" a relatively high resistive load in order to produce optimum power output. The plate tank coil is a variable rotary inductor with a sliding or rolling contact that traverse the length of the coil. The unused turns are shorted out. The variable-capacitor range is such that the proper reactance value can be obtained for any frequency between 3.5 and 30 mc. In practice, the capacitance is adjusted to the correct value for the operating frequency, and the circuit then tuned to resonance with the variable inductance. The use of continuously variable tank-circuit elements will permit a more uniform circuit Q across the entire tuning range, and a maximum amount of harmonic attenuation. The network elements are also compact, which will reduce the over-all dimensions of the amplifier and simplify the design.

When the two tubes are operated in parallel, as shown in Fig. 10-11, the required driving-signal peak voltage will be one-half that required for the same tubes in the push-pull circuit arrangement. The grid-bias and the plate- and screen-voltage requirements will be the same as for the push-pull arrangement. The effective plate load resistance, as mentioned previously, will be 2,000 ohms. If a loaded plate tank Q of 12 is desired, the pi-network capacitor, C1, will be approximately 280 mmf when the operating frequency is 3.5 mc. At 28 mc, the value of C1 will be approximately 35 mmf. An appropriate variable capacitor, which has a capacitance range from about 15 to 300 mmf, should be selected for C1. The air gap should be approximately 10 mils for each 100 volts applied to the 6146 tube plates.

Pi-network output capacitor C2 matches the impedance of the amplifier output to either a 50- or 75-ohm coaxial transmission line. To match the amplifier to a 50-ohm line at 3.5 mc, the value of C2 will have to be approximately 1,800 mmf, and at 28 mc—225 mmf. For a 70-ohm transmission line at 3.5 mc the capacitance required is approximately 1,300 mmf; and at 28 mc, 160 mmf. The table in Fig. 10-12 gives the proper values for C1, C2, and L1 for all the amateur bands from 3.5 to 30 megacycles. In actual practice, C1 and C2 are adjusted to the approximate values given in the table. The circuit is then tuned to resonance

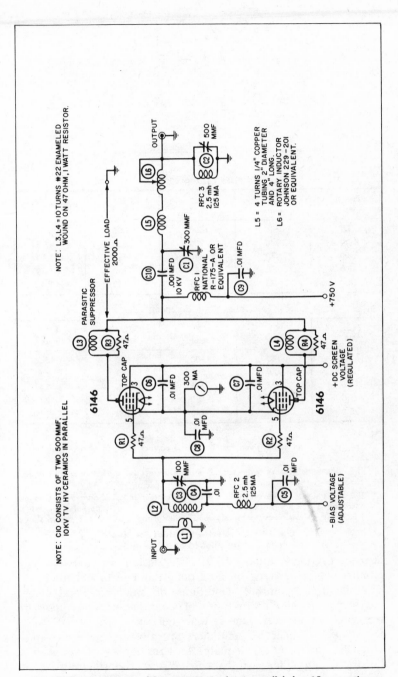

NOTE: L3, L4 = 10 TURNS #22 ENAMELED WOUND ON 47 OHM, 1 WATT RESISTOR.

NOTE: C10 CONSISTS OF TWO 500 MMF. 10KV TV HV CERAMICS IN PARALLEL.

L5 = 4 TURNS 1/4" COPPER TUBING 2" DIAMETER AND 4" LONG.
L6 = ROTARY INDUCTOR JOHNSON 229-201 OR EQUIVALENT.

Fig. 10-11. Low-power amplifier using 6146 tubes in parallel class-AB$_1$ operation.

201

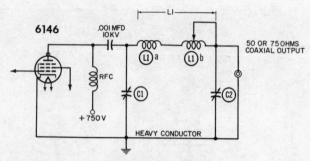

Freq. MC	C1 mmf	C2* mmf	C2** mmf	L1*** μh
3.5	280	1800	1300	8.5
7.0	140	900	650	4.25
14.0	70	450	325	2.10
21.0	50	300	220	1.38
28.0	35	225	160	1.05

Plate Load = 4000Ω

Freq. MC	C1 mmf	C2* mmf	C2** mmf	L1*** μh
3.5	140	1100	800	15.5
7.0	70	550	400	7.8
14.0	35	275	200	3.9
21.0	25	180	130	2.6
28.0	18	140	100	1.94

Notes:

* The approximate value given for C2 will be correct for a 50-ohm output impedance.

** The approximate value given for C2 will be correct for a 75-ohm output imped-
ance.

*** The approximate value given for L1 will be correct for a 50-ohm output imped-
ance. For a 75-ohm output impedance, multiply the inductance value shown by
1.03. L1 is the **total inductance value** and includes both L1A and L1B shown above.

**Fig. 10-12. Pi-network values for single
tube and parallel 6146 RF amplifier.**

at the operating frequency by L1. The design of pi-network tank
circuits will be covered in more detail later in this chapter.

While the operating conditions of single-sideband linear
amplifiers are similar to those of audio amplifiers, there are
important differences. One is that the input and output waveforms of the linear RF amplifiers are always sine waves, provided the circuit Q is adequate. As a result, any distortion in a
linear RF amplifier will likewise distort the single sideband
modulation envelope. The driving-power requirements for the RF

202

amplifier, particularly where grid current is drawn over a portion of the grid-voltage cycle, will be considerably different. In the audio amplifier, the audio-driver stage must supply an average sine-wave power equal to one-half the peak power. In the RF amplifier, the resonant input circuit will tend to average the power over the RF grid-voltage cycle, and the RF driver stage will have to supply only the actual average power to the grid. While audio specifications will generally give a reasonably good approximation of linear RF amplifier conditions, a comparison of the two amplifiers will be most useful when both circuits are operated in the class-A or -AB region.

When the tube is designed specifically for linear RF power-amplifier service, it is advisable to follow the "typical operation" data supplied by the manufacturer. If the tube must be oper-

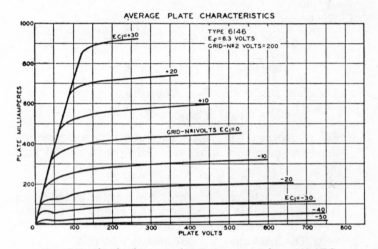

Fig. 10-13. Plate-family curves for 6146—screen voltage 200 VDC.

ated under different voltage or current conditions from those specified on the data sheet, it is best to consult with the manufacturer before the tube is placed in operation. Many of the later-production tubes such as the 4CX-1000A are very easily damaged if certain precautionary measures are not observed.

Many data sheets, particularly for the older tubes, do not include information for operating the tube in class-AB_1 or -AB_2 linear RF amplifier service. However, they do include a set of average plate-characteristic curves like those in Fig. 10-13, from which the required information can be calculated. As an example, we shall use the curves in Fig. 10-13 to calculate the operating values for a single 6146 used as a class-AB_2 linear RF amplifier.

The 6146 will be operated under ICAS conditions, with a plate voltage of 600, a screen voltage of 200, and a maximum single-tone DC plate current ($I_{P\ MAX}$) of 135 milliamperes. The step-by-step calculations are carried out as follows:

1. The DC plate input (P_I) will be equal to 600×0.135, or 81 watts.
2. The peak plate current ($i_{P\ MAX}$) will be equal to 3.14×0.135, or 0.424 ampere.
3. From Fig. 10-13, determine the peak positive grid voltage required to produce a peak plate current of 0.424 ampere. This is found to be approximately +5 volts. Determine the effective minimum plate-voltage value at the instant of peak plate current. This will be approximately 65 volts.
4. The power output (P_O) will be equal to

$$0.785 \, (E_P - e_{P\ min}) \times I_{P\ max}$$

$$= 0.785 \, (600 - 65) \times 0.135, \text{ or } 56.75 \text{ watts.}$$

5. The plate dissipation (P_P) will be equal to

$$(600 \times 0.135) - 56.75, \text{ or } 24.25 \text{ watts.}$$

6. For a zero-signal DC plate current which will give one-third the maximum rated plate dissipation at 600 volts:

$$25/ \, (3 \times 600) = .0139 \text{ ampere}$$

7. From the plate characteristic curves of Fig. 10-13 determine the value of DC grid bias required to produce 14 ma of zero-signal plate current with the plate at 600 volts. The bias value is approximately −51 volts.
8. The peak RF grid voltage will be equal to the bias voltage (51) plus the peak positive grid voltage (5), or 56 volts.
9. The effective plate load resistance will be:

$$\frac{E_P - e_{P\ min}}{0.5 \, i_{P\ max}}$$

$$= \frac{535}{.212} = 2523, \text{ or approximately 2500 ohms.}$$

10. If a loaded tank circuit Q of 12 is desired, the reactance (X_C) of the plate tank capacitor at the resonant frequency will be:

$$\frac{R_L}{Q} = \frac{2500}{12} = 208 \text{ ohms.}$$

11. At a frequency of 4.0 megacycles, the effective resonance value of the plate tank capacitor will be:

$$\frac{10^6}{6.28 \times 4.0 \times 208} = 191 \text{ mmf}$$

12. The inductance required to resonate the tank circuit at a frequency of 4.0 megacycles will be:

$$\frac{208}{6.28 \times 4.0} = 8.3 \text{ microhenrys.}$$

While the above calculations apply specifically to a single 6146 tube operated under class-AB$_2$ conditions, the operating conditions for class-AB$_1$ service are only slightly different. With the plate at 600 watts, and the screen at 200 volts, the grid bias will be approximately −50 volts for class-AB$_1$. In practical operation, the grid bias will be adjusted for a zero-signal plate current of approximately 26 ma. In class-AB$_1$ operation, no grid current will be drawn during any portion of the RF grid-voltage cycle, so the grid will not be driven positive. The peak RF grid voltage will be equal to the bias voltage.

When the power output is 1,000 watts or less, the amplifier is normally designed to operate in the class-AB$_1$ region because high power gain can be obtained without the distortion due to grid-current loading. During the past few years, several new transmitting tubes have been developed especially for use as class-AB$_1$ linear RF amplifiers. Two outstanding types, the 4CX-1000A and PL-172, are widely used in both amateur and commercial services. In the power range above 1,000 watts, class-AB$_2$ operation is generally used in order to obtain good plate efficiency with low distortion characteristics. However, a great amount of research and development is being directed toward improvement of high-power linear RF amplifier tubes. Tubes suitable for class-AB$_1$ operation at the higher power levels are expected to be available in the relatively near future.

A 1,000-WATT AMPLIFIER

While the circuit configurations and physical layouts of class-AB$_1$ and -AB$_2$ linear RF power amplifiers are similar, the exact design values will depend on the type of tube selected and the desired class of operation. The 1,000-watt class-AB$_1$ amplifier to be described in this section is a good example of modern design practice. The tube selected for this particular application is the 4CX-1000A, which has the desired rated plate dissipation of 1,000 watts. However, the same electrical and mechanical

205

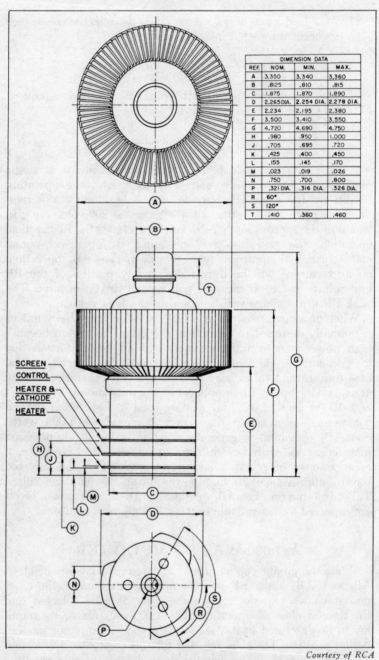

DIMENSION DATA			
REF.	NOM.	MIN.	MAX.
A	3.350	3.340	3.360
B	.8125	.810	.815
C	1.875	1.870	1.890
D	2.265 DIA.	2.254 DIA.	2.278 DIA.
E	2.234	2.195	2.380
F	3.500	3.410	3.550
G	4.720	4.690	4.750
H	.980	.950	1.000
J	.705	.695	.720
K	.425	.400	.450
L	.155	.145	.170
M	.023	.019	.026
N	.750	.700	.800
P	.321 DIA.	.316 DIA.	.326 DIA.
R	60°		
S	120°		
T	.410	.360	.460

SCREEN
CONTROL
HEATER &
CATHODE
HEATER

Courtesy of RCA

Fig. 10-14. Terminal arrangement and dimensional data for 4CX-1000A.

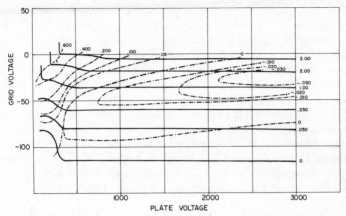

Fig. 10-15. Constant-current characteristics and class-AB₁ data
for 4CX-1000A.

design considerations will generally apply to similar linear amplifiers which use other types of tetrodes or pentodes at the 1,000-
watt power level.

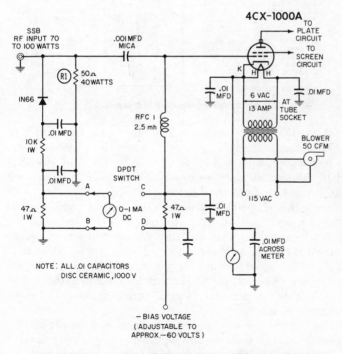

Fig. 10-16. Input circuitry of 1,000-watt RF amplifier using 4CX-1000A.

The 4CX-1000A is a radial-beam tetrode of ceramic and metal construction and is designed especially for class-AB$_1$ linear RF power-amplifier service. At its rated maximum plate voltage of 3,000 volts, it is capable of producing 1,680 watts of peak-envelope power. This tube is also suitable for use as an AF power amplifier. Two 4CX-1000A's operating in class-AB$_1$ will produce 3,360 watts of audio power with very low distortion. Forced-air cooling must be used for the anode and other ceramic-to-metal seals. The heater, screen, and control-grid leads are brought out to a special breechblock base and terminal arrangement. The tube requires a special socket as shown in Fig. 10-14. The constant-current characteristics and operating conditions for a typical class-AB$_1$ linear RF amplifier are shown in Fig. 10-15.

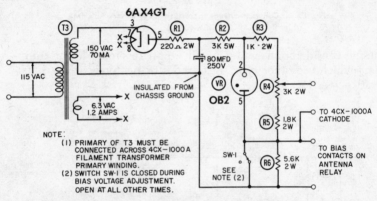

Fig. 10-17. Voltage-regulated bias supply.

The 4CX-1000A has a maximum grid dissipation rating of *zero* watts. This means that the grid must never be allowed to be driven into the positive region. In Fig. 10-16, the grid circuit is loaded by 50-ohm, 40-watt resistor R1. The value of R1 is such that the RF output from the Exciter (the SSB transmitter) will barely drive the 4CX-1000A grid into conduction. With normal plate, screen, and grid voltages, the plate power input of the amplifier will exceed the legal limits for the amateur service before grid current is drawn. As shown in Fig. 10-16, an RF voltmeter is included in the input circuit for monitoring the level of the driving signal. When the DPDT switch is thrown the meter will also indicate the presence of grid current during adjustment of the amplifier circuit.

Fig. 10-17 shows the voltage-regulated grid-bias supply for the amplifier. The grid will require approximately −60 volts for class-AB$_1$ operation. The actual bias-voltage value must be

208

adjusted to obtain the listed zero-signal plate current. As shown in Fig. 10-18, the OB2 voltage-regulator tube is connected across voltage divider R3-R4-R5. R4 is a 3,000-ohm, 2-watt wirewound pot used to adjust the negative bias applied to the grid of the tube. While the nominal bias value is given as −60 volts, in actual operation the bias value is adjusted to give the specified zero-signal DC plate current. During the standby period, R6 is included in the voltage-divider network, and the resultant bias is sufficient to cut off plate current. During the operating period, however, R6 is short-circuited by the bias contacts of the antenna relay. As a result the grid bias is restored to the normal operating value. If the static plate current of the amplifier were permitted to flow during the standby period, a high level of background noise would be developed in the station receiver, but the bias voltage is automatically changed by the VOX control system to prevent this.

Although the maximum rated power dissipation for the 4CX-1000A screen grid is 12 watts, the screen power should be kept well below this level. The actual screen dissipation is somewhat difficult to measure accurately, because a reversed (negative) screen current may be present under certain operating conditions. At lower values of plate potential, negative screen currents on the order of 25 milliamperes may be encountered. The product of the peak screen voltage and the indicated DC screen current will approximate the screen input power, except when the screen current is near zero or negative. According to the tube manufacturer, experience has shown that the screen will operate within the limits established for the 4CX-1000A if the screen current, plate voltage, and drive voltage approximate the "typical operation" values.

It is important that the screen supply voltage be maintained constant for any values of negative and positive screen currents that may be encountered. If the screen power supply exhibits a rising voltage characteristic with negative screen current, the DC plate current may rise excessively. The screen voltage can be stabilized by one of several different methods. The simplest is to connect a bleeder resistor from the screen to the cathode, and to adjust its value so that about 70 to 80 ma of bleeder current is drawn when 325 volts is applied to the screen. The 4CX-1000A screen voltage may be taken, if desired, from a 325-volt source in the low-power stages of the transmitter, provided the voltage is stabilized by a constant current drain of at least 70 to 80 ma.

Fig. 10-18 shows the screen power supply actually used with the 4CX-1000A linear amplifier. T1 is designed for audio-amplifier

209

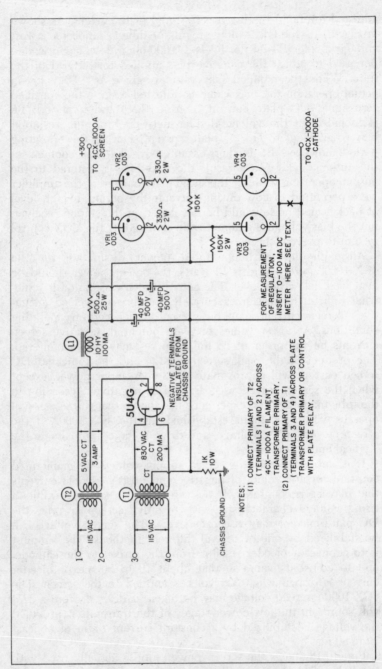

Fig. 10-18. Voltage-regulated screen supply.

power-supply service; and the secondary winding produces 830 volts AC, center-tapped, at 200 ma. Notice that a separate filament transformer, T2, is used for the 5U4G. Its primary terminals are connected in parallel with the primary terminals of the 4CX-1000A filament transformer (not shown). If the transformer used for T1 has filament windings, they should not be used since the primary voltages of T1 *must* be controlled simultaneously with that of the high-voltage plate transformer. This precaution is necessary, to prevent damage to the 4CX-1000A screen by the accidental application of screen voltage in the absence of plate voltage. A Stancor PC-8301 can be used for T1, and T2 can be a Stancor P6467.

Filter choke L1 is a Stancor Type C-1001 and is rated at 10.5 henrys at 110 ma. The filter choke is followed by an electrolytic capacitor rated at 40 mfd and 500 volts. The 500-ohm 25-watt resistor (R1) and the second electrolytic capacitor (C2) provide additional filtering action. The relatively large value of C2 is necessary to provide good regulation during peak excursions of the screen current.

The DC output voltage is regulated by means of the four OD3 (VR150) regulator tubes. The unusual circuit arrangement of these tubes is necessary, to prevent one or more of them from extinguishing during operation. It is extremely important that the regulators function during all conditions of negative or positive screen-current flow. The regulation may be measured by connecting a 0 to 100 DC milliammeter in series with the ground return of VR3 and VR4 and observing the tube current operation. When the linear amplifier is in the standby condition, the regulator tube current should be approximately 60 ma. If the current value is higher or lower, one or more regulator tubes may be defective, or it may be necessary to increase or decrease the values of R1, R4, and R5 until the proper current is indicated. When the linear amplifier is driven, the regulator current will decrease. If it falls to zero, this indicates excessive screen current and loss of regulation. It is imperative that the cause of this condition be corrected before operation is continued.

The 4CX-1000A has a relatively low plate impedance, which varies considerably with different values of plate voltage. Table 10-2 shows the typical operating conditions for *two* 4CX-1000A tubes in class-AB$_1$ audio-amplifier service. With the plate at 3,000 volts, the plate-to-plate load is given as 3,450 ohms. When one tube is used as a class-AB$_1$ with 3,000 volts on the plate, the plate load will be in the vicinity of 1,725 ohms. For a plate voltage of 2,500 volts, the plate load for a single 4CX-1000A will be on the order of 1,200 ohms.

Table 10-2.

Typical operating conditions for two 4CX-1000A tubes in Class AB₁ audio amplifier service.

MAXIMUM RATINGS	
DC Plate Voltage	3,000 Volts
DC Screen Voltage	400 Volts
DC Plate Current	1.0 Amp
Plate Dissipation	1,000 Watts
Screen Dissipation	12 Watts
Grid Dissipation	0 Watts

TYPICAL OPERATION (Sinusoidal wave, two tubes unless noted)				
DC Plate Voltage	2,000	2,500	3,000	volts
DC Screen Voltage	325	325	325	volts
DC Grid Voltage[1]	—60	—60	—60	volts
Zero-Signal DC Plate Current	500	500	500	ma
Max.-Signal DC Plate Current	2.0	2.0	1.8	amps
Zero-Signal DC Screen Current*	—4	—4	—4	ma
Max-Signal DC Screen Current*	70	70	70	ma
Effective Load, Plate-to-Plate	1,650	2,400	3,450	ohms
Driving Power	0	0	0	watts
Max-Signal Plate Output Power	2,040	2,900	3,360	watts

* Approximate values.   [1] Adjust grid bias to obtain listed zero-signal plate current.

The low plate impedance means that the plate tank capacitor will be large in value, and that the inductance value will be smaller. At 3.5 mc, a tank capacitor of approximately 330 mmf will be required in order to maintain the proper tank circuit Q. Since the peak voltage rating of the plate tank capacitor should be at least 5,000 volts, an air-dielectric variable capacitor of the proper capacitance and voltage ratings will be very large physically. In the amplifier described here, the problem was solved by the use of a *vacuum* variable plate-tank capacitor. The unit actually used is a Jennings Type UCS 400, which has a peak rating of 7,500 volts. Its RF current rating is 42 amperes. As shown in Fig. 10-19, the capacitance range of 10 to 400 mmf is provided by approximately twenty-five turns of the control shaft.

The plate tank inductance may be wound from ¼-inch copper tubing and tapped to give the proper inductance for the various amateur bands, or a heavy-duty rotary coil may be used instead. The B & W 852 bandswitching turret inductor is designed especially for the low-impedance 4CX-1000A plate circuit. When a tapped plate coil is used, the bandswitch must be a heavy-duty type with ceramic insulation and be capable of carrying at least 20 to 25 amperes of RF current. The most common source of supply for such switches is the government surplus market.

The rotary inductor and the tapped plate coil contain a considerable amount of distributed capacitance between turns. At the higher frequencies, this distributed capacitance makes it extremely difficult to maintain the proper Q in the plate tank circuit: To overcome the effects of distributed capacitance, a small-diameter coil consisting of four or five turns of heavy copper tubing is inserted in series with the main tank inductance and plate tank capacitor. The smaller coil is usually mounted at a 90° angle to the axis of the larger coil. It should be four or five inches away from the metal chasis.

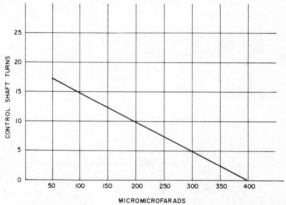

Fig. 10-19. Capacitance values versus control-shaft turns of Jennings UCS-10-400 vacuum variable capacitor over the 50- to 400-mmf range.

It is important to keep the internal RF resistance of the plate tank circuit as low as possible, to prevent excessive loss of output power. That portion of the amplifier plate circuit indicated by the heavy lines in Fig. 10-20 should be wired with ¼-inch copper tubing or strap. Thoroughly clean all connections with steel wool, and bolt them together with 6-32 brass machine screws and nuts. Solder each connection, using a good-quality radio solder and a high-wattage soldering iron. Take enough time to do a good job—a poorly soldered connection in the plate tank circuit will not only cause the tank coil to overheat, but will waste precious output power. Do not depend on the soldered connection for mechanical support of the copper tubing leads. During normal operation, a considerable amount of heat will be generated in the amplifier compartment. Over an extended period of operation, the heat may soften or melt the solder at the tank circuit connections. If the tank circuit should become open,

213

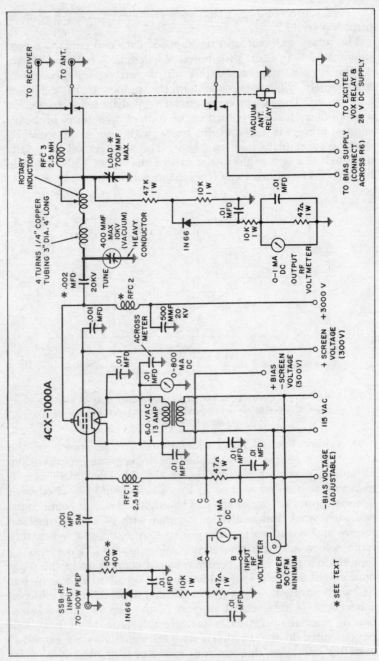

Fig. 10-20. 4CX-1000A linear RF power amplifier.

214

during the operation of the amplifier, the 4CX-1000A tube is quite likely to be ruined.

The plate coupling capacitor must have a sufficiently high voltage rating to safely pass the heavy RF plate current without overheating or breaking down. A satisfactory coupling capacitor can be made up from four 500-mmf, 20K-volt television high-voltage capacitors connected in parallel. Fig. 10-21 shows the location of the 2,000-mmf "sandwich." Do *not* use two 1,000-mmf capacitors in parallel; all four units are required in order to pass the heavy RF current.

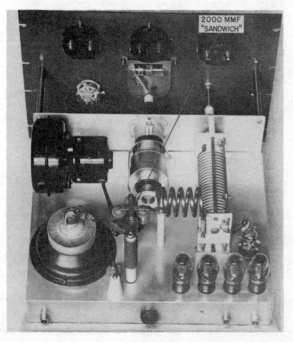

Fig. 10-21. Rear view of 4CX-1000A linear RF power amplifier showing the four 500-mmf capacitors.

The plate RF choke is designed especially for use with shunt-fed pi-network tank circuits and offers a high impedance at all frequencies between 3.5 and 31 mc. The RF choke used in Fig. 10-20 is a Raypar RL-100, which has a DC rating of 800 ma. Fig. 10-22 shows its proper placement and mounting. The "hot" RF lead from the choke top terminal to the tube plate and the coupling-capacitor "sandwich" must be dressed away from the choke winding at an angle of not less than 90° If copper strap or tubing is used for the plate lead, it should be

215

mounted under the terminal screw above the metal cap. The high-voltage end of the choke is bypassed to ground by a standard 500-mmf 20K-volt capacitor.

The rated heater voltage for the 4CX-1000A is 6.0 volts. The heater current drain is 9.5 amperes minimum and 11.5 amperes maximum and the minimum heating time is three minutes. The heater voltage, measured at the tube socket, should never be allowed to exceed ±5% of the rated value. The filament transformer in this amplifier is the Chicago Standard Transformer Type P-6463, which has a number of primary-winding taps. When the appropriate primary taps are used, the secondary voltage can be adjusted to exactly 6.0 volts. The P-6463 secondary

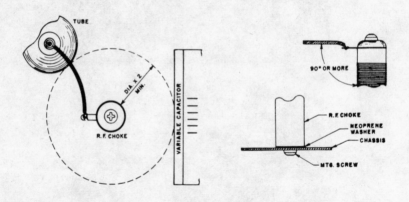

Fig. 10-22. Placement of RL-100 RF choke.

winding is rated at 13 amperes. It is recommended that the heater voltage be applied for not less than three minutes before other operating voltages are applied. From an initial cold condition, tube operation will stabilize after approximately five minutes.

Sufficient air cooling must be provided for the anode and ceramic-to-metal seals of the 4CX-1000A to maintain operating temperatures below the rated maximum values. The rated maximum temperature value of the ceramic-to-metal seals is 200° C. and of the anode core, 250° C. An air-flow rate of 28 cubic feet per minute (with inlet air temperatures up to 40° C.) will be adequate for operation at maximum rated plate dissipation at sea level. Under these conditions, 28 cubic feet per minute of air flow corresponds to a pressure difference across the tube and socket of 0.25 inch of water column. Experience has shown that for reliable long-life operation, the cooling air flow must be maintained during standby periods when only the heater voltage is applied to the tube. In this amplifier, the blower-motor winding is connected across the primary of the filament transformer; thus, air is applied to the tube seals simultaneously with the application of the heater voltage.

If there is any doubt about the adequacy of the supplied cooling, remember that operating temperature is the sole criterion of cooling effectiveness. Surface temperatures may be easily and effectively measured by using one of the several temperature-sensitive paints or sticks available from chemical or scientific supply houses. When these materials are used, extremely thin applications must be made. Otherwise they would interfere with

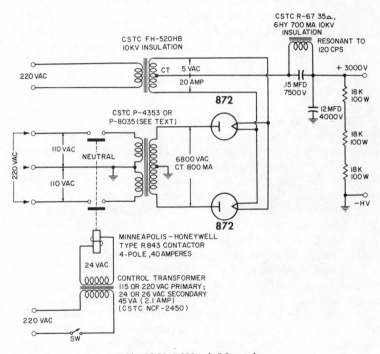

Fig. 10-23. 3,000-volt DC supply.

the transfer of heat from tube to air stream, and this would cause inaccurate indications. The anode cooler should be inspected periodically and cleaned when necessary to remove any lint or dirt which might interfere with effective cooling.

Fig. 10-23 shows a 3,000-volt DC power supply suitable for use with the 4CX-1000A linear RF power amplifier. The high-

217

voltage transformer is the Chicago Standard CSTC Type P-4353, rated at 600 ma DC for CCS and 800 ma DC for ICAS. If it is desired to operate the 4CX-1000A at 2,500 volts on the plate, the CSTC P-8035 will be suitable. This transformer is rated at 500 ma DC for CCS and 575 ma DC for ICAS. The use of lower-voltage plate power transformers to obtain a DC working voltage of 2,500 or 3,000 volts is *not* recommended in bridge-rectifier circuits unless the transformer is specifically designed for such circuits. In most cases, the center-tap connection to the high-voltage secondary will lack sufficient insulation to permit the use of the average plate power transformer in the bridge-rectifier circuit.

Two type 872-A half-wave mercury-vapor rectifiers are used, each with a rated filament voltage of 5.0 volts and a filament current of 7.5 amperes. In a full-wave single-phase circuit, such as that of Fig. 10-23, two 872-A tubes are capable of a maximum DC current output of 2.5 amperes. The filament transformer required for the two high-voltage rectifier tubes is the CSTC Type FH-520HB, which has a secondary rating of 5.0 volts at 20 amperes. The secondary winding must be insulated for at least 10,000 volts to ground.

The 4CX-1000A linear amplifier will present a widely varying load to the DC plate supply. During the standby period, the power-supply load will be reduced to that of the bleeder resistor only. When the amplifier is delivering full output power to the antenna, the load across the power supply will be only a few thousand ohms. However, during normal operation the load will continuously vary from the standby to full-load conditions. Unless the power-supply regulation is very good, the effective linearity of the amplifier will be so poor that the output signal will contain a high percentage of distortion products. In general, a 3,000-volt plate supply for a high-power linear amplifier—such as that described here—must not vary more than 200 volts between the extremes of no-load and full-load conditions.

It is possible to obtain satisfactory voltage regulation of a high-voltage power supply by a number of methods. However, the simplest and least expensive is to resonate the filter choke to approximately 120 cycles, as shown in Fig. 10-23. At resonance, the effective impedance of the filter choke to voltage changes will be increased by a factor equal to the Q of the choke. A 10-henry choke, for example, with a Q value of 3.0 will appear as 30 henrys when tuned to resonance. Another important advantage gained by resonating the filter choke is that a smaller-valued, and hence less expensive, output filter capacitor may be used.

218

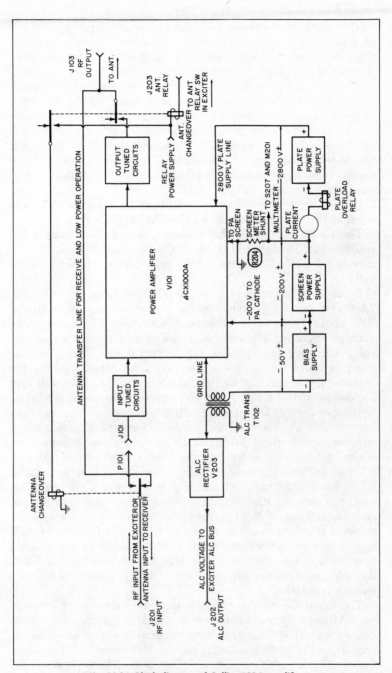

Fig. 10-24. Block diagram of Collins 30S-1 amplifier.

219

This method of voltage regulation, however, requires the use of quality components. The filter choke must have a low DC resistance and be constructed of good-quality iron in order to provide a high Q value. The inductance of an iron-core choke varies with the DC current which passes through its winding; this variation can be minimized by the use of a large air gap, as in a smoothing-type filter choke. The maximum DC current rating of the choke should be at least 100 to 200 ma higher than the average DC current drawn by the linear amplifier during normal operation. The choke (and its resonating capacitor) must have a high breakdown voltage rating, since the resonant voltage across the winding will be quite high. The recommended voltage rating of the choke and capacitor is at least two or three times the DC supply voltage.

The CSTC R-67 filter choke, shown in Fig. 10-23, has a DC resistance of 35 ohms and is rated at 6 henrys at a maximum DC current of 700 milliamperes. The insulation is rated at 10,000 volts.

Resonating capacitor C1 is an oil-filled type. Its 0.15-mfd, 7,500-volt value was found to be correct when used with the R-67 choke. If the exact inductance of the choke is known at the average operating DC current, dividing 1.77 by the inductance value will give the value of C1 in microfarads. However, the exact value of the capacitor can better be determined by the "cut and try" method, since the inductance of the choke will vary somewhat with the changes in DC current. The usual procedure is to operate the DC supply with no load other than bleeder resistor R1. Then several values of C1 are tried until a value is found which gives the *lowest* DC output voltage. Since filter chokes usually do not have a very high Q, the correct value of C1 will not be extremely critical. When the optimum value of C1 is found, the value of R1 may be decreased, if necessary, until the output DC voltage is approximately 90% of the input rms AC voltage. If the DC voltage is already at this value, the value of R1 is increased to the point where the DC output voltage begins to rise sharply with small changes in the bleeder resistance. When this point is reached, the resistance of R1 is the maximum which can be used and still obtain satisfactory voltage regulation.

The linear RF power amplifier described above, a 1,000-watt class-AB_1 unit, is suitable for construction by a technically qualified amateur. The design has been thoroughly proved in actual operation on the various amateur bands. The quality of the output signal will compare favorably with that of most better commercial amplifiers of similar design and power capabilities. However, a number of features included in the better commercial amplifiers would be difficult for the average amateur to incorporate in a home-built unit. An excellent example of a well-designed commercial linear RF power amplifier will be described in the next section.

THE COLLINS 30S-1

The Collins 30S-1 linear RF power amplifier is capable of maximum legal input power on any of the frequencies between 3.5 and 29.7 mc. It can be operated at full power input in either CW or single-sideband service with any exciter (such as the 32S-1) capable of 80 watts PEP output.

Fig. 10-24, shows the general circuit and control arrangement of the 30S-1. Although a 4CX-1000A tube is used, the circuit arrangement is entirely different from that of the amplifier described in the preceding section. In the 30S-1, the 4CX-1000A control grid is grounded for RF by a 220-mmf capacitor, and the screen is connected directly to ground. The plate, screen-grid, and control-grid supplies are connected in series. The junction between the plate and screen supplies is grounded through the screen-current meter shunt. This arrangement places the cathode at negative potential with respect to the screen grid. The bias supply is connected between the cathode and control grid. Provisions are included for RF negative feedback to improve linearity, and for automatic load control (ALC) to prevent overdrive.

As shown in Fig. 10-25, exciter RF is applied through a series of pi-network broad-tuned circuits, to the cathode of the 4CX-1000A. The input impedance of the cathode is approximately 100 ohms, and the S-line exciters have an output impedance of 50 ohms. To match the two, an ingenious method is used which is a combination of the interconnecting coaxial cable and pi-network arrangement in the amplifier cathode circuit. A 20.5-foot cable is supplied with the amplifier. This cable length, and the 30S-1 tuned input circuits, are such that even multiples of 180° phase shifts will be provided between the driver plate and power-amplifier grid. Even multiples are necessary because modulation components change the amplifier cathode impedance, and this change is translated into a shift in reactive impedance at the driver plate. This shift in impedance phase modulates the driver and in turn increases the total over-all distortion of the system. The pi-networks are automatically switched when the band-switch of the plate tank circuit is changed from one band to another.

221

The plate circuit of the power amplifier is tuned by a pi-network consisting of C120, L109, L104, C121, and C122. C121 and C122 are ganged together and are adjustable so that the pi-network can be matched to the antenna circuit impedance. Plate tank capacitor C120 can be adjusted to make the tank circuit resonant to the operating frequency. The RF output from the plate tank is connected, through K101, to the antenna when the control circuits are switched to the "transmit" function.

The 30S-1 amplifier contains both automatic load control (ALC) and RF negative feedback. ALC is a type of compressor circuit operating at radio frequencies. The modulation envelope is detected by rectification in the 4CX-1000A control-grid circuit. The RF component is then filtered out by L108 and C140, and the audio remaining is applied to the primary of T102. The lower end of the primary is bypassed to ground for RF by C128, and the DC return lead is connected to the −60-volt bias supply. T102 is a small 1 : 1 ratio audio transformer with primary and secondary impedances of 10,000 ohms each.

From the secondary of T102, the audio signal is applied to ALC rectifier V203, which is connected as a voltage doubler. Here the audio is rectified to produce a negative control voltage· which is a function of the modulation level. The negative voltage fed back from V203 to the ALC line of the exciter produces approximately 3 db of override control. R234, in series with V203 heater, reduces the no-signal DC level caused on the ALC line by the tube contact potential. Otherwise, this no-signal DC level might result in a delay voltage on the exciter ALC bus line.

The 3 db of ALC override control produced in the 30S-1 acts to reduce the exciter RF gain and thereby helps keep the drive level sufficiently low that the power amplifier is prevented from being driven into distortion.

A fixed amount of RF, fed back from the output to the input of the power amplifier by means of C103, produces a high degree of linearity in the amplified signal. Although there is no phase inversion between the cathode and plate circuits of a cathode-driven RF amplifier, there is between the cathode and grid circuit (provided the grid is not completely bypassed for RF). The feedback voltage will therefore be out of phase with the grid RF voltage. C103 and C104 form an RF voltage-divider circuit that maintains the RF feedback voltage at the proper amount.

Three DC power supplies and three AC filament supplies are included in the 30S-1. The power supply may be connected to a 115-volt, single-phase source; but a 230-volt, three-wire, single-phase source is recommended. High-voltage plate transformer T201 has two primary windings, which are connected in parallel

222

for 115-volt operation and in series for 230-volt operation. The 12-volt AC filament winding of the bias supply transformer, T203, supplies current for the heater of ALC rectifier V203, the pilot lamps in the two indicating meters, and those which light the two dials. This transformer also supplies current for relay power. The bias-voltage winding of transformer T203 is connected to selenium diodes CR207 and CR208 in a full-wave rectifier circuit that provides negative grid-bias voltage for the 4CX-1000A power-amplifier tube. The heater of three-minute time-delay relay K202 is supplied power from the 115-volt AC connections which also furnish power to filament transformer T202 in the high-voltage rectifier circuit. Filament transformer T103 supplies AC power for the heater of thermal overload relay K102. Taps on the primary of high-voltage plate transformer T201 are switched to provide the different voltages necessary for the power amplifier in CW or single-sideband operation. The high-voltage plate supply uses two type 3B28 rectifier tubes connected in a full-wave rectifier circuit and the screen grid supply uses eight 1N1492 silicon diodes in a full-wave bridge circuit. In the screen supply each rectifier is paralleled with a .001-mfd capacitor to protect it against high transient voltages.

Thermal overload relay K102 protects the 4CX-1000A from overdissipation and loss of cooling air. Its bimetallic strip has contacts connected in series with the interlock system. The thermal overload switch is located in the airstream from the 4CX-1000A tube. Current from T103 is passed through the heater of the thermal overload relay to keep the temperature of the heater just below that necessary to operate its contacts. If the airstream fails, the temperature of the bimetallic strip increases, opening the interlock circuit and thus removing the voltages from the 4CX-1000A. Also, if the plate dissipation of the tube is excessive, the higher temperature of the air stream will cause K102 to operate and break the interlock circuit.

In any amplifier using the 4CX-1000A, the various heater, bias, screen, and plate voltages must be applied and also removed in the proper sequence. In the 30S-1, when switch S202 is closed, 115-volt AC is applied to the heater of time-delay relay K202. After three minutes, the bimetallic contacts of the relay will close. (These contacts are in series with the interlock circuits and the coil of plate contactor K203.) When the "on" push button is depressed, plate contactor K203 is energized and its contacts will also close, applying power to step-start relay K201 through CR205. C203, connected across the coil terminals of step-start relay K201, requires a fixed charging time to rise to a high enough potential to energize the relay. When this time has elapsed K201 energizes and shorts out step-start resistors R201 and R233. (These resistors are wire-wound, 100 watts, and have a value of 8.2 ohms each.) Until relay K201 has closed, all power applied to T201 has been dropped through the two step-start resistors. In this manner, the high-voltage power supply starts at a low primary voltage and, after the step-start cycle has elapsed, switches to full voltage. This allows time for partial charging of C207 and C208 before application of the full secondary voltage to the 3B28 rectifier plates. During this time, the rectifier tubes are protected from high peak currents. High-voltage filter capacitors C207 and C208, which are 4 mfd each and rated at 3000 volts DC working voltage, are connected in parallel to provide a total capacitance of 8 mfd. R215, connected between the two filters and the negative high-voltage terminal, limits the inrushing current to the capacitors when power is first applied. The 8-henry filter, L202, is resonated to 120 cycles by C206 in order to improve the DC voltage regulation. The bleeder for the high-voltage supply consists of three wirewound, 100-watt resistors, of 18,000 ohms each, connected in series across the 3000-volt output terminals. High-voltage shorting switch S206, which is part of the safety interlock system, protects the operator from accidentally coming in contact with the 3,000 volts.

The amplifier cabinet cover and the power-supply front door operate safety interlock switches for operator protection. When the top cover is opened, interlock switch S103 breaks the circuit to the coil of plate contactor K203 and thereby removes all high voltages from the amplifier. Likewise, when the power-supply compartment (lower) door is opened, S205 breaks the same circuit and removes all high voltages. Both interlock switches are mechanically interlocked with switches which short out the high-voltage filters at the same time the interlock circuit opens. S103 is mechanically ganged with shorting switch S101, and S205 with S206. Without the shorting switches, the high-voltage charge would remain on the filters if one or more sections of the bleeder resistor were to open. It must be emphasized that an 8-mfd filter capacitor charged to 3000 volts (or possibly higher, if the bleeder were open) could be fatal if you should accidentally come in contact with its terminals. *Never* attempt to defeat the purpose of the interlock switches. Always remember that the voltages in this equipment are sufficiently high to kill instantly.

Both of the linear power amplifiers described in the two preceding sections are designed around the characteristics of the 4CX-1000A ceramic tetrode. When other types of tubes are used, the basic amplifier design must be modified to conform

224

with the requirements of the tube used. The 4CX-1000A has been selected as a good example for tetrode or pentode linear radio-frequency amplifier design because its requirements, particularly those of the control-grid and screen-grid circuits, are somewhat more stringent than those of most similar tubes of the 1,000-watt class.

GROUNDED-GRID CLASS-B

The simplest linear RF power amplifier uses either a high-*mu* power triode or a triode-connected tetrode in the grounded-grid circuit configuration. In addition to their comparative simplicity, these amplifiers are almost foolproof in operation since no tricky bias or screen voltages ordinarily are required. However, in spite of the fact that they have been in use for many years, their exact operating characteristics are not widely understood. The tubes most amateurs use in grounded-grid amplifiers are the 811 and 813. Tube manufacturers have been very reluctant to endorse the use of their tubes in this manner, however, since the grid dissipation ratings were almost always exceeded. During the past few years, a number of high-*mu* power triodes have been developed especially for use in grounded-grid class-B service. Included in this new group are the Eimac 3-400Z and 3-1000Z , and the Penta PL-6569 and PL-6580.

The Eimac 3-400Z is a compact power triode intended for use as a zero-bias class-B amplifier in either audio or RF applications. Operation with zero bias simplifies the associated amplifier circuitry since no grid-bias voltage supply is required. In addition to the circuit simplification, the use of grounded-grid circuitry is attractive from the viewpoint of power gain. When the 3-400Z is used as a cathode-driven linear amplifier, for example, a power gain as high as twenty times is possible.

The 3-400Z has a thoriated tungsten filament which operates from 5.0 volts and has a current drain of 14.5 amperes. Its special five-pin base is designed for use with the Eimac SK-400 air-system socket. The Eimac SK-416 chimney should also be used for most effective cooling. Maximum operating temperatures are 225° C. for the plate seal and 200° C. for the base seals. When the recommended socket and chimney are used, the minimum air-flow rate required in order to provide adequate cooling, at an inlet air temperature of 25° C., is 15 cubic feet per minute at a static pressure of approximately 0.40 inch of water, as measured in the socket at sea level. Cooling air must be supplied to the tube even during standby periods.

225

Air-flow rates in excess of the minimum requirements will, of course, prolong the life of the tube.

The average amplification factor of the 3-400Z is 200. The maximum ratings for use in grounded-grid, class-B linear RF power-amplifier service are 3,000 volts of DC plate voltage, 400 ma of plate current, 400 watts of plate dissipation, and 20 watts of grid dissipation. The upper-frequency limit for the maximum ratings is 110 mc. Typical operating data for plate voltages of 2,000, 2,500, and 3,000 volts are given in Table 10-3. Most "typical operation" data are obtained by calculation from the published characteristic curves and confirmed by direct tests. No allowance for circuit losses, either input or output, has been made. Exceptions are distinguished by a listing of "useful" as

Table 10-3.

Operating data for an EIMAC 3-400Z used in grounded-grid linear RF amplifier service.

	2,000	2,500	3,000	volts
DC Plate Voltage	2,000	2,500	3,000	volts
Zero-Signal DC Plate Current	62	73	100	ma
Max-Signal DC Plate Current*	400	400	333	ma
Max-Signal DC Grid Current*	148	142	120	ma
Driving Impedance	——**	——**	122	ohms
Resonant Load Impedance	2,750	3,450	4,750	ohms
Two-Tone DC Plate Current	265	274	——**	ma
Two-Tone DC Grid Current	87	82	——**	ma
Max-Signal Driving Power	——**	——**	32	watts
Peak Envelope Plate Output Power	——**	——**	655	watts
Peak Envelope Useful Output Power	445	560	——**	
Intermodulation Distortion Products Below PEP Level	—40	—35	——**	db

* Single-tone conditions.

** Data not available.

Zero-signal DC plate-current values are approximate only. Adjust for best linearity of output RF envelope.

opposed to "plate" output power. The values appearing in Table 10-3 have been obtained from existing equipment and the output power has been measured at the load. The typical constant-current characteristics for the 3-400Z power triode are shown in Fig. 10-26. These curves will be useful for calculating operating conditions which differ from those in the table.

The 3-1000Z is similar to the 3-400Z described above except for its higher power ratings. The 3-1000Z includes a thoriated tungsten filament which operates at 7.5 volts with a current drain of 21.3 amperes. The base is a special five-pin type designed for use with the Eimac SK-500 air-system socket. The

226

recommended chimney is the Eimac SK-516. The maximum operating temperatures are 225° C. for the plate seal and 200° C. for the base seals. When the recommended socket and chimney, are used, at least 20 cubic feet of air per minute must flow, at a static pressure of approximately 0.15 inch of water (as measured in the socket at sea level), in order for adequate cooling to be provided at an inlet air temperature of 25° C. Above 30 mc the required air flow is increased to 30 cubic feet per minute at a static pressure of approximately 0.35 inch of water, (as measured in the SK-500 socket). Cooling air must be supplied to the tube even during standby periods. As before, higher-than-minimum air-flow rates will prolong tube life.

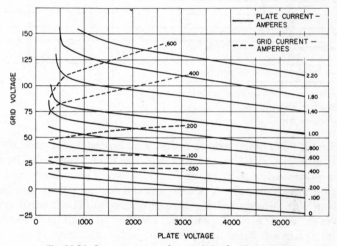

Fig. 10-26. Constant-current characteristics for Eimac 3-400Z.

The average amplification factor of the 3-1000Z is 200. The maximum ratings in grounded-grid class-B service are 3,000 volts of DC plate voltage, 800 ma of DC plate current, 1,000 watts of plate dissipation, and 50 watts of grid dissipation. The upper-frequency limit for the maximum ratings is 110 mc. Typical operating data for plate voltages of 2,500 and 3,000 volts are given in Table 10-4. The terminal connections for both the 3-400Z and 3-1000Z are given in Fig. 10-27. The typical constant-current characteristics for the 3-1000Z are shown in Fig. 10-28.

For greatest linearity and power output when either the 3-400Z or 3-1000Z is operated as a grounded-grid linear RF power amplifier, a resonant tank is recommended in the cathode circuit. With a single-ended amplifier configuration, it is suggested that for best results the cathode tank circuit be designed to operate at a Q of 5 or more.

227

Table 10-4.

DC Plate Voltage	2,500	3,000	volts
Zero-Signal DC Plate Current	162*	240*	ma
Max-Signal DC Plate Current**	——***	670	ma
Max-Signal DC Grid Current**	——***	300	ma
Driving Impedance	——***	55	ohms
Resonant Load Impedance	1,700	2,650	ohms
Max-Signal Driving Power**	——***	65	watts
Peak Envelope Plate Output Power**	——***	1,360	watts
Single-Tone DC Plate Current	800	——	ma
Single-Tone DC Grid Current	254	——	ma
Two-Tone DC Plate Current	550	——	ma
Two-Tone DC Grid Current	147	——	ma
Intermodulation Distortion Products Below PEP Level	—35	——	db
Peak Envelope Useful Output Power	1,050	——	watts

* Approximate value. Adjust for best linearity of output RF envelope.

** Single-tone conditions.

*** Not available.

The PL-6569 power triode is designed especially for grounded-grid, class-B service as a linear RF amplifier. This tube has a plate power-dissipation rating of 250 watts. The average amplification factor is 45. A small amount of negative grid-bias voltage will be required for class-B operation. The control grid, however, is at ground potential for the RF voltage. Because of its relatively high amplification factor and perveance, the PL-6569 will give power gains as high as 10 when used in the

Fig. 10-27. Socket-terminal connections for the 3-400Z and 3-1000Z.

grounded-grid RF-amplifier circuit. The tube is provided with effective internal shielding, and neutralization is not required in most ordinary grounded-grid applications.

The PL-6569 uses a thoriated tungsten filament which operates at 5.0 volts with a current drain of 14.5 amperes. The base is a giant five-pin type with a metal shell. The recommended socket is the Johnson 122-275, National HX-100, or equivalent. Forced-air cooling of the base and its seals is required for all classes of operation. Such cooling is normally provided by the use of a tube socket having holes which align with those of the base, and by using a small fan or blower to pressurize the chassis on which the tube is mounted. With an open chassis, the air stream from a small fan or blower can be directed at the tube socket. A minimum air flow of 5 cubic feet per minute is required through the socket and base while filament power is being applied. When operation is confined to frequencies below 30 mc convective air flow will provide adequate cooling of the glass envelope and plate seal. Above 30 mc, the air stream from a small fan or blower can be directed at the upper portion of the tube envelope. In any event, the temperature of the plate cap should never exceed 170° C. for any class of continuous service.

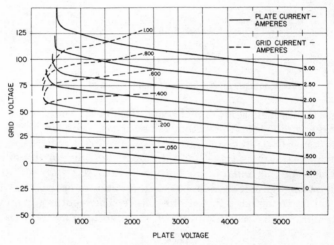

Fig. 10-28. Constant-current characteristics for 3-1000Z.

Fig. 10-29 shows a typical class-B circuit suitable for use with the PL-6569. Typical operating data for plate voltages of 2,500, 3,000, 3,500, and 4,000 volts are given in Table 10-5. The graph in Fig. 10-30 shows the typical constant-current characteristics for the PL-6569. From these curves, operating conditions for plate voltages different from those in the table may be calculated.

In Fig. 10-29, the control grid is supplied only with DC bias; RF is bypassed to ground. The RF driving signal is applied between the filament and ground, and the output power is taken from pi-network output capacitor C4. The filament transformer must either be of a low-capacitance type capable of a 15-ampere current flow at 5.0 volts, or be arranged so that suitable high-current RF chokes can be added between the transformer sec-

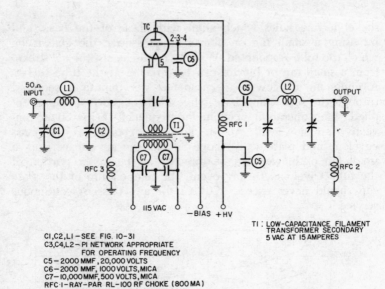

Fig. 10-29. PL-6569 used in a grounded-grid class-B RF-amplifier circuit.

C1,C2,L1 — SEE FIG. 10-31
C3,C4,L2 — PI NETWORK APPROPRIATE
FOR OPERATING FREQUENCY
C5 — 2000 MMF, 20,000 VOLTS
C6 — 2000 MMF, 1000 VOLTS, MICA
C7 — 10,000 MMF, 500 VOLTS, MICA
RFC 1 — RAY-PAR RL-100 RF CHOKE (800 MA)
RFC 2, RFC 3 — 2.5 MH RF CHOKE, 500 MA.

T1 : LOW-CAPACITANCE FILAMENT
TRANSFORMER SECONDARY
5 VAC AT 15 AMPERES

ondary terminals and the filament terminals. The driving RF voltage applied to the cathode circuit will appear in series with the RF output voltage. This means that a portion of the excitation power is transferred, through the tube, to the output circuit. The portion of the output power "fed through" from the driving circuit is related to the ratio between the tube excitation voltage and the output voltage. The feedthrough power is minimized by using a tube with a high amplification factor,

Table 10-5.

Operating data for the PL-6569 used in grounded-grid linear RF amplifier service, single-sideband suppressed carrier.

DC Plate Voltage	2,500	3,000	3,500	4,000	volts
DC Grid Voltage	−65	−75	−90	−105	volts
Zero-Signal DC Plate Current	40	35	30	24	ma
Max-Signal DC Plate Current	300	265	270	250	ma
Max-Signal DC Grid Current	80	50	68	42	ma
Max-Signal Peak RF Driving Voltage	180	170	220	205	volts
Max-Signal Driving Power (Approx.)	70	60	75	60	watts
Max-Signal Plate Power Input	750	800	945	1,000	watts
Max-Signal Plate Dissipation	250	250	250	250	watts
Max-Signal Power Output	550	600	760	800	watts

Maximum-signal values are for peak conditions, or for single-tone modulation at full signal.

230

so that minimum RF grid voltage is required. Since the ratio of RF output to excitation voltage is increased by using the highest possible DC plate voltage, the amplifier power gain is further improved.

In addition to the feedthrough power, the RF driving source must supply power for normal grid-driving purposes. This power is dissipated in the tube bias supply and grid, before it can appear in the output circuit. The power lost is ordinarily around two per cent of the output power.

The average input impedance of the PL-6569 is given by the formula:

$$Z_{input} = \frac{(\text{Peak RF driving voltage})^2}{2 \times \text{Driving power}}$$

Values of peak RF driving voltage and power for a number of operating conditions will be found in Table 10-5. For all

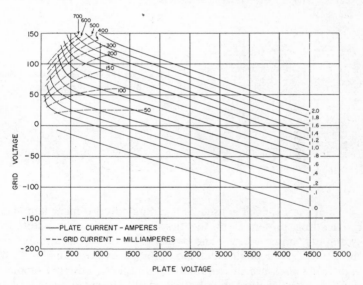

Fig. 10-30. Constant-current characteristics of PL-6569 tube.

practical purposes, however, the input impedance of the PL-6569 in the grounded-grid configuration may be taken as 300 ohms. The constant-current characteristics of the tube are shown in Fig. 10-30.

Fig. 10-31 shows the suggested pi-network capacitance and inductance values for a network feeding the PL-6569 from a "flat" 50-ohm coaxial line. The pi-network is composed of L1, C1, and C2 in Fig. 10-29. RFC3 will be required only when no

231

low-capacitance filament transformer is used. When a standard filament transformer and series-filament RF chokes are used, the ground and negative high-voltage returns are usually connected to the center tap of the secondary winding. The output tank circuit (L2, C3, and C4) can be designed from the pi-network data included earlier in this chapter.

As shown in Fig. 10-32, the grid of the PL-6569 terminates in three base pins. The corresponding three socket terminals should be connected together with a low-inductance lead, and bypassed to chassis ground with another low-inductance lead and a low-inductance capacitor (shown as C6 in Fig. 10-29. Multiple bypass capacitors may be used, if desired, but ordinarily are not needed.

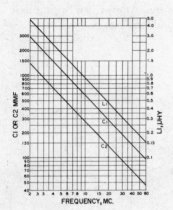

Fig. 10-31. Pi-network values for matching input circuit of grounded-grid class-B amplifier to flat 50-ohm line.

When the PL-6569 is used as a grounded-grid linear amplifier, the loading presented to the driving source makes additional swamping unnecessary. The typical operating conditions for the PL-6569 as a single-sideband amplifier as given in Fig. 10-30 and Table 10-5, are for continuously applied sinusoidal modulation. Increased output may be obtained, without excessive plate dissipation, by using the normal speech waveform of the single-sideband signal. When the modulation is intermittent and contains a high ratio of peak to average power (as in the average single-sideband signal), the plate loading and drive should be increased. However, the average plate dissipation should not be allowed to exceed 250 watts.

The PL-6580 power triode is similar to the PL-6569 except for its higher plate dissipation rating. The PL-6580 includes a thoriated tungsten filament which operates at 5.0 volts and a

232

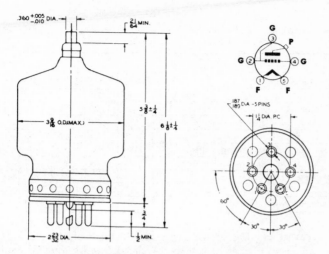

Fig. 10-32. Socket-terminal connections of a PL-6569 tube.

current drain of 14.5 amperes. The base is a giant five-pin type with a metal shell. The recommended socket is a Johnson 122-275, National HX-100, or equivalent, operated in conjunction with the PL-C1 glass-chimney socket cutout shown in Fig. 10-33. The constant-current characteristics of the PL-6580 are shown in Fig. 10-34 and its operating data given in Table 10-6.

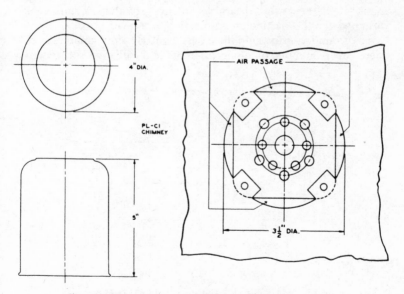

Fig. 10-33. Socket chassis cutout and mounting data for PL-6569.

233

Table 10-6.

Operating data for the PL-6580 used in grounded-grid linear RF amplifier service, single-sideband suppressed carrier.

DC Plate Voltage	2,500	3,000	3,500	4,000	volts
DC Grid Voltage	—50	—70	—85	—100	volts
Zero-Signal DC Plate Current	60	50	45	40	ma
Max-Signal DC Plate Current	350	335	300	300	ma
Max-Signal DC Grid Current	95	80	65	65	ma
Max-Signal Peak RF Driving Voltage	195	205	210	230	volts
Max-Signal Driving Power (Approx.)	75	73	68	72	watts
Max-Signal Plate Power Input	875	1,000	1,050	1,200	watts
Max-Signal Plate Dissipation	320	335	335	350	watts
Max-Signal Power Output	610	720	765	910	watts

Forced-air cooling of the seals at the base of the PL-6580 is required in all classes of service. At least 5 cubic feet of cooling air per minute should be passed through the base. Where the plate dissipation exceeds 250 watts, envelope cooling is also required. Adequate envelope cooling at 400 watts of plate dissipation requires 15 cubic feet of air per minute past the envelope and across the plate seal. Proper distribution of the air may be obtained by use of the PL-C1 chimney.

The power triodes discussed above are designed specifically for grounded-grid linear RF amplifier service. In new equipment, it is generally desirable to use standard components designed for the particular application wherever possible. However, grounded-grid amplifiers, particularly for amateur use, there are a number of older tubes which will give satisfactory

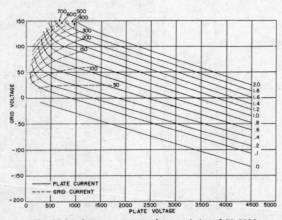

Fig. 10-34. Constant-current characteristics of PL-6580.

results. Quite likely the average amateur already has some of these tubes, or can obtain them at an insignificant cost from a government surplus dealer. The following information should enable the amateur to select the tube or tubes best suited to his own requirements.

Tube Selection

The tube selected for a grounded-grid amplifier must be capable of good linearity. Generally the best linearity will be obtained from either a zero-bias tube (in which grid current flows during the full 180° of the RF driving-voltage cycle), or a biased tube (in which no grid current flows even at the peak of the cycle). Either tube will provide good regulation of the driving voltage and thus improved linearity. Moreover, there will be no abrupt change of grid current, which would tend to produce higher-order harmonics.

A large number of triodes are not suitable for use in class-B grounded-grid service, either with or without fixed bias. Included in this group are the low-*mu* types such as the 100-TL, 250-TL, 304-TL, 450-TL, and the 211. They generally require excessive driving power, and lack the linearity capabilities required for modern linear amplifier service. Because of their internal construction, poor screening between the plate and cathode will be obtained when the control grid is connected to ground. This will result in instability and other effects which will further deteriorate the linearity of the amplifier.

Medium- and high-*mu* triode types such as the 100-TH, 250-TH, 304-TH, 810, 812, and 833A can be used as class-B linear RF amplifiers, but will require a negative grid bias in order to provide any degree of high peak output power. In fact, the amplifier will have to be driven well into the positive grid region. To do so requires a much higher driving power than normal since a large percentage of the driving-signal power is dissipated in the swamping network. In most cases, these tubes will operate best when the driving-signal power is reduced slightly below the level required to produce grid-current flow. However, the peak power output will be reduced considerably.

The most satisfactory tubes for zero-bias grounded-grid operation are the 805, 808, 811A, 838, 813, and the 4-1000A. The 4-1000A will be discussed in detail later in this chapter.

Triode-connected tetrodes and pentodes possess some definite advantages for use as zero-bias grounded-grid linear amplifiers:

1. The screen and/or suppressor provides excellent screening between the plate and cathode.

2. The grounded control grid closes the input circuit and thus prevents the driving signal from being coupled into the output circuit.
3. The grounded screen and suppressor grids close the output circuit to prevent feedback of the output voltage into the driver circuit.
4. A small amount of negative bias can be applied to the control grid to cut off the plate current during the standby period. This bias can be keyed in and out automatically by the VOX relay, or with a telegraph key for CW operation.
5. The control-grid current can be metered and the indication used to facilitate correct adjustment of excitation and loading.

The amateur's use of the power pentode and tetrode tubes as high-*mu* triodes in grounded-grid linear RF-amplifier service has stirred up considerable controversy among tube design engineers and manufacturers. In spite of the fact that the amateurs have been using such tubes as the 813, 4-125A, and the 4-400A as zero-bias grounded-grid high-*mu* triodes in class-B linear RF amplifiers for years, virtually none of the tube manufacturers will endorse their use in this manner. The reason is, of course, that the control grid of the tetrode or pentode, when connected as a high-*mu* triode, in practically all cases tends to draw a grid current greatly in excess of the manufacturer's maximum allowable rating. It is extremely doubtful whether a manufacturer will replace any tetrode or pentode that fails within the warranty period, if it was used in the high-*mu* triode connection and in a zero-bias type of grounded-grid circuit. But if the amateur has a reasonably large supply of surplus tubes or can afford to buy replacements, he will obtain excellent results from them.

Tetrodes such as the 813, 4-125A, 4-250A, 4-400A, and 4-1000A are the most suitable for use as high-*mu* triodes in the zero-bias grounded-grid configuration. The operating characteristics for the 4-125A, 4-400A, and 4-1000A tetrodes are shown in Table 10-7. (Each column represents different sets of operating conditions.) The operating characteristics of the 813 will be similar to those of the 4-125A and the ratings for the 4-250A (except for a lower plate dissipation) will be similar to those of the 4-400A. To illustrate the design procedure for a tetrode zero-bias amplifier, the next section will describe a practical amplifier of the 1,000-watt class using a triode-connected 4-1000A tetrode tube.

Table 10-7.

Operating characteristics of 4-125A, 4-400A, and 4-1000A tetrodes operated as zero bias triode-connected Class-B linear RF amplifiers.

4-125A				
DC Plate Voltage	2,000	2,500	3,000	volts
No-Signal DC Plate Current	10	15	20	ma
Single-Tone DC Plate Current	105	110	115	ma
Single-Tone DC Screen Current	30	30	30	ma
Single-Tone DC Grid Current	55	55	55	ma
Single-Tone Driving Power	16	16	16	watts
Driving Impedance	340	340	340	ohms
Load Impedance	10,500	13,500	15,700	ohms
Plate Input Power	210	275	345	watts
Plate Output Power	145	190	240	watts

4-400A				
(Ratings apply to 4-250A, within plate dissipation rating of 4-250A)				
DC Plate Voltage	2,000	2,500	3,000	volts
Zero-Signal Plate Current	70	80	90	ma
Single-Tone Plate Current	265	270	280	ma
DC Screen Voltage	0	0	0	volts
Single-Tone Screen Current	55	55	55	ma
DC Grid Voltage	0	0	0	volts
Single-Tone Grid Current	100	100	100	ma
Single-Tone Driving Power	38	39	40	watts
Driving Impedance	160	150	140	ohms
Load Impedance	3,950	5,000	6,100	ohms
Single-Tone Input Power	530	675	840	watts
Single-Tone Output Power	325	435	555	watts

4-1000A				
DC Plate Voltage	3,000	4,000	5,000	volts
Zero-Signal Plate Current	100	120	150	ma
Single-Tone Plate Current	700	675	540	ma
DC Screen Voltage	0	0	0	volts
Single-Tone Screen Current	105	80	55	ma
DC Grid Voltage	0	0	0	volts
Single-Tone Grid Current	170	150	115	ma
Single-Tone Driving Power	130	105	70	watts
Driving Impedance	104	106	110	ohms
Load Impedance	2,450	3,450	5,550	ohms
Single-Tone Input Power	2,100	2,700	2,700	watts
Single-Tone Output Power	1,475	1,870	1,900	watts

1,000-WATT GROUNDED-GRID AMPLIFIER

The amplifier to be described in this section has been designed around the operating characteristics of the 4-1000A tetrode, as given in Table 10-7. This tube is operated at a plate voltage of 4,000 volts and is capable of a single-tone output power of 1,870 watts. The single-tone input power has a maximum rating of 2,700 watts. This is of course greatly in excess of the 1,000 watts of maximum legal input power specified by the FCC for use on the amateur frequency bands. However, there are some very definite and worthwhile advantages to be gained from the excess power capabilities of this amplifier. In the first place, a linear RF power amplifier—as far as distortion characteristics are concerned—is somewhat similar to a good-quality high-fidelity audio power amplifier. It is customary for the latter to have power-output capabilities far in excess of those required for the average level of musical reproduction, so that the occasional high peaks of audio power will be reproduced. In the linear RF amplifier, we are specifically interested in the production of high peak power output without distortion. The peak power output of a good-quality amplifier will be in the vicinity of 2,000 to 3,000 watts PEP—depending on the characteristics of the operator's voice—when the input power is at the legal amateur limit. The 4-1000A grounded-grid amplifier will easily produce a peak power ouput in the 2,000- to 3,000-watt range without waveform distortion or flattening. If the single-sideband exciter is a good quality 100-watt transmitter the ALC indicating meter can be monitored during transmission to prevent the amplifier input power from being driven beyond the legal amateur limit. At plate power inputs of 1,000 watts or less, the control-grid dissipation of the 4-1000A will be well within the manufacturer's rated maximum dissipation limits for maximum tube life.

The 4-1000A includes a thoriated tungsten filament which operates at 7.5 volts with a current drain of 21 amperes. A suitable filament transformer is the Stancor Type P-6457 transformer, which is rated at 7.5 volts at 21 amperes. The Triad type F-28U will also be suitable. The base is a giant five-pin type with a metal shell. The recommended socket is the Eimac SK-500 air-system type with the SK-506 chimney. The tube is cooled by radiation from the plate and by circulation of forced air through the base and around the envelope. The cooling air must be supplied to the tube even when the filament alone is on during the standby periods. The base-seal temperatures must be maintained below 150° C. and the temperature of the plate seal below 200° C. The problem of cooling is greatly simplified by using the recommended air-system socket and chimney, which are designed to maintain the correct balance of cooling air for the various parts of the tube. For maximum rated plate dissipation of the tube, this

238

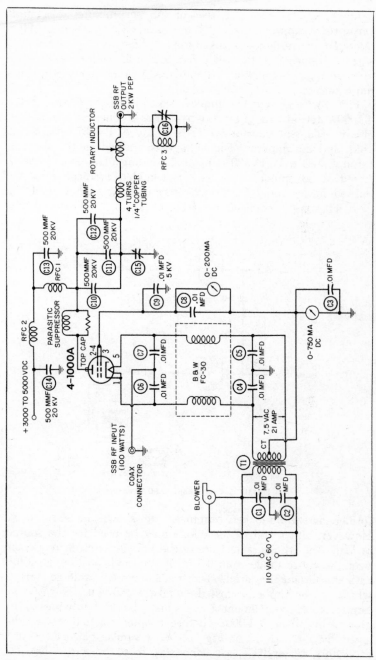

Fig. 10-35. Schematic of a grounded-grid 4-1000A class-B linear RF power amplifier.

239

system requires 45 cubic feet of air per minute at a static pressure of approximately 1.2 inches of water column. When operated as a grounded-grid linear amplifier for amateur single-sideband purposes, the tube requires less cooling,, since the average plate dissipation will be considerably below the maximum rating.

Fig. 10-35 shows the simplest possible arrangement of the 4-1000A tetrode in grounded-grid class-B linear RF amplifier circuit. Filament transformer T1 is a Stancor P-6457 rated at 7.5 volts and 21 amperes. The voltage is applied to the filament through a B & W FC-30 twin dual-winding filament RF choke. Rated at 30 amperes, this unit is shielded (indicated by the dashed lines) and contains four terminals at each end of the case. The proper connections of the choke to the filament trans-

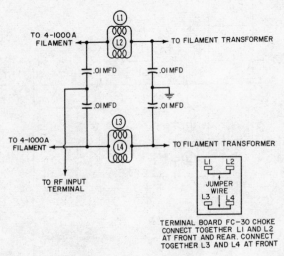

Fig. 10-36. Connections to FC-30 choke.

former and tube-socket terminals are shown in Fig. 10-36. However, either end of the choke may be used for the source or load. The RF characteristics of the FC-30 permit it to operate over the entire range from 3.5 to 30 mc, with no tuning of the cathode circuit required. The maximum RF voltage (rms) which can be applied across the choke is 150 volts. The 7.5-volt terminals of the filament transformer should be bypassed to ground by .01-mfd, 1,000 volt disc ceramic capacitors, as indicated by C4 and C5 of Fig. 10-36. A similar pair of .01-mfd capacitors, C6 and C7, are connected in series across the filament terminals of the 4-1000A socket. The center junction of these capacitors is connected to the inner-conductor terminal of the chassis coaxial input connector. In this manner, the RF driving signal is simultaneously applied to both sides of the tube filament. The center tap of the 7.5-volt transformer winding is also bypassed to ground by a .01-mfd capacitor. The 0- to 750-ma DC plate-current meter is connected from the center tap of the filament-transformer secondary winding to ground, and the 0- to 200-ma DC grid-current meter is returned to the center tap of the filament transformer. When the two milliammeters are connected as shown, the plate-current meter will indicate only the plate current drawn by the tube, and the grid-current meter will indicate only the rectified RF (DC) current drawn by the two grids. If the grid-current meter is returned to ground instead of to the filament-transformer center tap, the plate-current meter will indicate only the plate current during the standby period. When the amplifier is driven, however, the plate-current meter will indicate the combined plate and grid currents. This would not only give false indications of the linear-amplifier power input, but would also cause a great amount of confusion in making the proper excitation and loading adjustments. Placement of the plate-current meter in series with the +4000-volt power-supply return lead is *not* recommended.

The parasitic suppressor connected between the plate terminal of the 4-1000A and the plate tank circuit may or may not be required. In the model amplifier, the original plate RF choke (RFC1) was a hand-wound solenoid one inch in diameter and approximately six inches long. A strong VHF parasitic oscillation occurred which was eliminated by use of a parasitic suppressor consisting of ten turns of No. 14 copper wound on a two-watt, 47-ohm carbon resistor. The turns were evenly spaced over the length of the resistor, and the two ends of the coil were soldered to the resistor terminals, as shown in Fig. 10-36. Before the parasitic was eliminated by installing the suppressor, the amplifier caused severe interference with nearby television receivers. However, the home-made RF choke was later replaced with the Raypar Type RL-100 RF choke, which is specified, and the parasitic condition did not reappear. The parasitic suppressor was then removed from the circuit, and no interference with television reception has since occurred. The presence or absence of parasitic oscillations will generally be determined by the wiring of the grid or plate leads which are individual characteristics of a particular amplifier. The tendency toward parasitic oscillation in any type of linear RF amplifier can be reduced by the use of low-impedance (to VHF) grid and plate leads. It is customary to use at least one-quarter inch copper strap for the high-power amplifier plate and grid leads. The use of vacuum-type variable tank capacitors, instead of the ordinary air-dielectric type, will aid considerably in preventing VHF parasitic oscillations.

COLLINS 30L-1

The Collins 30L-1 is a portable RF linear power amplifier, including the plate power and bias supplies. It is capable of 1,000 watts PEP input power in SSB or 1,000 watts DC input in CW service with any exciter, such as the KWM-2/2A, 32S-1, 32S-3, etc., which will supply 70 watts of driving power. The 30L-1 covers the amateur bands between 3.5 and 29.7 mc. In addition, the amplifier may be operated outside the amateur bands over certain ranges of frequency. The power-amplifier stage uses four 811A triodes connected in parallel with cathode drive.

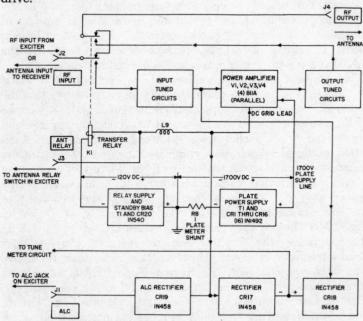

Fig. 10-37. Block diagram of Collins 30L-1 linear amplifier.

The block diagram of the 30L-1 is shown in Fig. 10-37. The front view of the unit is shown in the photograph (Fig. 10-38).

The input tuned circuits, shown in Fig. 10-37 and 10-40, are broadband pi-network circuits used to couple the exciting signal into the cathode circuits of the power-amplifier tubes. The tuned

242

input circuits provide increased efficiency, reduced distortion, and a better impedance match for the exciter than normally would be obtained with an untuned input. Tuning adjustments are not required except for operation outside the amateur bands.

The output tuned circuits are also pi-networks resonated at the operating frequency in use. This circuit is adjusted by the tuning control on the front panel. A four-gang variable capacitor is adjusted by the loading control to match the pi-network tank circuit to the impedance presented by the antenna and feed system in use. Output from the plate tank circuit is made through the contacts of antenna changeover relay K1 to the antenna when the control circuits are energized.

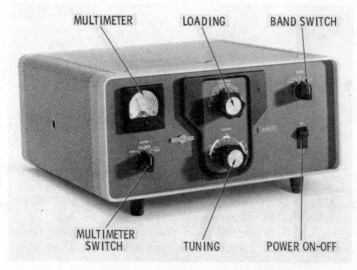

Fig. 10-38. Collins 30L-1 linear amplifier showing operating controls.

Two DC power supplies and one AC filament supply are included in the 30L-1. The amplifier may be operated from either a 115-volt AC single-phase or a 230-volt AC, three-wire, single-phase source. Where possible, the 230-volt, three-wire connection is recommended. Power transformer T1 has two primary windings. They are connected in parallel for 115-volt, and in series for 230-volt, operation. The 6.3-volt secondary winding provides filament power for the 811A tubes through an RF choke, and also powers the pilot lamp in the meter. Another secondary winding applies voltage to semiconductor rectifier CR20. This is a half-wave circuit connected to supply blocking bias to the amplifier tubes under receive conditions and operating bias when transmitting. It also furnishes power for changeover relay K1.

243

Voltage from the third secondary winding is applied to two semiconductor rectifier strings connected in a full-wave voltage-doubler configuration. Parallel capacitors are used to equalize the reverse voltages impressed across the diode junctions and to protect the diodes against damage by transients. The output of this supply provides approximately 1,600 volts DC under load for the amplifier-tube plates.

The control and interlock circuits of the 30L-1 are shown in Fig. 10-39. The front-panel "on-off" switch breaks one side of

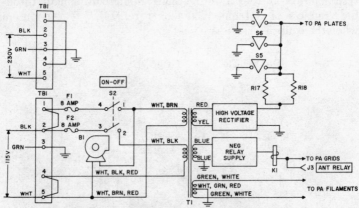

Fig. 10-39. Control circuits of 30L-1 linear amplifier.

the AC line in the "off" position. In the "on" position, AC power is applied to the power-transformer primaries and the tube-cooling fan, B1. Overload protection is provided by eight-ampere fuses F1 and F2. These are used for both 115-volt and 230-volt AC operation.

The 30L-1 amplifier contains automatic load control (ALC) circuits to prevent distortion of the output waveform and to permit a high average level of modulation and optimum power output. Under modulation, RF voltage is taken from the 811A grids, rectified, and filtered to provide a negative DC control voltage which is proportional to the modulation level. This voltage is applied to the control grid of a low-level RF-amplifier tube, or tubes, in the exciter. The time constants of the ALC circuit have a fast-attack, slow-release characteristic. The ALC threshold is controlled by the amount of reverse bias on CR19. The reverse-bias voltage is developed across a 1,500-ohm resistor in the plate-supply bleeder network and can be varied by a potentiometer. This adjustment is normally made at the factory for optimum operation with exciters such as the KWM-2/2A, and rarely will require adjustment in the field.

244

HEATHKIT SSB AMPLIFIER HA-14

In keeping with the current trend toward higher-power single-sideband service, the Heathkit HA-14 SSB linear amplifier is designed to provide high output power for mobile- and fixed-station use. Nearly all of the modern single-sideband exciters and transceivers now available can be used as a driver for this linear RF amplifier.

The HA-14 linear amplifier is small and compact for easy mounting in most automobiles. The companion HP-14 DC power supply used with it makes an excellent combination for mobile use. If desired, the HP-24 AC power supply may be used with the HA-14 to provide a small desk-top 1,000-watt PEP amplifier.

Fig. 10-41. Heathkit® SSB amplifier model HA-14. This compact unit is supplied in kit form.

The photograph, Fig. 10-41, shows the front view of the HA-14 and the operating controls. The schematic, Fig. 10-42, shows the circuit. The amplifier unit is basically made up of three circuits: the input circuit, the output circuit, and the antenna changeover and cutoff bias circuit. Each circuit is described individually.

Tubes V1 and V2, types 572-/T160L, are connected in parallel in a cathode-driven (grounded-grid), class-B configuration. Driving power for each band is coupled through a broadband network consisting of a coil and associated capacitors, and through capacitor C13 to the tube cathodes. Coils L1 through L5, with their associated capacitors, make up these impedance-matching networks, which reduce distortion and increase efficiency.

The proper input network as well as the correct output circuit coil tap for each band is selected with the front-panel band-switch. The coils in the input networks are aligned at the factory.

245

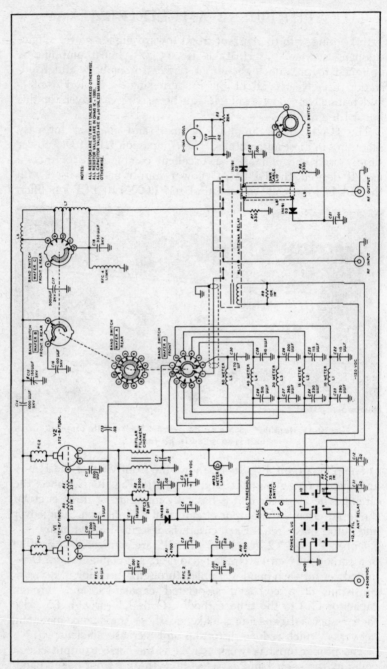

Fig. 10-42. Complete schematic of Heathkit® HA-14 linear amplifier.

246

To keep the capacitance of the filament supply from shunting the RF driving power to ground, the filament winding is isolated from the cathode circuit by a bifilar-wound filament choke. Also, this choke provides a cathode current path to ground.

High voltage is applied to the plates of tubes V1 and V2 through RF chokes RFC1 and RFC2, and parasitic chokes PC1 and PC2. Tuning capacitor C15 is connected on the input side of tapped final coils L6 and L7. Capacitor C16 is switched in parallel with the tuning capacitor on the 80-meter band.

Loading capacitor C18 is on the output side of final coils L6 and L7. Capacitor C17 is switched in parallel with the loading capacitor on the 80-meter band. Output power is applied through antenna changeover relay RL1 and through the SWR (standing-wave-ratio) bridge circuit to the RF output connector. The SWR bridge consists of coils L8, L9, and L10, capacitors C20 and C21, resistors R6 and R7, and crystal diodes D2 and D3. The RF choke, RFC4, is connected from the output side of the final coils to ground to provide a direct DC path to ground in case capacitor C14 should short.

The antenna changeover relay, RL1, is controlled by a VOX relay in the exciter used with the linear amplifier. When transmitting, the VOX relay grounds the antenna relay; when receiving, the antenna relay is ungrounded.

While receiving, cutoff bias voltage from the power supply is applied through the coil of relay RL1 and through resistors R2, R3, and R4, and choke RFC3, to the grids of V1 and V2. The antenna relay contact is ungrounded and no current will flow through the coil of relay RL1, which allows the relay to remain open. Thus, it connects the RF output jack (antenna) to the RF input jack of the linear amplifier and through the exciter change-over relay to the receiver input.

When transmitting, the antenna relay contact is grounded by the VOX relay of the exciter. This allows current to flow through the coil of relay RL1 and actuate the relay. When actuated, relay RL1 connects the RF output jack (antenna) to the output circuit of the linear amplifier. Grounding the antenna-relay contact also grounds the grids of tubes V1 and V2 through RFC3 and resistors R3 and R4. This removes all but −2 volts from the grids of the tubes. This −2 volts, which is developed across resistor R9, is operating bias, which limits the resting plate current to approximately 90 milliamperes.

When operating with the linear amplifier turned off, there is no bias voltage to operate relay RL1; and the RF input jack remains connected to the antenna, through the RF output jack. In this manner, low-power operation from the exciter into the

247

antenna is provided without changing any cables or connections. Since the linear amplifier uses instant-heating tubes, high power may be used at any time by merely turning on the amplifier.

During modulation, the ALC control voltage is developed across a voltage divider which consists of capacitors C8 and C9. A sample of this voltage is rectified by diode D1. This diode is reverse-biased with approximately $+6$ volts DC to form a threshold level. A negative DC control voltage is produced which is proportional to the modulation level. This control voltage is then applied back to the ALC input of the exciter.

Relative power and SWR are measured with a bridge circuit consisting of coils L8, L9, and L10, diodes D2 and D3, resistors R6 and R7, and capacitors C20 and C21. Control R5 sets the sensitivity of the meter. The "forward" position is used when adjusting the tuning control for maximum output of the linear amplifier. This meter function is also used to establish a "set" meter level for making SWR measurements.

Because coil L9 of the bridge circuit is connected in series between the RF input and RF output jacks when the linear amplifier is turned off, the meter can be used to measure relative power and SWR when operating on the exciter alone. This method of checking SWR is preferred for accurately determining antenna performance.

In the bridge circuit, RF current is inductively and capacitively coupled from L9 to L8 and L10. The RF currents in L8 and L10 are rectified by diodes D2 and D3 and then filtered by capacitors C20 and C21. For relative power measurements, rectified RF voltage from L10 is applied to the meter. For SWR measurements, rectified voltage from L8 is applied to the meter.

SB2-LA LINEAR AMPLIFIER

Sideband Engineers' SB2-LA (Fig. 10-43) is a linear amplifier designed primarily for use with the SB-34 single-sideband transceiver (described in Chapter 12) and similar equipment. The unit is self-contained in a case 5¾ inches high, 12 inches wide, and 12½ inches deep. The weight is 40 pounds. The input power ratings are 1,000 watts peak on SSB, 300 watts on AM, and 400 watts on CW, FM, or FSK. It operates on all authorized amateur frequencies within the range of 3.5 to 21.45 mc.

The self-contained power supply operates from a nominal 117-volt, 50- to 60-cycle AC source. However, for mobile applications, a solid-state inverter (SB3-DCP) is available as an accessory item. The linear amplifier is designed to operate into a 50-ohm unbalanced antenna load with a VSWR of 2:1 or less.

Installation of the SB2-LA linear may be made in any auto-

248

mobile with a negative-ground 12-volt supply. The amplifier and inverter are normally installed in the trunk of the vehicle; installation in the cab is not recommended since the amplifier generates a considerable amount of heat. Ventilation precautions for the amplifier must be observed; in addition, a reasonable amount of air flow must be provided around the inverter. Detailed instructions are included by the manufacturer.

Fig. 10-43. SB2 linear amplifier (left) and SB-34 SSB transceiver (right).

High-power mobile operation with units such as the SB-2LA presents a problem because of corona discharge and excessive loss due to loading-coil heat when conventional whip or center-loaded antennas are used. In most cases, conventional center-loaded mobile antennas will be destroyed when fed a full kilowatt of RF energy. The *Top Sider* series of mobile antennas, made by Webster, is designed especially for use with high-power mobile linear amplifiers. The use of a conventional whip antenna may be possible on 20 and 15 meters, provided that a plastic top cap is installed to suppress corona.

The SB2-LA linear amplifier circuit (Fig. 10-44) consists of six parallel-connected type 6JE6 tubes, operated Class AB_1 (no grid current), with a passive grid input circuit and a pi-section output network. Because of the high perveance of the 6JE6 tubes, efficient operation is obtained with low anode voltage and high current. Thus, most of the expensive and bulky components normally required for linear amplifiers of this power capability are eliminated. Power supplies required for the heater, bias, and anode circuits of the unit are self-contained.

Since the amplifier-tube grids require no power for operation, a bank of noninductive resistors connected to the input jack

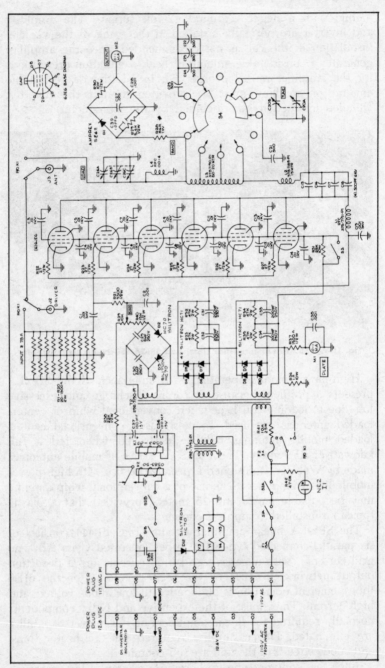

Fig. 10-44. SB2-LA linear amplifier.

absorbs the power generated by the transceiver (or exciter). These resistors are arranged to present an essentially resistive input impedance of approximately 75 ohms. Antiparasitic resistors are provided in each grid lead. Fixed bias is shunt-fed to the grids from a small voltage-doubler supply. A bias adjustment is provided on the rear panel.

The output network of the amplifier is a conventional pi-section coupler, although the electrical (and physical) sizes of the various components are unusual. Because of the low plate-load impedance required (about 300 ohms), the input capacitor need is large in value; likewise, the inductance required is small. Since the plate voltage is relatively low, a small air gap is completely adequate for the input capacitor.

The bandswitch selects the amount of inductance for each band, provides extra fixed amounts of load capacitor on 80 and 40 meters, and adds a fixed input capacitor on 80 meters.

A small diode, together with a resistor-capacitor network, actuates the output meter, which provides a relative indication of the voltage existing on the output terminal.

Anode power for the amplifier is obtained from two series-connected voltage-doubler rectifier circuits. Output voltage under load is 800 volts nominal at 1.2 amperes. Rectification is by parallel-connected silicon diodes, and filtering is accomplished by large-value electrolytic capacitors. The bias voltage is also obtained from the main power transformer. The bias supply also uses a voltage-doubler circuit. A resistor in the primary of the main power transformer protects the silicon diodes from the high surge current produced when the unit is first turned on. Relay contacts short this resistor when actually transmitting so that full output voltage is produced.

In the standby (receive) condition, cutoff bias is applied to the amplifier tubes to prevent tube noise. When transmitting, the bias is reduced to the correct value by grounding a voltage-divider network, consisting of resistors R38 and R40 and bias potentiometer R39, through K2. Grounding this lead also actuates relay K1. Energizing voltage for this relay is supplied by diode D12 and the heater supply voltage. This diode also prevents the high negative voltage existing on pin 9 (when in receive) from shorting the heater line. In mobile operation, the actuating voltage for K2 is obtained directly from the battery source. Sections of the filament and power switches are inserted into the control line to relay K2 so that the relay does not close except when the filament switch is on and the power switch is in the "high" position.

Chapter 11

Single-Sideband Communications Receivers

The preceding ten chapters have been largely concerned with the fundamentals of single-sideband generation and the details of the transmitting portion of the system. The single-sideband receiver also requires special design attention if the full capabilities and advantages of the SSB communications systems are to be realized. Although the ordinary AM communications receiver will receive single-sideband signals, the overall reception is generally not satisfactory. One of the most important and stringent requirements in a single-sideband receiver is that of stability. In ordinary AM communications, the channel width for voice transmission is at least 4 to 6 kc; hence a frequency drift of a few hundred cycles will hardly be noticeable as far as intelligibility of the demodulated audio is concerned. However, in the SSB receiver a frequency drift of only 20 cycles is noticeable. When the drift approaches 50 cycles, the audio quality deteriorates rapidly. Beyond 50 cycles, the audio signal becomes unintelligible. The high degree of stability in the single-sideband receiver is required because of the narrow channel width of the single-sideband signal, and also because local-carrier reinsertion is necessary in the demodulation process. In the SSB receiver, the frequency drift of both the variable-frequency oscillator (VFO) and carrier-reinsertion oscillator (BFO) must be kept to the minimum.

In our study of SSB generators we learned that for maximum intelligibility the audio signal must be properly shaped and otherwise processed. The RF sideband signal is further shaped in a precision filter. The carrier is accurately positioned on the filter skirt for proper bandpass characteristics of the transmitted signal. The conversion oscillators and balanced mixers were very carefully designed to keep to a minimum any distortion or spurious components generated in these stages. Finally, the linear RF power amplifiers are very carefully designed and adjusted to produce an undistorted replica of the SSB signal at a higher

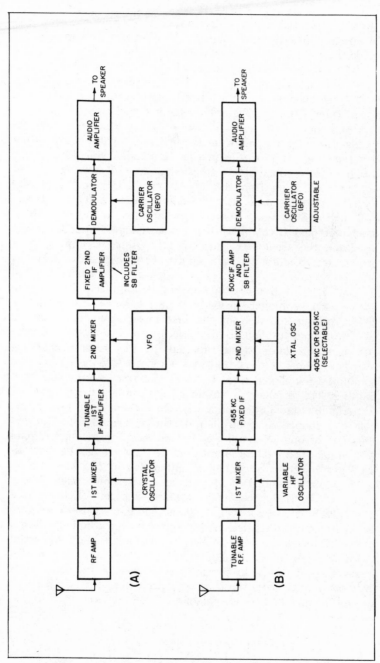

Fig. 11-1. Block diagram of two basic single-sideband receiver designs.

253

power level. It is obvious that unless the receiver is designed to process the received signal and recover the original intelligence with an equal degree of precision, the full capabilities of the system will not be realized.

The block diagram in Fig. 11-1 illustrates two approaches to the problem of single-sideband receiver design. In A, the signal from a tuned RF amplifier is mixed with the signal from a crystal-controlled oscillator. The crystal frequency is selected so that the output signal from the first mixer will appear within the range of the tunable first-IF amplifier, which usually is designed to be tuned over a frequency range of about 1.0 mc or less in the region from 1.5 to 4.0 mc. The signal from the amplifier is then mixed with the one from the VFO in the second mixer. This new signal is now applied to the input of a fixed bandpass IF amplifier usually designed to operate at 455 kc. From the second IF amplifier, the signal is applied to a product demodulator and AF amplifier. From here the audio is fed into the speaker.

B, of Fig. 11-1, the VFO operates in the high-frequency region, usually 455 kc higher or lower than the received signal. The 455-kc output signal from the first mixer is amplified in an IF "strip" and applied to the grid of the second mixer. The conversion-oscillator signal applied to the second mixer is usually crystal-controlled and may be either 405 or 505 kc. The resultant 50-kc signal from the second mixer is amplified by a highly selective 50-kc IF amplifier and applied to the product demodulator and audio amplifier. The IF amplifier usually includes a shaped or controlled bandpass characteristic for the rejection of one sideband (upper or lower) of a conventional AM signal. This is accomplished by switching the crystal-oscillator injection frequency to either 405 or 505 kc.

The main advantage of the arrangement shown at A of Fig. 11-1 is its improved frequency stability, since all VFO's operate at relatively low frequencies. This method is most useful in communications receivers designed to operate over a limited portion of the RF spectrum, such as the amateur bands or the commercial or military frequencies. The method shown at B is more common in receivers designed to cover a wide range of frequencies. In order to illustrate the basic design principles, a description of several commercial single-sideband receivers follows.

THE COLLINS 75S-3

The Collins 75S-3B and 75S-3C receivers, an example of which is shown in Fig. 11-2, are the companion units to the 32S-3 transmitter described in a previous chapter. Reception of SSB, CW, and AM signals is provided on all amateur bands from 3.4 to 30 mc. The 75S-3C is identical to the 75S-3B except that it is equipped with an extra high-frequency crystal mounting board on the chassis, a crystal board selector switch on the front panel, and associated components.

Fig. 11-2. Collins 75S-3B SSB receiver.

The 75S-3 receivers (Figs. 11-3 and 11-4 [see foldout]) are double-conversion superheterodynes with injection voltage for the first conversion provided by a crystal-controlled oscillator. A bandpass IF circuit, 200 kc wide, couples the first and second mixers. Injection voltage for the second mixer is supplied by a VFO with a tuning range of 200 kc. The 455-kc output frequency of the second mixer is coupled through the IF system to separate SSB and AM detectors. Injection voltage for the product detector is provided by either a crystal-controlled or a tunable BFO.

The RF-amplifier grid, high-frequency mixer grid, and crystal-oscillator plate circuits are resonated by slug-tuned coils. The slugs are mechanically ganged and linked to the "preselector" tuning knob. The required tuning range of these circuits is obtained by switching appropriate values of fixed capacitance in parallel with the coils. The total 3.4- to 30-mc tuning range of the receiver is divided into five segments for bandswitching purposes. The tuned circuit LC ratio is thereby varied within appropriate limits for each of the five segments.

Signals within the particular 200-kc band selected are amplified by V2, the RF amplifier, and coupled to the control

255

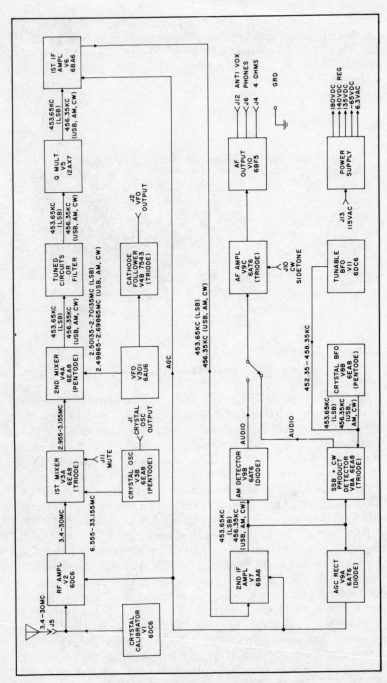

Fig. 11-3. Block diagram of Collins 75S-3B.

grid of V3A, the first mixer. Injection voltage is coupled to the cathode of V3A. Products of mixing are selected in the plate circuit of V3A and tuned to 3.155 to 2.955 mc, the bandpass IF frequency. The signals are then coupled to the control grid of the second mixer, V4A, with VFO injection voltage applied to the cathode.

High-frequency crystal oscillator V3B provides injection voltage for the first mixer. The crystal-oscillator output is always 3.155 mc higher than the lower edge of a selected band. On bands below 12.0 mc, the oscillator plate circuit is tuned to the crystal frequency. At 12.0 mc and higher, the plate circuit is tuned to the second harmonic of the crystal frequency. The secondary winding of T2 couples injection voltage to the first-mixer cathode circuit and furnishes a DC return path to ground for mixer tube V3A. Dummy load R41 simulates the load presented by a transmitter when connected for transceiver operation.

Crystal-controlled BFO V8B and associated circuitry supply injection voltage for the product detector. Crystals Y15 and Y16 provide the proper BFO frequency relationships to the mechanical filter passband to yield optimum audio response from the product detector. Crystal Y15 (453.650 kc) is used for lower sideband reception, and Y16 (456.350 kc) for upper sideband. Capacitor C95 and coil L12 form a broadly resonant circuit at 455 kc. Oscillator voltage is developed across R49 and coupled by C100 to the cathode of V8A, the product detector tube.

The crystal-calibrator circuit provides marker signals at multiples of 100 kc. Variable capacitor C61 provides for adjustment to zero-beat with WWV. The output of this oscillator is coupled to the receiver antenna circuits.

The VFO uses fixed capacitance and variable inductance to produce the required tuning range of 2.50135 to 2.70135 mc for LSB reception and 2.49865 to 2.69865 mc for USB, AM, and CW reception. Capacitor C303, in the frequency-determining network, is paralleled by variable capacitor C308 in series with diode CR301. This diode switches C308 in or out of the circuit, depending on the polarity of the bias voltage impressed across its junction. With the "mode" switch in the LSB position, diode CR301 is reverse-biased and switches capacitor C308 out of the frequency-determining network. This condition will result in the tunable 2.50135- to 2.70135-mc signal desired. With the "mode" switch in the USB, AM, or CW position, diode CR301 is forward-biased and switches C308 into the frequency-determining network, lowering the output frequency to the tunable 2.49865- to 2.69865-mc signal desired. Note that when C308 is properly adjusted, it shifts the VFO frequency by an amount equal to the frequency separation of crystals Y15 and Y16. This allows either sideband to be selected without retuning or recalibrating the dial. The VFO output voltage is coupled to the cathode of second mixer tube V4A and to the control grid of cathode follower V4B. The cathode follower prevents loading of the VFO circuits by cable capacity when operated in transceiver service.

Tube V11 and associated circuitry comprise a 452.35- to 458.35-kc tunable BFO. The BFO tuning control is potentiometer R81. This control varies a positive DC voltage applied to the junction of voltage-variable capacitor CR4. The junction capacity of this device is proportional to the applied voltage. Adjustment of R81 therefore varies the output frequency of the BFO. Voltage for the tuning circuit is stabilized by a regulator consisting of zener diode CR5 and resistor R82. Switch S13 completes the cathode circuit of either V8B or V11, thus turning on the desired BFO and turning off the other. The output circuits of both oscillators are coupled to the product detector.

Output from the second mixer is connected to either one of three mechanical filters, FL1, FL2, or FL3, or to a tuned circuit consisting of transformers T4 and T5. Mechanical filter FL1 (tuned to 455 kc with a nominal bandpass of 2.1 kc) is selected for SSB reception, while FL2 and FL3 are optional filters to be used for CW operation. For AM operation, two cascaded 455-kc transformers (T4 and T5) provide an increased bandwidth of approximately 5 kc. Output from these circuits is coupled through the Q-multiplier to the first IF amplifier, V6. The cathode of V6 is returned to ground through potentiometer R57, which is used to set the gain of this stage at a point producing the proper AGC threshold. The S-meter circuit is connected from the screen circuits of V6 and V7, the two IF amplifiers, to the cathode of V7. Under no-signal conditions, the voltage developed across R13 is equal to that developed across R21, and the meter reads zero. Application of AGC causes the cathode current of V7 and the combined screen current of V6 and V7 to decrease. The voltage across R13 increases, the voltage across R21 decreases, and the meter reads upscale by an amount proportional to the signal strength. Output voltage from the second IF amplifier is coupled to the product detector, V8A. It is also coupled to separate AM and AGC diode detectors. Injection voltage is applied to the cathode of the product detector.

The notch filter is composed of coil L8 and associated capacitors and resistors. The rejection notch occurs at the resonant frequency of this circuit and is centered at 455 kc. Capacitor C132 is mechanically coupled to the "rejection tuning" control, which allows the notch frequency to be moved across the receiver IF passband. Potentiometer R77 is adjusted to provide optimum Q and depth of notch. Switch S10 shorts the filter circuit in the "off" position. The Q-multiplier is a feedback circuit which includes L8. This circuit multiples the Q of L8 approximately ten times, thereby obtaining a much deeper and narrower rejection notch than would be provided by the filter alone. The notch shape provided by this circuit allows unwanted signals to be rejected with minimum disturbance to desired signals.

Signal voltage is coupled from the secondary of transformer T6 to one of the diode plates in V9 and rectified. This rectified signal voltage is then coupled, through filter network R50 and C49, to the AGC network consisting of resistors R24 and R88 and capacitors C50, C137, and C153. The AGC network develops the desired AGC signal and then applies it to the RF and IF amplifier stages. The parallel combination of R88 and C153 presents the fast charge-discharge rate desired for elimination of small-time-duration interference, while the parallel combination of R24 and C50 presents a longer RC time constant, allowing for a smoothly developed AGC signal. Generation of AGC voltage is delayed until the signal voltage at the diode plate exceeds the cathode bias on V9. Potentiometer R57 in the cathode of the first IF amplifier tube is normally adjusted so that AGC action is initiated with a receiver input signal of approximately 1.5 microvolts. This point is referred to as "AGC threshold."

Manual control of RF gain is also accomplished through the AGC line. A voltage-divider circuit consisting of resistors R33, R55, and RF gain control R56 is connected across the negative 65-volt bias line. At the maximum gain setting, this circuit places a one-volt static bias on the AGC line to furnish proper operating bias for RF amplifier V2. At lower control settings, increased bias is provided which reduces the gain. The DC grid return for the first mixer stage and "mute" jack J11 are connected to the junction of resistors R33 and R58. When the receiver function switch is placed in the "standby" position, a ground at J11 causes the receiver to operate in a normal manner. Removal of this ground causes cutoff bias to be applied to the mixer grid and increased bias on the AGC line, thus muting the receiver.

Audio voltage from the appropriate detector is selected by S8A on the "mode" switch and is coupled to the audio gain control. The CW sidetone jack, J10, is also connected to this point. A sidetone audio voltage of approximately 0.2 volt will produce a normal listening level at average gain settings. Audio is amplified in a two-stage amplifier consisting of tubes V8 and V10. Three audio outputs are provided. Jack J8 is a 4-ohm outlet for a speaker. The headphone jack is connected to a resistive divider across the 500-ohm tap on the output transformer. The divider provides a load for V10 when the impedance of the headphones used is relatively high. ANTIVOX jack J12 is also connected to the 500-ohm tap. At normal audio-gain settings, 5 to 15 volts of audio is available at J12 for use with the ANTI-VOX circuits in an associated transmitter.

The internal power supply furnishes filament, plate, and bias voltages for the receiver. Three high-voltage values are developed, consisting of a 180-volt DC unregulated voltage at the hot side of C59B, a 140-volt regulated voltage at the plate side of zener diode CR6, and a 135-volt DC unregulated voltage at the hot side of C59A. The high-voltage winding of transformer T8; diodes CR1, CR2, and CR6; resistor R86; and the filter network consisting of capacitors C59A, C59B, and C59C, resistor R51, and choke L6 make up the full-wave rectifier system which generates the three high-voltage values mentioned above. Bias voltage is obtained by rectifying a small portion of the AC voltage appearing from one leg of the high-voltage secondary to ground. The tube filaments and pilot lamps are connected in a way which allows operation from a 6-, 12-, or 24-volt source. Filament plate and bias voltages may be obtained from an external source such as a mobile power supply.

HALLICRAFTERS SX-146 RECEIVER

The SX-146 (Fig. 11-5) is basically a single-conversion super-heterodyne receiver with a 9.0-mc filter-type IF system. The VFO

Fig. 11-5. Hallicrafters Model SX-146 SSB receiver.

supplies injection directly on 80 and 20 meters and is premixed with the output of an overtone crystal oscillator on 40, 15, and 10 meters.

The signal applied to the antenna terminals is stepped up in voltage by antenna transformer T1. This signal is applied to the grid of RF stage V1, where it is amplified. The output of this stage is transformer-coupled through T2 to the grid of triode mixer V2A, where it is mixed with the cathode-applied injection. Both T1 and T2, in combination with their associated series and shunt inductances, are tuned to resonance by the two-section preselector capacitor (Fig. 11-6).

The 9.0-mc output of the mixer is fed through terminating coil L9 to one of three switch-selected filters. The output of the filter is fed through terminating coil L10 to IF amplifier V3. The plate circuit of V3 is tuned to 9.0 mc by L11. From L11, the 9.0-mc IF signal is fed to IF amplifier V4 for further amplification.

The output of V4 is fed through a double-tuned 9.0-mc transformer (T3) to the AM detector-AVC rectifier (V5A) and through a capacity divider to product detector V5B.

The output of the product detector, or the AM detector, is selected by the "operation" switch and fed through the audio gain control to V9A and V9B for audio amplification. The output of V9B is transformer-coupled through the phone jack to the 3.2-ohm speaker terminals.

Carrier insertion for CW or SSB reception is supplied by crystal oscillators V6A and V6B. These oscillators supply cathode injection to the product detector.

Diode CR1 is in series with the output of the AM detector to provide clipping of impulse noise. This noise limiter functions only on AM and will be most effective when used in conjunction with the 5.0-kc filter. Diode CR2 is used as a gate diode in the AVC circuit to prevent the positive bias applied to CR1 from appearing on the AVC line.

Injection for mixer V2A is supplied as follows: On 80 and 20 meters, the output of the 5.0- to 5.5-mc VFO (V7) is coupled through the band-selector switch to cathode-follower V2B. The output of V2B is connected to the cathode of mixer V2A and to the "slave" output or external oscillator-input receptacle, depending on the setting of the "internal-external" rear-mounted slide switch.

For 40-meter operation, the output of the VFO is subtracted from the 21.5-mc output of crystal oscillator V8A in premixer V8B. The output of premixer V8B is fed through a 16.0- to 16.5-mc bandpass transformer, T4, to the cathode follower. For 15-meter operation, the output of the VFO is added to the 25.0-

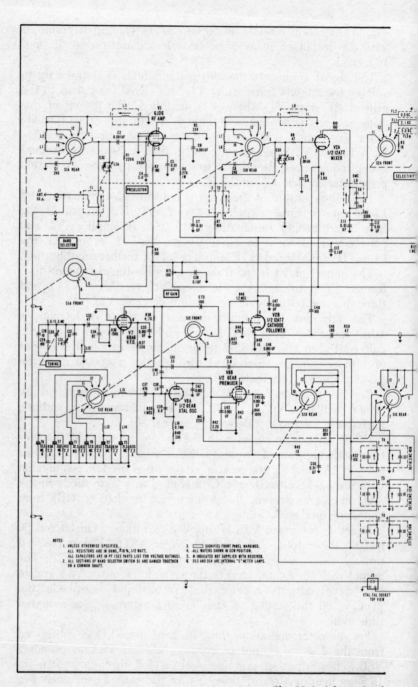

NOTES:
1. UNLESS OTHERWISE SPECIFIED,
   ALL RESISTORS ARE IN OHMS, ±10 %, 1/2 WATT.
   ALL CAPACITORS ARE IN PF (SEE PARTS LIST FOR VOLTAGE RATINGS).
2. ALL SECTIONS OF BAND SELECTOR SWITCH S1 ARE GANGED TOGETHER
   ON A COMMON SHAFT.
3. ☐ SIGNIFIES FRONT PANEL MARKINGS.
4. ALL WAFERS SHOWN IN CCW POSITION.
5. ✦ INDICATES NOT SUPPLIED WITH RECEIVER.
6. DS3 AND DS4 ARE INTERNAL "S" METER LAMPS.

Fig. 11-6. Schematic of

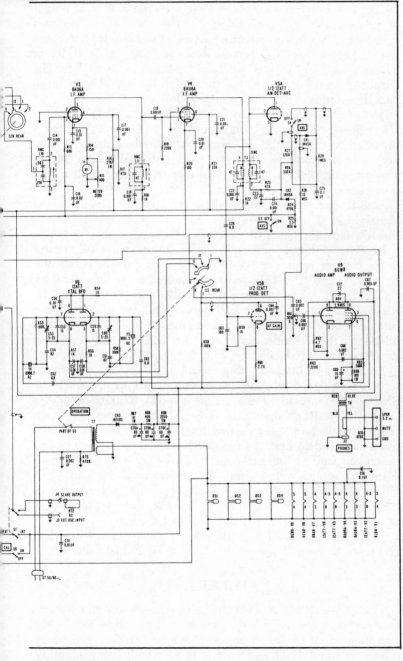

Model SX146 receiver.

mc output of crystal oscillator V8A in premixer V8B. The output of premixer V8B is fed through a 30.0- to 30.5-mc bandpass transformer, T5, to the cathode follower. For 10-meter operation, the output of the VFO is added to the 32.0-, 32.5-, 33.0-, or 33.5-mc output of crystal oscillator V8A in premixer V8B. The output of premixer V8B is fed through a 37.0- to 39.0-mc bandpass transformer, T6, to the cathode follower.

AVC voltage is applied to RF amplifier V1 and IF amplifier V3 to provide automatic gain control. An AVC "on-off" switch is provided to disable the AC circuit if desired. A meter is connected in the cathode circuit of AVC-controlled V3 for signal-strength indication. A unique feature of the meter circuit is that it is connected at a point that has extremely fast-attack, fast-release time constants, which allow the meter to closely follow signal peaks. The long-time-constant AGC circuitry is applied to the RF stage and has little effect on meter operation.

Receiver muting is accomplished by inserting a 470K resistor in the cathode returns of V1, V2A, and V4 to provide cutoff bias for these stages. The 470K resistor is shorted in normal operation.

The RF gain, or receiver sensitivity, may be changed by varying the setting of the RF gain control. As this control is rotated counterclockwise from maximum, additional resistance is added to the cathode circuits of V1 and V4. More bias is developed, thus reducing the amplification of these stages.

An 82-ohm resistor and plug assembly is supplied and should always be plugged into the "slave" output jack except when the SX-146 is connected to the companion HT-46 transmitter, for slave (transceiver) operation. This termination resistor keeps the mixer injection at the desired level when the receiver is used as an independent unit. A slide switch located on the rear-chassis apron and marked "internal-external oscillator" is used to remove plate and screen voltage from the crystal oscillator and VFO. When placed in the "external" position, all internal injection is removed from mixer V2A, allowing injection to be supplied from an external source through the "external oscillator" jack.

Band-gain equalization is provided by automatically adding resistance in the cathode circuit of V1 on 40 and 20 meters.

R. L. DRAKE R-4A

The Drake R-4A is an extremely versatile communications receiver designed to provide every feature desirable in the reception of all modes of amateur communications. It contains a linear permeability-tuned solid-state VFO with 1-kc readability, and premixed injection with a crystal-controlled high-frequency

264

oscillator for stability on all bands. A 100-kc crystal calibrator is included. The passband tuner-filter has four selectivity positions, and a built-in notch filter provides the desired selectivity and interference rejection. A built-in noise blanker eliminates most noise on CW, SSB, and AM reception.

As supplied, the unit gives complete coverage of the 80-, 40-, 20-, and 15-meter bands as well as the 28.5-mc to 29.0-mc portion of 10 meters. Ten accessory crystal sockets are provided for coverage of other 500-kc frequency ranges between 1.5 and 30 mc such as the 160-meter amateur band, the MARS frequencies, WWV, short-wave broadcasts, etc. These sockets can be programmed to give up to 5 megacycles of continuous coverage for convenient use with VHF converters.

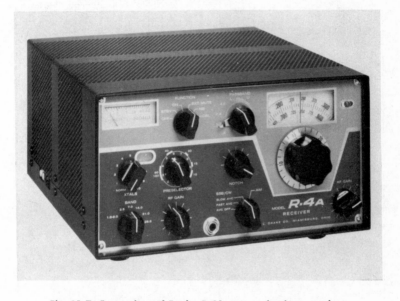

Fig. 11-7. Front view of Drake R-4A communications receiver.

Complete AVC action and accurate S-meter indication can be obtained on all modes. The AVC action is fast-attack slow-release for SSB or AM, and fast-attack fast-release for CW. If desired, the AVC can be completely disabled for CW reception. A crystal-lattice filter following the first mixer provides excellent overload characteristics by providing selectivity ahead of the gain-producing stages. When used with the Drake T-4 *Reciter,* transceive operation may be obtained. When the R-4A is used with the T-4X transmitter, either transceive or independent receive and transmit functions are possible.

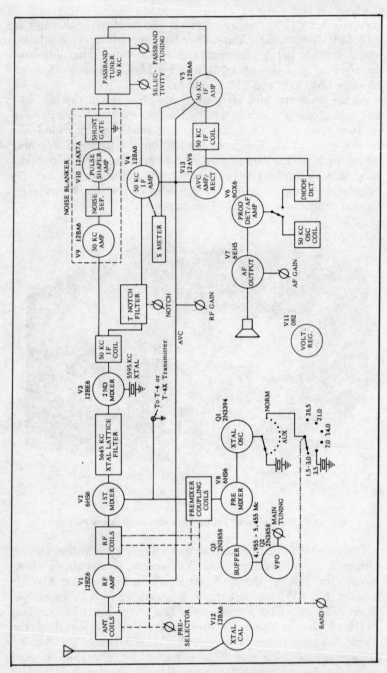

Fig. 11-8. Block diagram of Drake R-4A receiver.

The front view of the R-4A (Fig. 11-7) shows the dial and operating controls. The block diagram (Fig. 11-8) illustrates the general over-all design arrangement. The schematic is shown in Fig. 11-9. The following description refers to the above illustrations.

A signal entering the antenna is applied to the grid of the low-noise 12BZ6 RF amplifier (V1) through a tuned circuit formed by coil T1 and capacitors C21 through C31. The amplified output signal is then applied to the grid of the 6HS6 first mixer (V2) through a tuned circuit consisting of coil T2 and capacitors C1 through C11. A signal from the premixer system is applied to the 6HS6 first-mixer cathode, 5645 kc above the incoming signal frequency applied to its control grid. The mixing of these two signals results in a 5645-kc IF output signal.

The premixer system consists of a 4955- to 5455-kc solid-state permeability-tuned VFO unit (T13), a switchable overtone crystal oscillator (Q1), the premixer (V8), and the premixer output circuitry composed of T3 and T4 and their tuning and coupling capacitors. The VFO signal is applied to the cathode of premixer V8, and the output of crystal oscillator Q1 is applied to the grid. The crystal frequencies are selected so that the difference-frequency output of the premixer is 5645 kc higher than the frequency of the incoming signal. RF coils T1 and T2 and premixer coils T3 and T4 are permeability-tuned and are ganged together. The ganged assembly is tuned by the "preselector" control on the front panel.

The 5645-kc IF-signal output from V2 is applied to the grid of the 12BE6 second converter (V3) through a crystal filter. The filter provides selectivity for the desired cross-modulation and overload-protection characteristics while the signal is still at a relatively low level. The 12BE6 cathode, control grid, and screen grid are connected in a Pierce oscillator-circuit configuration controlled by a 5595-kc crystal. The incoming 5645-kc IF signal and the 5595-kc oscillator output mix to produce the final 50-kc IF output.

The 50-kc IF output signal from the second converter (V3) is applied to the grid of the 12BA6 IF amplifier (V4) through the T-notch filter composed of T8 and its associated circuitry. The output of V4 is fed, through the passband tuner (T9) to the grid of the final 12BA6 IF amplifier (V5). The passband tuner consists of four high-Q LC circuits. Passband tuning is accomplished by ganged permeability tuning of the coils, and variable selectivity of changing the coupling between the tuned circuits.

The amplified 50-kc signal from the final IF amplifier, V5, is applied to the AM detector composed of diode D7 and its

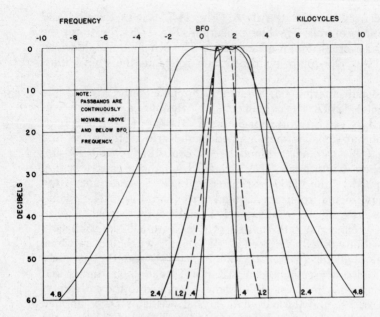

Fig. 11-10. IF selectivity curves for R-4A receiver.

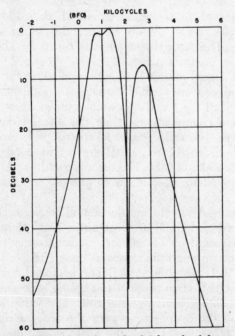

Fig. 11-11. Effect of notch on the 2.4-kc selectivity curve.

associated circuitry, to AVC amplifier V13, and to the switch S2 rear. When the SSB-CW-AM switch is in the SSB-CW positions, the output of V5 feeds into grid 3 of the 6GX6 product detector tube, V6. The cathode, grid 1, and grid 2 are connected in a 50-kc Hartley oscillator circuit. The incoming 50-kc IF signal is mixed with the 50-kc oscillator signal to produce audio output. When the SSB-CW-AM switch is in the AM position, the 50-kc oscillator is disabled and the output of the AM detector circuit is connected to grid 3 of V6, which now functions as an audio amplifier.

The Drake R-4A selectivity curves are shown in Fig. 11-10. The effect of the adjustable notch filter on the 2.4-kc selectivity curve is shown in Fig. 11-11.

The noise-blanker circuit in the R-4A attenuates a received noise pulse by shunting to ground the output of V4 during the pulse. In other words, the receiver is turned off during the pulse.

The 50-kc IF output from the second converter, V3, is fed to the grid of the 12BA6 noise-blanker IF amplifier, V9. Here the signal is amplified to a level sufficient to operate the pulse detector and separation circuit composed of D1 and D2 and their associated circuitry. This circuit functions in such a manner that when a noise pulse of a higher level than the accompanying signal is received, a negative pulse is presented to the grid of noise shaper V10A. This stage is normally conducting and a negative pulse causes a large positive pulse to appear at the plate. This positive pulse is applied to the grid of pulse amplifier V10B. The 18K resistor (R66) and the 100K resistor (R65) form a voltage divider which applies positive cathode bias to V10B and diode D3, preventing them from conducting. When a positive pulse is applied to the grid of V10B, the bias is overcome, causing both V10B and D3 to conduct. When D3 conducts, it shunts to ground the output of V4 through C104 and C105.

The R-4A contains a full-wave rectifier power supply using two 1N3194 diodes. The power transformer has a dual primary. As supplied, the primaries are connected in parallel for 120-volt line operation and in series for operation on 240 volts AC.

THE HAMMARLUND HQ-180

The Hammarlund HQ-180 shown in Fig. 11-12 is a triple-conversion superheterodyne receiver designed for reception of CW, AM, and SSB signals. A total of eighteen tubes are used, including the rectifier and voltage-regulator tubes in the self-contained power supply. The circuitry includes a 100-kc crystal calibrator plus controls for selectable sideband, adjustable bandwidth (0.5 to 6 kc), and slot filter and depth. Also included are an adjustable AVC decay time constant, an effective noise limiter, and a tuning control with expanded scales for the 80-, 40-, 20-, 15-, and 10-meter amateur bands.

The antenna input coupling and the RF amplifier stage provide the necessary preselection and gain for high performance and for rejection of undesired signals. In Fig. 11-13, the grid and plate circuits of the RF amplifier are both tuned, and individual tuning coils are selected for each band. The antenna compensation capacitor, adjustable from the front panel, permits the input circuits to be resonated for optimum performance with the particular antenna in use.

A high degree of high-frequency oscillator stability is ob-

Fig. 11-12. Hammarlund HQ-180 receiver.

tained through the use of a separate mixer, V2, and an independent oscillator, V12. The output signal from the 6BZ6 RF amplifier, V1, is applied to the grid of the 6BE6 mixer, V2. The conversion-oscillator signal voltage for the first mixer stage is taken from the cathode circuit of high-frequency oscillator V12. When receiving signals are in the range from 540 kc to 7.85 mc, the oscillator signal is located 455 kc above them. In the tuning range from 7.85 mc to 30.0 mc, however, the oscillator signal is 3,035 kc higher than the received signal frequency.

When operating on the 7.85- to 30-mc bands, the difference frequency of 3,035 kc is fed through a crystal filter and is mixed with the 2,580-kc oscillator signal in 6BE6 converter V3. The

270

resultant 455-kc IF signal at the plate of V3 is coupled, through transformer T3, to the 6BA6 455-kc IF amplifier. When operating on the bands between 540 kc and 7.85 mc, the 6BE6 converter, V3, ceases to function and the 6BA6 gate tube, V18, becomes a regular 455-kc IF amplifier.

The output signal from V3 or V18 is applied to a single-stage 455-kc IF amplifier. The gain of V4 is controlled by 10,000-ohm pot R15 which is ganged with sensitivity control R6. The output of V4 consists of two 455-kc IF transformers, T4 and T5, which are interconnected by a network of resistors, capacitors, and coils. This network, called the "slot filter," forms a balanced bridge type of bifilar "T" trap which provides very high attenuation to an undesired signal within the bandpass of the IF circuit. The depth of the attenuation slot is controlled by R26. The slot-filter response, shown in Fig. 11-14A, is extremely deep and sharp. The slot is normally located outside the bandpass of the 455-kc IF circuit. During reception, when heterodyne interference on AM or "monkey chatter" on single-sideband is present, the slot frequency may be moved to any position in the IF bandpass to "trap out" the undesired signal. On CW reception, the slot filter is useful in reducing or eliminating adjacent-channel interference.

In Fig. 11-13, the 455-kc IF signal from the T5 secondary is applied, through C28, to the grid of V5. Note that the coupling capacitor, C28, is only 7mmf. The second converter stage is more or less conventional, since the 6BE6 tube is also used as a 395-kc conversion oscillator. The incoming 455-kc IF signal is mixed with the 395-kc oscillator signal, and a difference frequency of 60 kc appears in the 6BE6 plate circuit. The three-stage 60-kc IF amplifier includes two 6BA6 tubes, V6 and V7, and one 6BV8 tube, V8. The six tuned circuits, T6, T7, T8, T9, T10, and T11 are capacitively coupled and individually shielded. The use of high-C tuned circuits with the addition of ferrite shielding provides long-term stability and freedom from the effects of external electrical or magnetic fields. The resonant circuits are stagger-tuned in a multiplicity of combinations which are selectable by means of the selectivity and sideband- selector switches on the front panel. The over-all response curves in the various switch positions are shown in Fig. 11-14B.

The double-diode sections of V8 serve as two AM detector-diode circuits. One diode is used with the AVC and signal-level meter system and the other is for detection of AM signals. This arrangement produces minimum distortion in the audio-output signal.

When the Reception switch is turned to the SSB or CW

position, the AM detector is disabled, the 60-kc IF signal is applied to the grid of V9, and V13A is placed in operation. Notice in Fig. 11-13 that the 60-kc IF signal is applied to the grid of one 12AU7 (V9) triode section and that the BFO signal is applied to the grid of the other. The two cathodes of V9 are connected together and returned to ground through a common 820-ohm resistor, R39. Reinsertion of the carrier component into the 60-kc SSB signal takes place in the cathode circuit of V9, and the two RF voltages appear across R39. Variable capacitor C129 varies the frequency of the BFO over a range from zero-beat to ±2 kc. The circuit of the beat-frequency oscillator is in the series-tuned Colpitts arrangement.

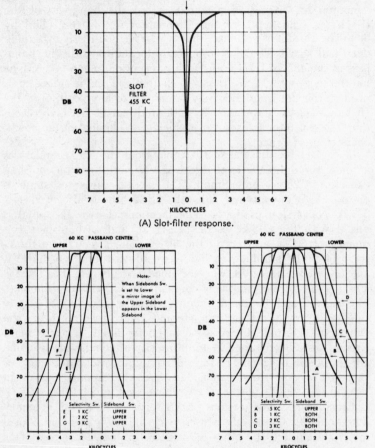

(A) Slot-filter response.

(B) IF response.

Fig. 11-14. Slot filter and passband curves for Hammarlund HQ-180.

272

The AVC system of an SSB receiver is somewhat more complex and critical than the corresponding AM AVC system. In the HQ-180, the AVC system minimizes fading and signal-level variations by controlling the gain of V1, V4, V5, and V6. The fast attack (charge) and adjustable decay time constant can be used for best performance with the particular type of signal being received. A slow-decay AVC system is required for SSB signal reception. The AVC voltage applied to V1 is delayed to prevent AVC action on extremely weak signals. This delay is necessary to maintain maximum sensitivity and signal-to-noise ratio in the receiver input circuits.

The "S" meter assists in the tuning of the receiver by giving an indication of the relative strength of the incoming signal. It is

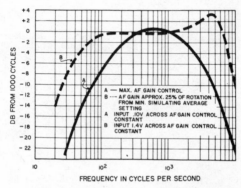

A — MAX. AF GAIN CONTROL
B .... AF GAIN APPROX. 25% OF ROTATION FROM MIN. SIMULATING AVERAGE SETTING
A   INPUT .10V ACROSS AF GAIN CONTROL CONSTANT
B   INPUT 1.4V ACROSS AF GAIN CONTROL CONSTANT

DB FROM 1000 CYCLES

FREQUENCY IN CYCLES PER SECOND

Fig. 11-15. Audio-level response curves.

connected in a stable balanced bridge circuit and utilizes the current amplification of V13B. This arrangement gives an indication of signal strength on all positions of the AVC time-constant switch. However, the signal-level meter calibration is valid only when the RF gain control is turned to maximum. The signal-level meter, which is calibrated to 40 db over S9, is adjusted at the factory so that a signal input of approximately 50 microvolts gives a reading of S9. The scale calibrations are arranged so that each unit indicates approximately a 6-db increase, which is equivalent to doubling the level of the incoming signal.

The first audio amplifier, V16, uses a 6AV6 tube in a resistance-coupled circuit. The 6AQ5 audio output provides an undistorted level of at least 1 watt. A unique feature of the HQ-180's audio amplifier is the variable negative-feedback system. The audio-output signal response for various settings of the audio gain control is shown in Fig. 11-15. Notice that maximum negative feedback is provided at low settings of the audio-gain control for best-quality reception on strong signals. As the audio gain is advanced, the negative feedback decreases so that on weak signals, the audio amplifier will provide additional selectivity. This improves intelligibility on weak or noisy signals. A further advantage is critical damping of the speaker. By thus eliminating "hangover" effects, the reproduction of speech is greatly improved. The negative feedback also reduces distortion of the reproduced audio, particularly at the lower-level settings of the audio control.

The Hammarlund HQ-180 is designed for complete coverage of all frequencies from 540 kc to 30 mc. The use of a separate

Fig. 11-16. Hammarlund SPC-10 SSB converter.

tuning dial provides "bandspread" tuning on the various amateur bands. The HQ-170 is very similar to the HQ-180 except that it is designed for coverage of the amateur bands only and does not include the 6BA6 455-kc gate tube, V18.

SINGLE-SIDEBAND CONVERSION

Many amateurs own good-quality communications receivers which were originally designed for AM communications work. The Hammarlund SPC-10 SSB converter shown in Figs. 11-16 and 11-17 (see foldout section) has been specifically designed for conversion of these older communications receivers to modern single-sideband operation.

The SPC-10 is a single-conversion superheterodyne converter designed to accept signals in the range from 450 to 500 kc with levels from 0.005 to 2 volts. The processing of the signal in the 60-kc IF circuits, and the sideband selection and detection, are carried out in a manner similar to that of the HQ-180 receiver.

The 455-kc signal from the communications receiver IF circuit is applied to the converter IF gain control, R11, and to a bifilar "T" trap, L1, which is part of the slot-filter circuit. The "T" trap filters out interfering signals before they appear at the V1 mixer grid. The trap is adjustable over the entire range from 450 to 500 kc by the slot-frequency tuned circuit L2-C11. Capacitor C11 is the vernier, or "fine tuning," control on the front panel, and R8 controls the depth of the slot.

The conversion-oscillator frequency is adjustable over the range from 390 to 440 kc by means of coil L6 and the vernier, or "fine tuning" capacitor C4, also mounted on the front panel. Stable operation of both the oscillator and mixer circuits is accomplished by use of low-LC-ratio resonant circuits which are temperature compensated to minimize frequency drift.

A three-stage IF amplifier consisting of two 6BA6 tubes, V2 and V3, and a 6AZ8 tube, V11A, follows the 6BE6 mixer. The IF amplifier includes six high-Q tuned circuits—T1, T2, T3, T4, T5, and T6. The associated switching circuits add or subtract capacitance in the tuned circuits to provide various degrees of selectivity over the IF passband, as shown in Fig. 11-14. The 60-kc IF signal is simultaneously applied to the control grids of the 6AZ8 third IF amplifier, V11A, and the 6AZ8 AVC IF amplifier, V4A. The parallel operation of these two amplifiers provides separate channels for the audio and AVC signals. AVC IF amplifier V4A is coupled to AVC diode V4B by means of tuned transformer T8. The AVC control voltage is applied to the signal grids of V1 and V2. The AVC voltages also controls the 12AU7 meter amplifier, V10B. AVC switch S3 grounds the AVC voltage in the "off" position; and the other positions provide slow, medium, and fast AVC action by changing the time-constant networks across AVC diode load resistor R77.

When AM or MCW signals are received, the 6AZ8 diode-detector output signal is applied to the plate of the 6AL5 noise limiter, V7. A DC voltage from the AM detector is also applied to noise-limiter control R50, and then to the cathode circuit of the 6AL5. The purpose of the DC voltage is to control the degree of noise-limiting action. The audio signal is then coupled to the remaining 6AL5 diode plate through the common-cathode connection and load. When noise-limiter switch S5 is in the "on" position, the 6AL5 functions as a series-type limiter which provides clipping of both the positive and negative noise pulses. When the switch is in the "off" position, the signal passes through the circuit unchanged. The audio-output signal from the noise limiter is applied to audio gain control R12 and to the grid of the 6AV6 first audio amplifier, V8.

In SSB or CW operation, the plate voltage is applied to the 12AU7 BFO, V10A, and the 12AU7 product detector, V5. The BFO signal is applied to one grid of V5, and the 60-kc IF signal from the plate of V11A is applied to the other grid. The audio-output signal from V5 represents the product of the applied IF and BFO signals at the 12AU7 grids. The audio signal from the product detector is applied to the noise limiter through R57 and S4. The operation of the audio circuits beyond this point is exactly the same as previously described.

12AU7 meter amplifier V10B forms one leg of a bridge circuit consisting of resistors R69, R70, R71, and R73. The output of V10B is controlled by the AVC voltage, which provides a meter indication by unbalancing the bridge. R70 balances the bridge circuit, to provide the required null adjustment for the meter. This adjustment must be made only when no AVC signal voltage is present. The sensitivity of the tuning meter is controlled by R72, which limits the current through the meter movement.

SSB RECEIVER SUMMARY

Obviously it is impossible to describe in detail every single-sideband communications receiver being manufactured today. Even though each manufacturer will approach the design problems in his own particular manner, the two receivers and the adapter described above should enable the reader to become reasonably familiar with modern communications receiver design. The stability and bandpass requirements will, in general, be similar to those of the single-sideband transmitter circuits discussed in the preceding chapters.

Other than the more stringent stability and bandpass requirements of the SSB receiver, the most noticeably different circuit is the product detector. In our study of SSB generators, we found that the RF envelope of the single- (or double-) sideband signal contains an entirely different set of components from those in the ordinary AM signal. The suppressed-carrier signal cannot be rectified or "detected" in the ordinary AM diode circuit, since this would produce highly distorted and unintelligible audio. Instead a special circuit arrangement, called the product detector, must be used to recover the audio from the single- or double-sideband RF signal. In this arrangement, the sideband signal is *mixed* with the local carrier generator (BFO) signal, and the resultant audio is the product of the two RF input signals.

Fig. 11-18 shows a triode product detector similar to the one in the Collins and Hammarlund receivers described previously.

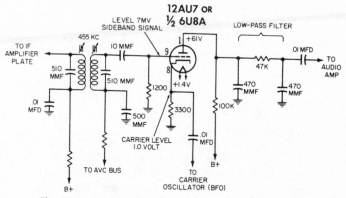

Fig. 11-18. Simplified schematic of a product detector.

The single-sideband IF signal is applied to the 12AU7 control grid, and the signal from the local carrier generator (BFO) is applied to the cathode. The injected carrier should be in the same relationship to the sideband signal as the carrier which was suppressed at the transmitter. The ratios between the SSB IF-signals and injected carrier-signal levels must be such that minimum distortion will appear in the recovered audio signal. In most cases minimum distortion of the audio signal will require an injected-carrier voltage of several times the level of the IF signal. The action of the product detector can be more clearly understood by referring to the vector diagram in Fig. 11-19 during the description which follows.

During the modulation process at the transmitter, an AF and RF signal were mixed to produce a pair of RF sidebands. The carrier was suppressed by the balanced modulator, and

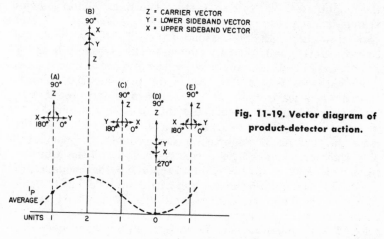

Fig. 11-19. Vector diagram of product-detector action.

277

only the sideband(s) transmitted. At the receiver, the sideband(s) are mixed with a local carrier in a product demodulator and the original audio-modulation signal thus recovered. The demodulation process is very similar to modulation except that the RF sidebands are mixed with an RF carrier to obtain the audio modulation as the product, whereas in modulation the audio-modulation signal is mixed with an RF carrier to obtain the RF sidebands as the product.

In Fig. 11-19, vector Y represents the lower-sideband RF signal, and vector X the upper-sideband RF signal. Together these two vectors represent the double-sideband, suppressed-carrier IF signal applied to the control grid of the product detector shown in Fig. 11-18. The actual frequencies of Y and X will depend on the audio frequency being transmitted and the IF bandpass of the particular receiver in use. The third vector, Z, represents the RF carrier signal, which is applied to the cathode of the 12AU7 product detector. This is the carrier component which was suppressed at the transmitter and must be reinserted at the receiver during demodulation.

Notice in Fig. 11-19 that at time A, X and Y are 180° out of phase. Since the two sideband voltages are equal in amplitude but opposite in phase, the sideband-signal voltages will cancel. Carrier voltage Z remains, however, and will affect the 12AU7 plate current. The average plate current (dotted sine wave) will assume an arbitrary value of one unit. At time B all three vectors (X, Y, and Z) are adding in magnitude. In this illustration the amplitude of each sideband voltage, or magnitude of each sideband vector, is considered to be equal to one-half the amplitude of the carrier voltage. The three vector voltages at time B will add to produce an arbitrary plate-current value of two units, as indicated by the solid vertical line below the dotted sine wave. At time C the two sideband voltage vectors X and Y have reversed their positions with respect to those of time A—X is now at 0° and Y is at 180°. Again the two sideband voltages cancel, which leaves only carrier component Z and produces an arbitrary plate-current value of one unit. At time D vectors X and Y are adding at 270° but carrier vector Z is at 90°. Since the magnitude of X and Y combined is exactly equal to the magnitude of Z, the carrier and sideband voltages cancel and the arbitrary plate-current value is zero. Time E represents the beginning of the next modulation cycle, and the carrier and sideband vector positions are the same as shown at time A. Notice that the *average* of the instantaneous values of the 12AU7 plate current (dotted line) follows a sine-wave pattern, but only when the audio modulation applied at the transmitter is a sine wave. When

278

speech is being applied at the transmitter, the 12AU7 average plate current will follow the speech audio-wave pattern.

It is important that the phrase "average of the instantaneous values of plate current" be thoroughly understood. Since the product demodulator acts essentially like a mixer, a number of signals will appear in the 12AU7 plate current. The most prominent will be the two RF (or IF) sideband signals represented by the vectors X and Y, and the RF carrier signal represented by vector Z. The carrier signal will add to each sideband signal and produce RF sum signals in the 12AU7 plate current. These signals appear as a pair of sidebands displaced above and below the injected-carrier second-harmonic frequency by the amount of the original modulation frequency. Also appearing in the plate current will be the RF difference signals—which are equal to the carrier minus the lower sideband, and the upper sideband minus the carrier. The difference frequency plate-current component (dotted sine wave in Fig. 11-19) is equal to the original audio-modulation component at the transmitter. Fig. 11-20 indicates the relative positions of the various plate-current signal components in the frequency spectrum. In the demodulation process, it is only necessary to recover the intelligence, or audio, portion of the transmitted signal. This is done by feeding the output of the product detector to a low-pass filter which removes the RF components. The output signal from the low-pass filter should be the same as the original audio signal applied at the transmitter.

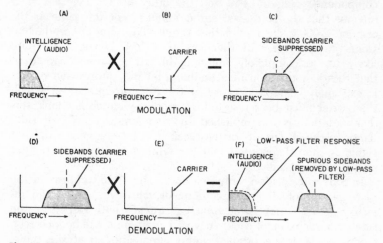

Fig. 11-20. Spectrum positions of intelligence, carrier, and sideband signals during modulation and demodulation.

279

In the preceding discussion, the demodulation of a double-sideband, suppressed-carrier RF signal was analyzed. Assuming that the receiver IF is designed for a nominal frequency of 60 kc, and that the bandpass is sufficient to pass the upper and lower sidebands without attenuation, then a 2,000-cycle modulation tone at the transmitter will produce receiver IF sidebands at 58 and 62 kc. In order to recover the original 2,000-cycle audio from the output of the product detector and low-pass filter, a precise 60-kc RF carrier must be reinserted into the double-sideband IF signal. Without offering complex mathematical proof, it can be stated that the *two* audio difference signals —obtained by subtracting the 58-kc lower-sideband signal from the 60-kc carrier signal, and the 60-kc carrier signal from the 62-kc upper-sideband signal—will add in the product-detector output circuit and appear as *one* signal. This statement will be true only when the carrier frequency is equidistant from either sideband frequency—or, in our numerical example, at exactly 60 kc. It will be interesting to determine what will happen to the demodulated audio signal when the inserted carrier is *not* at the proper frequency.

Suppose the receiver IF sideband frequencies are 58 and 62 kc, but the inserted-carrier frequency is only 59 kc. The audio-signal component recovered from the lower sideband will be equal to 59 kc minus 58 kc, or 1,000 cycles; and 62 kc minus 59 kc, or 3,000 cycles from the upper sideband. The audio signal at the output terminals of the low-pass filter will consist of *two* components, one of 1,000 and the other of 3,000 cycles. It is obvious that the recovered audio signal is not the same as the original 2,000-cycle modulation signal. The audio reproduction from the receiver will then be so distorted that it is quite likely to be completely unintelligible. It should be apparent that the demodulation of a double-sideband, suppressed carrier is extremely difficult because of the exact frequency at which the carrier must be reinserted. In modern communications, this demodulation is accomplished by removing one of the sidebands in the IF circuits of the receiver. The remaining sideband signal is then demodulated in the same manner as the regular single-sideband signal.

In SSB transmission, only *one* audio signal will appear in the plate circuit of the product detector. However, when the injected carrier is not at the proper frequency with respect to the sideband, the pitch of each recovered audio tone will be incorrect, compared with the original audio signal applied at the transmitter. As an example, suppose that the audio-modulation signal at the transmitter is a 2,000-cycle sine-wave tone and that the IF signal which appears at the grid of the receiver product detector is the 62-kc upper sideband only. We know that when the injected-carrier frequency is 60 kc, the 2,000-cycle audio tone will be recovered. But if the injected-carrier frequency is, say, 59.95 instead of 60 kc, then the audio-signal frequency recovered will not be 2,000 cycles, but 2,050 cycles. All other audio frequencies in the demodulator output will be shifted upward, in the spectrum, by an amount equal to the frequency error in the injected carrier. For single-sideband reception, injected-carrier frequency errors of 20 cycles or less generally are not noticeable in the recovered audio. When the error is greater than 20 cycles, however, the recovered audio will be shifted, in its spectrum, to the point where the reproduced sound will sound unnatural. If the error is 50 cycles or greater, the reproduced sound may even be unintelligible.

Chapter 12

Single-Sideband
Transceivers

In the preceding pages we discussed single-sideband transmitter and receiver design from the viewpoint of separate integral units. It is obvious that much of the circuitry of the two separate units, such as the IF stages, the sideband filters, the injection oscillators, etc., is virtually identical. Although many amateurs still prefer separate transmitter and receiver units, the single-sideband transceiver is rapidly becoming more and more popular, especially for mobile or other communications services where a small compact unit is required. The operation of a single-sideband transceiver is essentially bilateral. With the exception of the receiver RF amplifier and the high-level transmitting stages, the signal stages may amplify in either direction. During the receive function they amplify in one direction; on transmit they amplify in the opposite direction. The same tuned circuits are used for both transmitting and receiving. The various injection oscillators operate continuously, supplying the local-oscillator signals to the proper mixer stages. The transceiver has several important advantages over the separate transmitter and receiver units, the most outstanding of which are compactness, lower cost for the over-all station, and rapid break-in operation. Because the frequency-determining VFO is common to both the receiving and transmitting functions, it is only necessary to tune the receiver to the frequency of the station with which contact is desired and start talking. The transmitted signal is automatically placed on the same frequency as that of the distant station.

At this time a number of manufacturers are producing single-sideband communications transceivers. As might be expected, each manufacturer has his own ideas as to the features required in the service application for which the instrument was designed. As a result, the circuit details of the various equipment are somewhat different. It is obviously impossible to describe in detail all of the transceivers being manufactured today. Consequently, we have selected a limited number of transceivers of different manufacture to illustrate good engineering and design practice. One of these units, the Collins KWM-2/2A, has been in production for several years and contains many circuit refinements. It is an excellent example of a transceiver designed for the use of vacuum tubes. Another transceiver shown here is the Sideband Engineers' SB-34. This instrument is a very good example of current transceiver design practice using solid-state (transistor) techniques. Although every precaution has been taken to insure accurate descriptions of the various pieces of equipment, space does not permit complete functional details of all circuits. The reader is advised to write to the manufacturer of any specific equipment in which he may be interested and request the latest technical information.

COLLINS KWM-2/2A

Fig. 12-1 shows the front view of the Collins KWM-2/2A. The block diagram of the transceiver is shown in Fig. 12-2. The

Fig. 12-1. Collins KWM-2/2A transceiver.

KWM-2/2A is a single-sideband or CW transceiver operating in the range between 3.4 and 30.0 mc. It consists of a double-conversion receiver and a double-conversion exciter-transmitter. The transmitter and receiver circuits use common oscillators and a common mechanical filter, as well as a common RF amplifier. The transmitter and receiver low-frequency IF is 455 kc. The

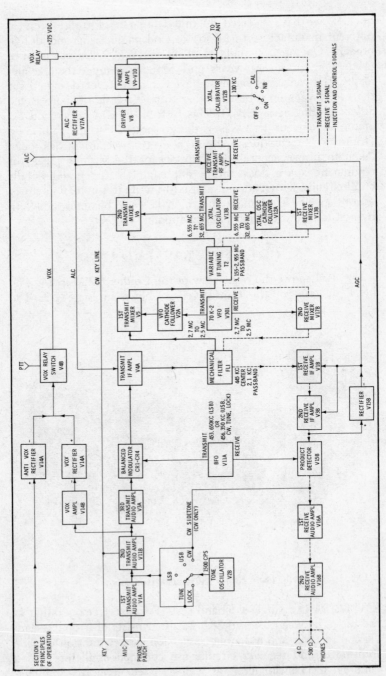

Fig. 12-2. Block diagram, Collins KWM-2/2A transceiver.

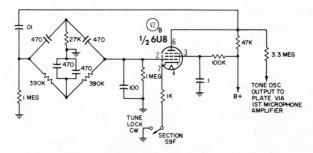

Fig. 12-3. KWM-2/2A tone oscillator circuit.

high-frequency IF for both is 2.955 to 3.155 mc. This is a band-pass IF which accommodates the full 200-kc bandwidth.

Refer to Fig. 12-2. Microphone or phone-patch input signals are applied to the grid of first-transmit audio amplifier V1A, amplified, and then coupled to the grid of second-transmit audio amplifier V11B. Output from V11B is applied, through the speech-amplifier gain control, to the grid of third-transmit audio amplifier V3A, which is a cathode-follower circuit. The low-impedance audio signal from the cathode follower is applied to the resistive balance point of balanced modulator CR1-CR4. In the "tune," "lock," and CW positions of the emission switch, audio output from tone oscillator V2B (Fig. 12-3) is fed to the

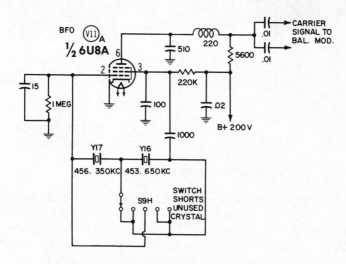

Fig. 12-4. KWM-2/2A beat-frequency oscillator (BFO).

285

grid of the second audio amplifier. The amplified tone-oscillator signal is taken from the plate of V11B and coupled to the grid of VOX amplifier V14B to activate the VOX circuits in CW operation. This 1,500-cps audio signal is also fed to the grid of first-receiver audio amplifier V16A for CW monitoring.

Audio signal voltage from the cathode of V3A and the BFO carrier generator voltage (Fig. 12-4) are applied to the carrier-balance diode-quad modulator (CR1, CR2, CR3, and CR4). Both upper- and lower-sideband signals from the balanced modulator are coupled through an IF transformer to the grid of IF amplifier V4A. The amplified double-sideband suppressed-carrier signal from V4A is fed to mechanical filter FL1. The 2.1-kc passband of FL1 is centered at 455 kc. This passes either the upper or the lower sideband, depending on the sideband selected when the emission switch connects the proper BFO crystal. The BFO crystal frequency required for the upper sideband is 456.350 kc, and 453.650 kc for the lower sideband. The single-sideband output of FL1 is applied to the grids of first transmit mixer V5 in push-pull (Fig. 12-6).

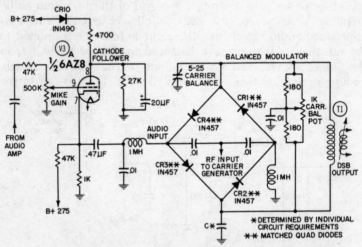

Fig. 12-5. KWM-2/2A balanced modulator.

The 455-kc single-sideband signal is fed to the first transmit mixer (Fig. 12-6) in push-pull; the plates of the mixer are connected in push-pull, but the VFO signal from cathode follower V2A is fed to the two mixer grids in parallel. The mixer cancels the VFO signal energy and translates the 455-kc single-sideband signal from the mechanical filter to a 2.955- to 3.155-mc single-sideband signal. The variable IF tuning circuit, T2, between the first and second transmit mixers, provides broadband response to the 200-kc variable IF output (2.955- to 3.155-mc range) from first transmit mixer V5. The bandpass IF signal is fed to one of the grids of second transmit mixer V6, and the high-frequency injection-signal energy from crystal oscillator V13A is fed to the cathode and other grid. The high-frequency injection signal cancels within the mixer, and only the bandpass IF signal is translated to the desired band.

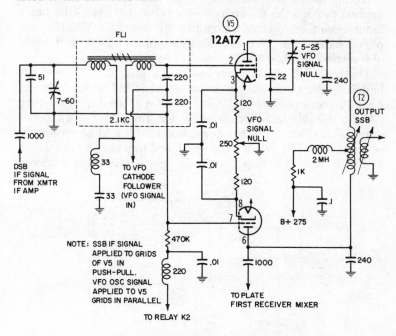

Fig. 12-6. KWM-2/2A first transmitter mixer.

A series of slug-tuned circuits couples V6 to V7, V7 to V8, and V8 to the power amplifier. These circuits are ganged to the exciter tuning control. The signal is amplified by RF amplifier V7 and driver V8 to drive power amplifiers V9 and V10. Output from the parallel power amplifiers is tuned by a pi-network and fed to the antenna through the contacts of transmit-receive relay K3. Negative RF feedback from the power-amplifier plate circuit to the driver cathode circuit reduces distortion in the output signal. Both the driver and power-amplifier stages are neutralized to insure good stability. When the RF driving voltage to the power amplifier becomes great enough that positive peaks drive the amplifier grids positive, the grids begin to draw current and the signal is detected. This produces an audio envelope. The

287

audio envelope is rectified by ALC rectifier V17A, which is connected to produce a negative DC voltage. This voltage, after being filtered and passed through an ALC time-constant network, is used to control the gain of V4A and V7. This system allows a high average level of modulation without driving the power-amplifier tubes well into the grid-current region, which would result in increased distortion.

During the receive function, signal input from the antenna is applied through the transmit-receive relay contacts to the tuned input circuit of receiver-transmitter RF amplifier V7. The amplified signal from V7 is fed through a tuned circuit to the grid of receiver first mixer V13B.

The input RF signal is applied to the grid of V13B, and the high-frequency oscillator injection signal is fed to the cathode. The difference product of the first mixer is applied from the tube plate to variable IF transformer T2. The RF output of T2, in the range of 2.955 to 3.155 mc, is applied to the grid of second receiver mixer V17B, across a parallel-tuned trap circuit (not shown in Fig. 12-2). This trap circuit minimizes a spurious response

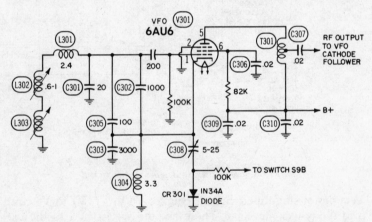

Fig. 12-7. Collins 70K-2 oscillator (VFO) circuit.

which would otherwise result from harmonics of the high-frequency crystal oscillator. When signal input is applied to the grid of V17B and VFO injection voltage is applied to the cathode, a 455-kc difference-signal product is produced. The 455-kc product is fed from the V17B plate to mechanical filter FL1.

The IF signal output from FL1 is applied to the grid of first IF amplifier V1B. The IF signal is amplified by V1B and V3B and then fed to AGC rectifier V15A and product detector V15B. The crystal-controlled BFO signal from V11A is applied to the

288

cathode of the product detector, and the product of mixing is the detected audio signal. Output voltage from the AGC rectifier circuit is fed to the two receiver IF amplifiers and, through relay contacts, to the receiver-transmitter RF amplifier. This AGC voltage controls the gain of the receiver and prevents overloading.

Output from the product detector is applied through an audio gain control to the grid of first audio amplifier V16A. The amplified audio from V16A is coupled to the grid of audio output amplifier V16B, which produces the power to operate a speaker, headphones, or phone patch.

This transceiver circuit contains five oscillators. They are the tone oscillator, the beat-frequency oscillator, the variable-frequency oscillator, the high-frequency crystal oscillator, and the crystal calibrator.

The tone oscillator operates when the emission switch is in the "lock," "tune," or CW position. It is a phase-shift oscillator operating at approximately 1.5 kc. Its output is fed to the transmitter audio circuits for CW operation. Because of the 1,500-cps tone applied to the balanced modulator during CW operation, the actual transmitted frequency will be 1.5 kc above the KWM-2/2A dial frequency calibration. Some of the output from the tone oscillator is applied to the receiver audio circuits for sidetone monitoring in CW operation.

The beat-frequency oscillator (BFO) is crystal controlled at either 453.650 or 456.350 kc, depending on which crystal is selected by the emission-switch section. The switch shorts out the unused crystal. These crystal frequencies are matched to the bandpass of mechanical filter FL1 so that the carrier frequency is placed approximately 20 db down on the skirts of the filter response. This 20-db carrier attenuation is in addition to the 30-db suppression provided by the balanced modulator.

The variable-frequency oscillator uses fixed capacitance and variable inductance to tune the range of 2.5 to 2.7 mc. The series combination of capacitor C308 and diode CR301, shown in Fig. 12-7, is connected in parallel with capacitor C303. The diode switches C308 into or out of the circuit, depending on the polarity of a bias voltage impressed across the diode junction. When the upper-sideband emission is selected, the bias is positive and C308 is switched into the circuit. The capacitor then is adjusted to shift the VFO frequency by an amount equal to the frequency separation of the two BFO crystals. This allows the selection of either sideband without upsetting the tuning or dial calibration.

High-frequency oscillator V13A is crystal controlled by any one of 14 crystals selected by the bandswitch. Output from the high-frequency crystal oscillator is fed to the transmitter second mixer and to the crystal-oscillator cathode follower. The cathode follower provides isolation and impedance match between the crystal oscillator and the receiver first-mixer cathode. The output frequency of the oscillator is always 3.155 mc higher than the lower edge of the desired band. This high-frequency injection signal is the crystal fundamental frequency for all desired signals below 12 mc. For operating frequencies higher than 12 mc, the crystal frequency is doubled in the plate circuit of the oscillator.

The 100-kc crystal calibrator, V12A, is the pentode section of a type 6U8A tube. Its output is coupled to the antenna coil. The calibrator may be trimmed to zero-beat with WWV by means of a small adjustable capacitor.

Audio voltage from second microphone amplifier V11B is coupled to the VOX gain control and amplified by VOX amplifier V14B. The amplified signal is fed to the VOX rectifier, which is one of the diodes of V14. The positive DC output of the VOX rectifier is applied to the grid of VOX relay amplifier V4B, causing it to conduct current and actuate the VOX relay. The contacts of the VOX relay switch the receiver antenna lead, the other relay coils, and the bias voltage. Other relays switch the metering circuits from receive to transmit, the low plate voltages from receive to transmit tubes, and the AGC and ALC leads.

The ANTIVOX circuit provides a threshold voltage to prevent the speaker output (picked up by the microphone circuits) from tripping the KWM-2/2A into the transmit function. Some of the receiver audio-output voltage is fed to the ANTIVOX gain control. The signal from the slider of this control is rectified by the ANTIVOX rectifier, which is the other diode of V14. Negative DC output voltage from the ANTIVOX rectifier, connected to the grid of V4B, provides the necessary ANTIVOX threshold. The ANTIVOX gain control adjusts the value of the threshold so that the speaker output will not produce enough positive DC output from the VOX rectifier to exceed the negative DC output from the ANTIVOX rectifier and cause V4B to actuate the VOX relay. However, speech energy into the microphone will cause the positive VOX voltage to overcome the negative ANTIVOX voltage and produce the desired action of the VOX relay. The final adjustments of the VOX and ANTIVOX circuits will depend on the operating habits of the individual, his voice characteristics, and the particular type of microphone used.

SBE SB-34

The SB-34 single-sideband transceiver is manufactured by Sideband Engineers, South San Francisco, California, and is designed for operation in the A3 portions of the 80-, 40-, 20-, and 15-meter amateur bands. The SB-34 operates either upper or lower sideband; selection is made by a front-panel switch. There is no carrier shift when the emission is changed from one sideband to the other. The peak effective power output exceeds 60 watts on the 80-, 40-, and 20-meter bands, and 50 watts on the 15-meter band.

The SB-34 is self-contained, requiring only a microphone and an antenna for operation. It will operate from either a 117-volt AC or a 12-volt DC (negative-ground) power source; the two-way power supply is an integral part of the unit. Selection between the two power sources is automatically made when the proper line cord is connected. Provision for use of a VOX unit and a 100-kc calibrator is included. These units are available as accessory items.

All stages of the SB-34 except the transmitter driver and power amplifiers are transistorized. The use of bilateral amplifiers and mixers, which amplify in one direction on transmit and in the other direction on receive, permits the use of a single bandpass circuit train. Duplication of circuitry is eliminated through the use of common circuit elements for both receive and transmit functions. Exceptional receiver performance is obtained through the use of post-alloy diffused transistors and a 2.1-kc Collins mechanical filter. The entire transceiver package is less than one-half cubic foot in volume and weighs approximately 18 pounds. The construction is of heavy-gauge steel and aluminum. Printed-

Fig. 12-9. SB-34 transceiver.

circuit boards are used extensively for the wiring to provide a rugged and compact package. The SB-34 is shown in Fig. 12-9.

All transistors in the SB-34 circuit operate in the common-emitter configuration except receiver RF amplifier Q11. This stage is operated common base, as shown in Fig. 12-10.

A typical bilateral stage may be understood by referring to the 456-kc amplifier. Q5-Q6, shown in Fig. 12-11. With the microphone button released, the base bias resistor of Q5 is returned to a line which carries a +12-volt potential. The transistor cannot conduct. The base bias resistor of Q6, however, is returned (through the volume control) to a line which is essentially

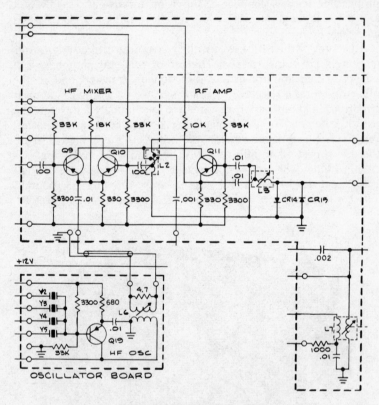

Fig. 12-10. SB-34 tuner board.

ground potential with the microphone button released, and Q6 is in conduction and able to amplify. Thus, with the microphone button up, a signal appearing at the mechanical filter will be amplified and delivered to IF transformer T2. With the microphone button pressed (transmit position), the two bias-control

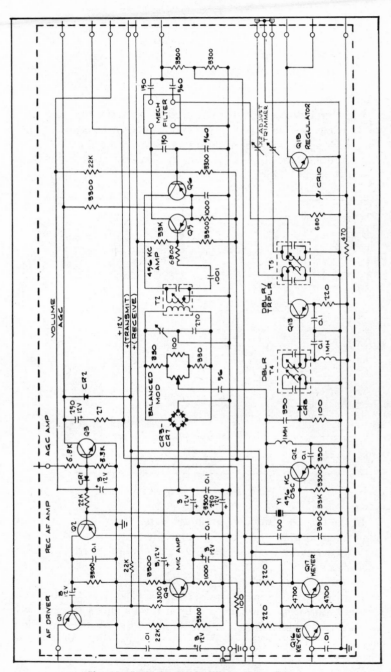

Fig. 12-11. SB-34 456-kc bilateral amplifier.

lines are inverted in polarity so that Q6 is cut off and Q5 is able to conduct. Therefore, a signal appearing at T2 is amplified by Q5 and impressed on the filter. Similarly, the amplifying direction of the VFO mixer (Q7-Q8, Fig. 12-12) and the high-frequency mixer (Q9-Q10, Fig. 12-13) are controlled by the two bias-control lines.

Unilateral stages that are required to operate only on receive or transmit are turned off when not needed by returning their base bias resistors to the appropriate bias-control line. The transmitter tubes are disabled during receive by applying a high negative bias to their grids.

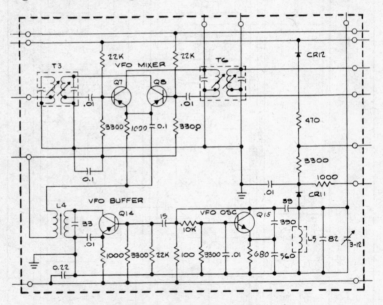

Fig. 12-12. SB-34 VFO mixer (VFO board).

In the transmit function, an audio signal from the microphone, controlled in amplitude by the microphone gain control, is amplified by microphone amplifier Q4 and applied to ring-balanced modulator CR3-7. Crystal oscillator Q12, operating at 456.380 kc, provides a carrier signal to the modulator. Carrier balance is obtained by a potentiometer and a trimmer capacitor. Double-sideband, suppressed-carrier output from the balanced modulator is amplified through T2 by bilateral amplifier Q5-Q6. The amplified signal is then passed through the mechanical filter, which suppresses the upper sideband.

Output from oscillator Q12 is also applied to frequency doubler CR8. The doubled carrier frequency from this stage is then either

294

doubled again or tripled by Q13. With the mode selector switch set at "USB," the frequency is tripled; with the switch on "LSB," the frequency is doubled. Thus, on "USB," a 2738.2-kc (456.38 × 6) signal appears at the output of T5. On "LSB," an 1825.5-kc output appears at T5.

Doubler-tripler transformer T5 is connected in a ring with the mechanical filter, mixer CR9, and transformer T3 which is tuned to 2281.9 kc. With the mode selector in "LSB," output from T5 is additively mixed with the lower-sideband signal from the filter to produce a lower-sideband signal at 2281.9 kc. With the mode selector set on "USB," the T5 output is subtractively mixed with the filter output to generate an upper-sideband signal, still at 2281.9 kc. Thus, the mode selector, by adjusting Q13 to either double or triple, determines the mode of the sideband signal. Since all of the frequencies involved are derived by a single oscillator, the carrier frequency cannot shift and no retuning is necessary when switching sidebands.

The 2281.9-kc upper- or lower-sideband output from T3 is applied to VFO mixer Q7-Q8. Also applied to this mixer is an injection signal which is tunable from 5456.9 kc to 5706.9 kc. This injection voltage is generated by VFO Q15 and isolated from the load by VFO buffer Q14. Tunable transformer T6, connected to the output of VFO mixer Q7-Q8, tunes the frequency range 3175 through 3425 kc. This frequency range is the result of subtractively mixing the incoming 2281.9-kc sideband signal with the VFO injection. Transformer T6 is gang-tuned with the VFO and thus is always accurately tuned to the desired frequency.

The 3175- to 3425-kc sideband signal from Q7-Q8 is applied to high-frequency mixer Q9-Q10. Also applied to this mixer is injection voltage from high-frequency crystal oscillator Q19. The frequency generated by this oscillator may be 7200, 10,475, 17,-525, or 24,625 kc, depending on the position of the bandswitch. Here again, the 3175- to 3425-kc incoming signal is subtractively mixed to produce the final output frequency. Output from mixer Q9-Q10 appears across tuner coil L2. The resonant frequency of L2 is controlled by a large variable capacitor and by a special slug which penetrates into the coil an amount depending on the setting of the bandswitch. The large variable capacitor is mechanically linked to the bandswitch through a Geneva movement so that rotating the capacitor shaft tunes the coil through a limited range, bracketing the selected operating band. Changing the bandswitch to the next band tunes a limited range, bracketing this band, etc. On 80 meters, the slug is almost fully penetrated into the coil and the capacitor is near maximum capacity. On 40 and 20 meters, the slug and capacitor are at near midrange, and on 15 meters the slug is fully withdrawn and the capacitor is near minimum. By this unique method of tuning and bandswitching, the Q and LC ratio of L2 and the variable capacitor are near optimum on all bands, and the resonant impedance remains essentially constant across the entire tuning range. This tuning arrangement is ganged with, and duplicated in, the antenna and driver-coil circuits, resulting in exciter train tuning with only one control.

In the receive function, with the microphone button released, a signal from the antenna is loosely coupled from the transmitter pi-section network to the top of L3. Diodes CR14 and CR15, across L3, conduct only when extremely strong signals are present and do not otherwise affect the circuit. The signal at L3 is coupled to the emitter of Q11, which operates as a common-base amplifier. The amplified signal from Q11 is applied to high-frequency mixer Q9-Q10 through L2. With the injection from Q19, this stage converts the signal to a frequency within the range 3175 to 3425 kc. The converted signal is then mixed by Q7 and Q8 to 2281.9 kc with injection from the VFO Q14 and Q15. The converted signal is finally mixed by diode CR9 to 456.38 kc, the reference frequency, in a manner exactly opposite to that described for this stage during the transmit function. Output from the filter is then amplified by Q5 and Q6 and coupled through T2 to ring modulator CR3-CR7.

With BFO injection from the carrier oscillator, the ring modulator now functions as a detector and produces an audio output which is applied to the base of Q2. The audio signal from the collector of Q2 is coupled to the base of Q1, the audio driver. This stage, in turn, drives the transistor audio power amplifier, which increases the signal to speaker level.

The volume control sets the gain of the high-frequency mixer, the 456-kc amplifier, and, to a small extent, first audio amplifier Q2. Other signal stages operate at full gain except in the presence of AGC action.

RF amplifier Q11 and IF amplifier Q5-Q6 are gain-controlled by AGC amplifier Q3. An audio signal appearing across the speaker terminal causes Q3 to conduct heavily. The voltage at its collector is normally close to that of the supply, $+12$ volts. When Q3 conducts, however, the collector potential falls rapidly and charges the 250-mfd capacitor (connected between the collector and 12-volt bus) to some value less than 12 volts. This AGC voltage is connected to the emitters of the RF amplifier and the 456-kc amplifier; and as the AGC voltage falls toward ground potential, the gains of these stages are reduced until the audio output is stabilized. The AGC action is proportioned such that the RF

296

amplifier becomes largely cut off in the presence of even moderate signals so that the following stages are protected from signal overload. If the signal fades, causing the audio output to drop, Q3 conducts less and the 250-mfd capacitor slowly discharges toward the +12-volt potential, causing the gains of the stages to be restored as necessary to maintain the audio level.

When the volume control approaches the fully clockwise position, diode CR1, connected to the base of Q3, begins to limit the amount of audio applied for AGC action. With this occurring, more audio output is produced for a given amount of AGC. Finally, with the volume control fully clockwise, the base of Q3 is clamped off and full audio output is produced.

Diode CR2, in the collector of Q3, conducts when the unit is switched to transmit. This conduction charges the 250-mfd capacitor to the 12-volt potential so that when the set is switched back to receive, full receiver gain is instantly available.

Two transistors, Q16 and Q17, perform the functions necessary to switch the transceiver from receive to transmit, thus eliminating the conventional relay. The base of Q16 is coupled through a current-limiting resistor to the cathode of driver tube V1. With the microphone button released, V1 draws no cathode current and its cathode is at ground potential. Transistor Q16, therefore, is cut off and the potential at its collector is +12 volts. This potential is supplied to the control line that requires +12 volts on receive. Also, the collector potential at Q16 is applied to the base of Q17, causing this transistor to conduct to saturation. Its collector potential, therefore, is essentially grounded. The control line requiring ground potential on receive is connected to the collector of Q17.

When the microphone button is pressed, the high negative bias on driver tube V1 is removed and the stage conducts. The cathode potential of V1 rises to approximately +6 volts and, with this voltage applied to the base, transistor Q16 conducts to saturation. The control line that was +12 volts is now at ground potential. In addition, since the potential on the base of Q17 is removed, this stage cuts off and the control line that was grounded on receive is now +12 volts.

The SB-34 contains a power supply designed to operate from either 117 volts AC or 12 volts DC (negative ground). With 12-volt DC operation, transistors Q21 and Q22 are connected as a common-emitter power oscillator. Starting bias for this oscillator is obtained from a small resistor and the heater current of driver tube V1. All of the transmitter-tube heaters and input voltage to the oscillators are applied through the "XMTR" switch so that the receiver portion of the transceiver may be operated with reduced power consumption. A high-voltage winding of T7 is connected to voltage tripler circuit CR17, CR18, and CR19 to supply approximately +450 volts to the transmitter tubes and +150 volts to the screen grids of V2 and V3. Another small secondary winding is half-wave rectified by CR20 to supply negative bias to the transmitter tubes.

With 117-volt AC operation, T7 is energized by a second primary winding. The feedback and collector windings of the transformer are connected essentially in series and full-wave rectified by the collector-base diodes of Q21 and Q22 to provide a high-current +12-volt output. This voltage operates the transistorized stages and the transmitter tube heaters. The high-voltage and bias systems operate as described above. The "XMTR" switch, in this mode of operation, is not connected and the transmitter tube heaters are energized at all times.

A special regulator circuit is provided to stabilize the voltage to the VFO, Q14 and Q15. Regulator Q18 operates a shunt regulator across the +12-volt bus to provide an output of +7.0 volts. The current to the base of Q18 is determined by the current flow through zener diode CR10; and since this zener diode in itself is not a perfect regulator, the output voltage from Q18 would normally vary slightly as the supply voltage changed. To overcome this variation, a small variable resistor is inserted in the series-dropping resistor line to the regulator transistor. The effect of this variable resistor is to insert an additional amount of base current to the transistor to offset the slight change that occurs in the zener diode because of supply-voltage changes. Thus, with proper adjustment of the resistor, regulation becomes perfect for input supply voltages of 11.5 to 15.0 volts.

The SB-34 includes a "pitch" control on the front panel. Its purpose is to permit a slight adjustment in the receiver frequency with respect to the transmitter frequency. The control may be switched in or out as desired. A small silicon diode, CR11, is connected between the "hot" end of VFO coil L5 and a voltage-divider network which may be adjusted to a value between the regulated voltage (+7 volts) and ground. The diode is connected so that a reverse bias is applied and therefore appears as a small capacitor, the actual value of capacitance varying according to the amount of reverse bias applied.

The voltage-divider network supplying bias to the diode contains, in one leg, the "dial-correct" potentiometer. This leg is active on both transmit and receive. The other leg of the network is divided into two sections, one operating on transmit and the other on receive. On transmit, the leg consists of a 470-ohm resistor and diode CR12, which conducts only on transmit. On re-

298

ceive, the leg consists of either an adjustable resistor (when the "pitch" control switch is off) or the "pitch" control (when the "pitch" control switch is on) and diode CR13.

The over-all effect of the pitch-control network is to permit a slight variation in VFO frequency on both transmit and receive by the "dial-correct" control, and a variation on receive only by the pitch control. The adjustable resistor, activated when the pitch switch is off, is factory adjusted so that the VFO frequency on receive is exactly the same as on transmit.

The single-sideband transceivers described above are factory-built and aligned, and are ready to operate. In the early days of amateur radio, before single sideband, it was customary for the average amateur to design and build most of his station equipment "from scratch," laying out the design on paper and then punching the chassis and assembling the components into a complete unit. Because of the complexities of single-sideband circuitry, it is virtually impossible for the average amateur to completely design and construct a modern receiver, transmitter, or transceiver unless he has access to laboratory or engineering facilities and equipment. Fortunately, however, remarkable progress has been made by the various kit manufacturers, such as EICO and the Heath Company. The two firms mentioned produce a wide variety of amateur-radio transmitter, receiver, and transceiver kits, as well as other electronic products, in which all of the difficult design work has been carried out in the laboratory. In most cases, the critical circuits are already wired and adjusted so that only a minimum of test equipment is necessary to complete the construction and adjustments of the final unit. These manufacturers supply detailed step-by-step instructions and drawings which, if carefully followed, will enable even a relatively inexperienced person to construct a complex piece of modern single-sideband communications equipment. The descriptions of the single-sideband transceiver kits which follow are necessarily brief. It is suggested that the reader who is interested in building his own SSB equipment write to the manufacturer for more detailed information.

EICO 753 TRI-BAND TRANSCEIVER KIT

The EICO 753 transceiver incorporates a filter-type single-sideband transmitter and a single-conversion receiver for operation on the 80-, 40-, and 20-meter amateur bands. It is equally suited for mobile- or fixed-station use. In fixed-station use, the 751 AC-supply speaker console is required for 117-volt, 60-cps AC line operation. In mobile use, the 752 DC supply designed for a 12-volt DC positive- or negative-ground source is required. Both of these supplies have been designed especially for use with the 753 transceiver and provide the requisite filtering and regulation. The front view of the EICO 753 transceiver is shown in Fig. 12-14. In order to follow the technical description given below, refer to the block diagram, Fig. 12-15.

In the transmit position, two stages of microphone-signal amplification are provided by V1A and V1B. A sample of the speech waveform is taken from the plate of V1A, ahead of the speech-amplifier gain control, and applied to V3A, the VOX amplifier.

Fig. 12-14. EICO 753 transceiver.

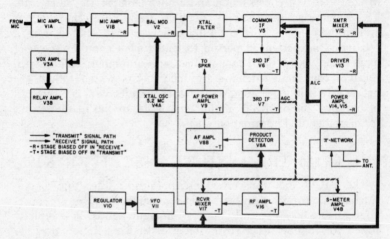

Fig. 12-15. Block diagram EICO 753.

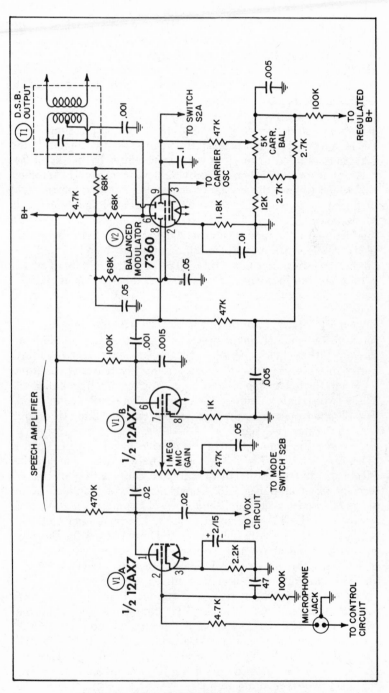

Fig. 12-16. EICO 753 balanced modulator circuit.

301

The amplified speech signal from V1B is applied between the deflection plates of the 7360 beam-deflection tube balanced modulator, as shown in Fig. 12-16. The 5.2-mc crystal-controlled carrier oscillator signal is fed to the control grid of the 7360. The DC bias on the dynamically grounded plate is adjusted with R20 to control the balance of the modulator. This balance is automatically upset when transmitting in the AM mode by the connection of R42 from one deflection plate to ground. The output signal from the balanced modulator is taken from across the two anodes of the 7360 and coupled to the four-pole crystal filter by means of T1.

Amplification at 5.2 mc is provided by common IF amplifier V5, which follows the crystal-filter output. The bias on the grid of this stage is modified by the ALC control voltage, which acts to decrease the stage gain when the peak input power to the final RF amplifier approaches the 200-watt level. Both the output of the common IF amplifier and the output of the VFO, V11, are applied to transmitter mixer tube V12, the output circuit of which is tuned to the frequency of operation. A dual-section tuning capacitor tunes this stage and also the following driver plate circuit.

Two VFO ranges are used. The 8.7- to 9.2-mc range provides for both 80- and 20-meter operation, and the 12.2- to 12.5-mc range yields 40-meter operation. On the 80-meter band, the transmitter mixer selects the difference frequency between the 9-mc VFO and the 5.2-mc modulated signal from common amplifier V5. These two signals are added for operation on the 20-meter band. For 40-meter operation, the mixer subtracts the 5.2-mc IF output from the 12-mc VFO signal.

To trace the signal path in the receive position, refer to the block diagram, Fig. 12-15. The same pi-network that matches the output of the transmitter to the antenna couples the antenna to receiver input amplifier V16. Conversion of the amplified input to the 5.2-mc IF is accomplished in receiver mixer V17, which is fed by both the RF stage and the VFO. The plate circuit of V17 is tuned to 5.2 mc with the same transformer used for the balanced-mixer output signal. After the signal passes through the crystal filter, three stages of IF amplification are provided by V5, V6, V16, and V17, as well as by S-meter amplifier V4B.

One section of V8 functions as a product detector in the CW and SSB modes. Signal from third IF stage V7 is applied to the grid of V8A, while the output of 5.2-mc crystal oscillator V4A is injected at the cathode. For AM reception, the cathode of V8A is grounded, causing this stage to function as a grid-leak detector. The 5.2-mc oscillator is disabled for AM reception. V8 and V9 provide a two-stage audio amplifier.

HEATHKIT SB-110

All of the single-sideband transceivers described above are designed for operation on the lower-frequency amateur bands. The Heathkit SB-110 is designed especially for use on the amateur 6-meter band. This instrument is a complete self-contained transmitter and receiver. Both DC and AC power supplies are available to provide either or both mobile- and fixed-station operation. The transceiver is capable of single-sideband and CW operation. It may also be used as an exciter for a 6-meter linear amplifier.

Both VOX and PTT (push-to-talk) operation are provided. An ANTIVOX circuit prevents the received signal at the speaker from switching the transmitter on during VOX operation. The linear master oscillator and the crystal-controlled heterodyne oscillators are preassembled and prealigned to assure accurate, stable operation. Other features include a large tuning knob, a smooth-operating dial mechanism, and backlash-free tuning. The

Fig. 12-17. Heathkit SB-110 transceiver.

dial may be accurately calibrated from the built-in 100-kc crystal calibrator. A total of seventeen tubes and one transistor are used. The use of circuit boards and wiring harnesses provides a clean, compact chassis layout and greatly simplifies assembly of the kit.

The block diagram of the SB-110 is shown in Fig. 12-18. Since the transceiver circuitry is somewhat complex, small sections of the over-all schematic are included to make the technical description easier to follow. Note that the block diagram shows the receiver circuits across the top and the transmitter circuits across the bottom. An upper-sideband signal at a frequency of 50.11 mc

303

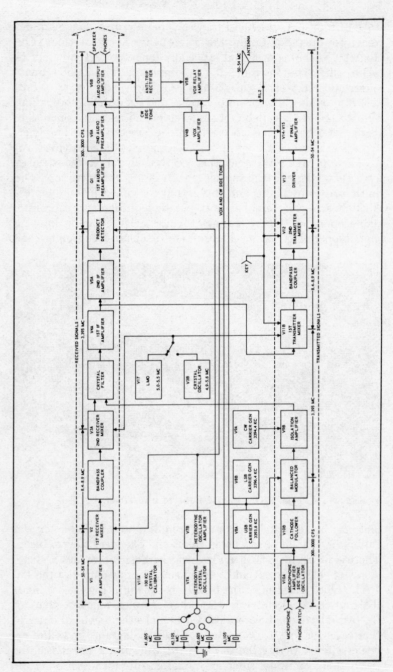

Fig. 12-18. Block diagram SB-110.

will be used to trace through the transceiver to show what action the various stages have on this signal. The transmitter stages will be explained first to show how they develop a single-sideband signal. The frequency chart, Chart 12-1, shows the various frequencies found throughout the transceiver.

Relay amplifier V5B, which controls transmit-receive relay RL1, is held in cutoff in the receive mode by a positive voltage at its

Chart 12-1. Frequency Chart of SB-110.

Band Segment mc	Carrier Generator Crystal Filter (Fixed) kc		LMO (Between 5 - 5.5) mc		Bandpass Coupler (Between 8.395 - 8.895) mc	Heterodyne Oscillator (Crystal Fixed) mc	2nd Transmitter Mixer- Transmitted Signal mc
50.0	USB	3393.6	5.1114	LMO	8.5050	41.605	50.110
	LSB	3396.6	5.1086	Shift	8.5050	41.605	50.110
	CW	3394.4	5.114	2.8 kc	8.5058	41.605	50.1108

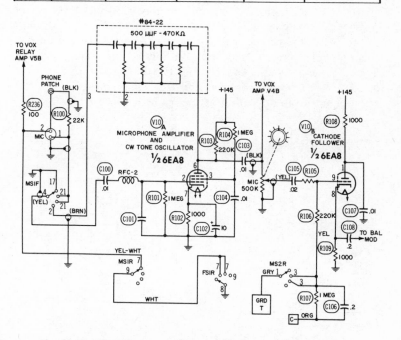

Fig. 12-19. Microphone amplifier and CW tone oscillator SB-110.

cathode. This tube is made to conduct and place the transmitter "on the air" by either the PTT (push-to-talk) or the VOX method. For PTT operation, the cathode of V5B is connected to ground through R236 (refer to Fig. 12-20) and the push-to-talk switch on the microphone. For VOX operation, a positive voltage is applied to the grid to overcome the cutoff bias at the cathode of V5B.

When relay amplifier V5B conducts, it applies power to transmit-receive relay RL1, causing all circuits to be switched to the transmit mode of operation. The antenna is automatically connected to the transmitter section of the transceiver.

During transmit, the following stages of the receiver section are turned off by relay RL1, which removes their B+ voltage: RF amplifier V1, first receiver mixer V2, second receiver mixer V3A, and second IF amplifier V5A. First audio amplifier Q1 is left in operation; but the following stage, second audio amplifier V6A, is biased to cutoff by relay RL1, which disconnects the grid of V6A from ground. This action disables both stages. First IF amplifier V4A and audio output amplifier V6B operate for both receive and transmit operations.

The audio signal from the microphone is fed to the mode switch (refer to Fig. 12-19) and, in the LSB and USB switch positions, the signal is coupled through the switch and through C100 and RFC2 to the grid of V10A. The frequency response of this amplifier stage is limited on the low end by capacitor C100 and on the high end by capacitor C101. RFC2 and capacitor C101 form a filter circuit to prevent any RF signals picked up by the microphone from appearing at the V10A grid.

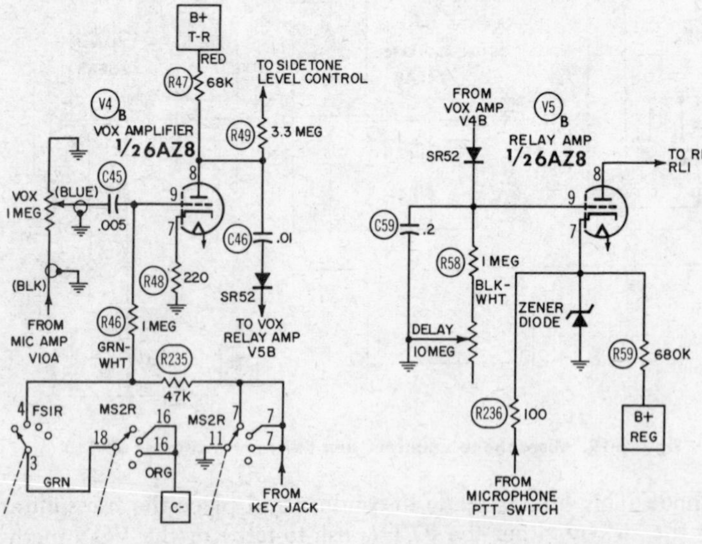

Fig. 12-20. VOX amplifier and relay amplifier SB-110.

The amplified microphone signal from V10A is fed to the speech-amplifier gain control and to the grid of cathode follower V10B. Cathode follower V10B, which applies the audio signal to the low-impedance circuit of the balanced modulator, is disabled by the mode switch for CW and "tune" operation.

When the mode switch is placed in the CW position, a printed phase-shift network is connected between the V10A plate and grid, causing it to function as an 800-cps audio oscillator.

In the VOX position, the transmitter is turned on and off by the amplified microphone signal. The signal from V10A is applied through the VOX control to the grid of V4B, the VOX amplifier (Fig. 12-20A). From the V4B plate the signal is coupled to

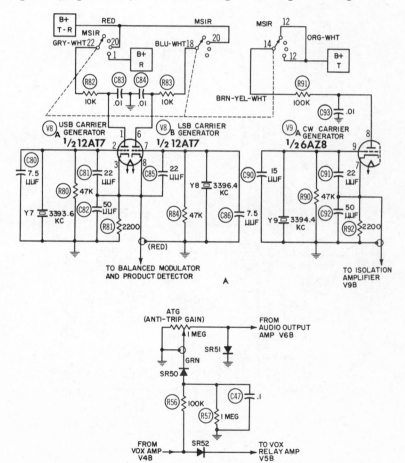

Fig. 12-21. Anti-VOX and carrier generator SB-110.

307

the diode, SR52 (Fig. 12-20B). The diode rectifies the audio signal and produces positive DC pulses which are filtered and fed to the grid of V5B, the relay amplifier.

Relay amplifier V5B is held at cutoff by a zener diode-controlled positive voltage at its cathode. When the positive voltage from V4B appears at the grid, V5B conducts and places transmit-receive relay RL1 in the transmit position.

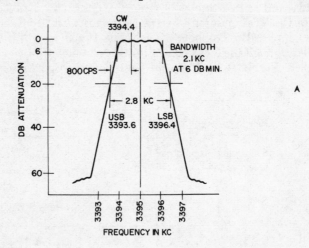

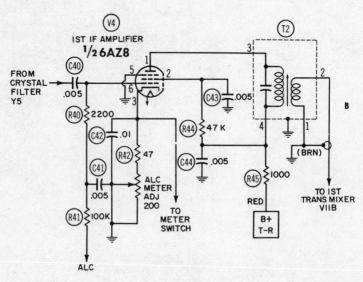

Fig. 12-22. Crystal filter response SB-110 (A) and 1st IF amplifier (B).

When the function switch is in the PTT position, the negative bias voltage is connected to the V4B grid. This bias cuts off the tube when the mode switch is placed on "USB" or "LSB," and no audio (VOX) signal passes through the tube to trigger relay amplifier V5B.

A 12AT7 tube is used as two separate crystal-controlled carrier-generator oscillators (Fig. 12-21B). The upper-sideband carrier, 3393.6 kc, is produced by V8A, while the lower-sideband carrier, 3396.4 kc, is produced by V8B. The output of V9A, the CW carrier generator, is coupled to the grid of isolation amplifier V9B. The correct carrier generator is placed in operation by the mode-switch wafer, which controls the B+ supply voltage to

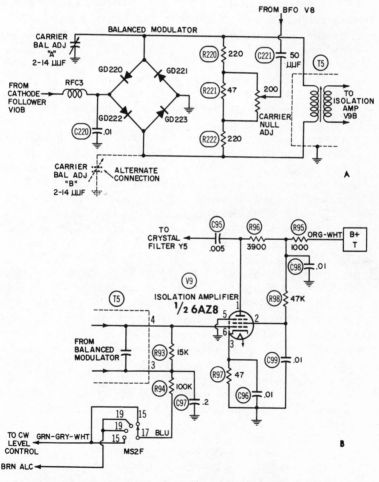

Fig. 12-23. Balanced modulator (A) and isolation amplifier (B) SB-110.

309

the plates of these tubes. The positions of the upper-sideband, lower-sideband, and CW carriers on crystal-filter response are shown in Fig. 12-22A. The upper- and lower-sideband carrier positions are at the −20-db points on the filter skirt. The CW carrier is positioned at the top of the filter response, where it is passed with very little attenuation. Note that the frequency of the CW carrier is 800 cycles higher than the frequency of the upper-sideband carrier. For transceive operation on CW, the receiver must be tuned 800 cycles below the frequency of the received CW signal. This causes an 800-cycle beat note to be produced in the receiver. The transmitter CW carrier generator automatically compensates for this 800-cycle frequency difference and transmits a signal that is 800 cycles above the receiver dial setting. This allows the transmitted and received signals to be on the same frequency, yet allows the receiver to produce an audible tone.

Diodes GD220 through GD223 are connected in a ring-type balanced modulator circuit, as shown in Fig. 12-23A. The audio signal is fed to the junction of diodes GD220 and GD222. This point is bypassed for RF by the 0.01-mfd capacitor, C220. The crystal-oscillator carrier signal is applied to the slider of the 200-ohm carrier-null potentiometer. The potentiometer is adjusted for minimum carrier signal at the secondary of transformer T5. With audio applied, a double-sideband suppressed-carrier RF signal appears at the modulator output and is coupled to the isolation-amplifier grid by means of T5 (Fig. 12-23B). The purpose of isolation amplifier V9B is to amplify the double-sideband signal and provide impedance matching to the crystal-sideband filter. The gain of V9B, in transmit, is controlled by the ALC voltage.

The crystal filter (Fig. 12-22) has a center frequency of 3395 kc and a usable bandpass of 2.1 kc (3393.95 kc to 3396.05 kc at the −6-db points). In the USB mode, this filter passes only the sum frequencies (3393.6-kc carrier frequency plus all audio frequencies from 350 to 2450 cps). In the LSB mode, the filter passes only the difference frequencies (the 3396.4-kc carrier frequency minus all audio frequencies from 350 to 2450 cps). In sideband operation, the carrier suppression in the balanced modulator plus the 20-db suppression at the crystal filter gives a total carrier attenuation of at least 55 db. In the CW mode, a carrier of 3394.4 kc passes through the crystal filter with no attenuation other than insertion losses.

The 3393.6-kc upper-sideband signal from the crystal filter is applied to the grid of first IF amplifier V4A. The amplified signal is then coupled through T2 to the grid of first transmitter mixer V11B (Fig. 12-24A). Here the sideband signal is mixed

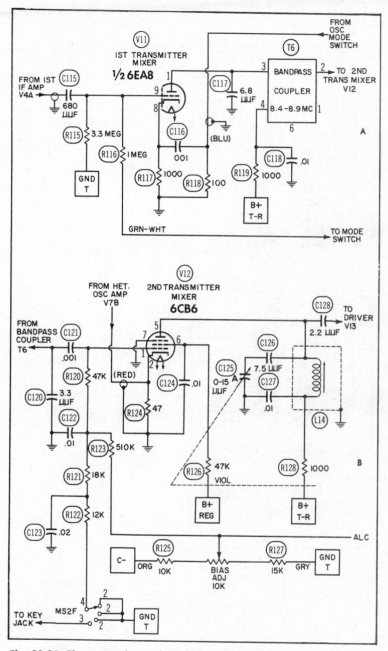

Fig. 12-24. First transmitter mixer (A) and second transmitter mixer (B) SB-110.

311

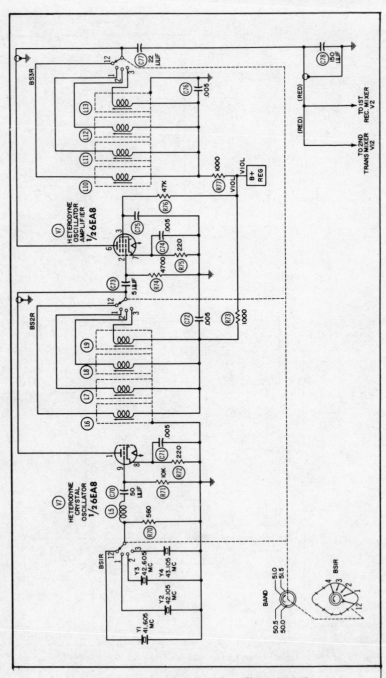

Fig. 12-25. Heterodyne crystal oscillator SB-110.

312

with the RF output from a VFO which is tunable over the range from 5.0 to 5.5 mc. Assuming a VFO signal of 5.114 mc (see Chart 12-1) at the cathode of V11B and the 3393.6-kc sideband signal at the grid, the sum-signal product will appear at 8.5 mc. The 8.5-mc sideband signal is then coupled through bandpass coupler T6 to the grid of second transmitter mixer V12 (Fig. 12-24B). In V12, the 8.5-mc signal is mixed with a crystal-controlled heterodyne oscillator signal of 41.605-mc frequency to produce a single-sideband signal at the operating frequency of 50.1 mc. The 50.1-mc operating-frequency single-sideband signal is fed to driver V13 and to final amplifiers V14 and V15. From the final-amplifier pi-network, the signal energy is applied, through the receive-transmit relay, to the antenna.

In the receive position, the 50.1-mc signal is coupled from the antenna to input coil L1 through a resonant trap. The trap offers a high degree of signal rejection at the IF frequencies in the 8.4- to 8.9-mc range. The RF circuits associated with V1 are tuned for maximum sensitivity over the range between 50 and 54 mc.

The amplified 50.1-mc signal is applied to the grid of first receiver mixer V2 and mixed with the 41.605-mc heterodyne oscillator signal to produce a difference-frequency product of 8.5 mc.

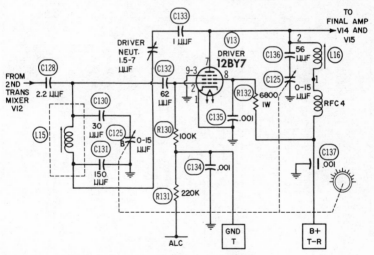

Fig. 12-26. Driver amplifier.

Bandpass coupler T1 applies the 8.5-mc incoming signal to the grid of second receiver mixer V3A. A 5.11-mc VFO injection voltage is fed to the V3A cathode. These two signals are mixed in V3A, and the difference frequency, 3.395 mc, is coupled through crystal filter FL1 to the IF amplifiers. The 3.395-mc sig-

313

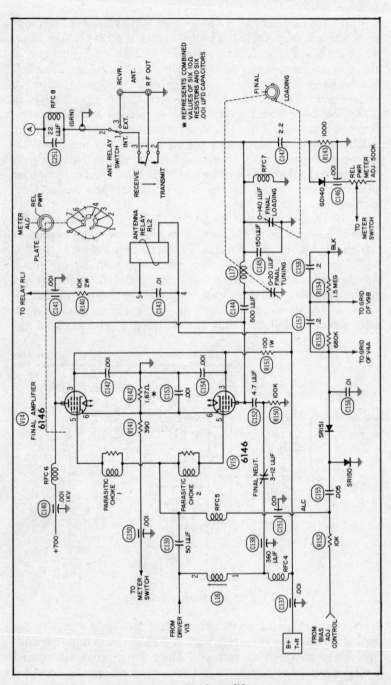

Fig. 12-27. Final amplifier.

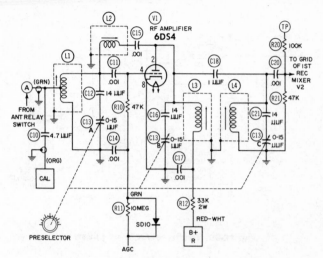

Fig. 12-28. First receiver RF amplifier SB-110.

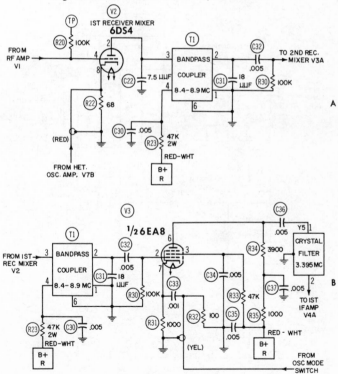

Fig. 12-29. First receiver mixer (A) and second receiver mixer (B).

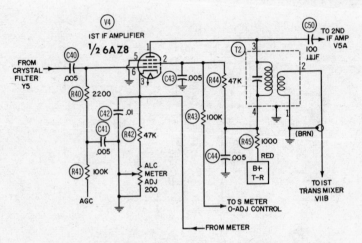

Fig. 12-30. First receiver IF amplifier.

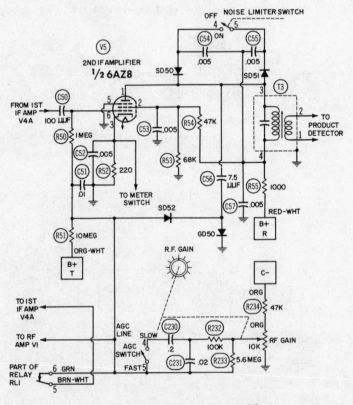

Fig. 12-31. Second receiver IF amplifier.

316

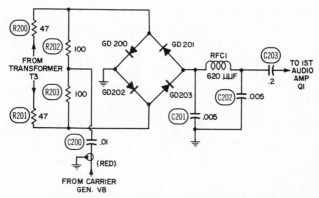

Fig. 12-32. Schematic, product detector.

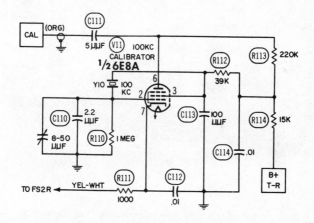

Fig. 12-33. Crystal calibrator.

nal is amplified by first and second IF amplifiers V4A and V5A; and, from the plate of V5A, the amplified signal is applied through transformer T3 to the product detector.

The IF signal at the product detector is 3.395 mc and is applied through resistors R200 and R201. The carrier-generator oscillator signal (3393.6-kc USB or 3396.4-kc LSB) is coupled to the product detector through resistors R202 and R203. These two signals are mixed by diodes GD200 through GD203. The resulting audio frequency (the difference-frequency product) is coupled through the RF filter network, consisting of C201, C202, and choke RFC1, to the first audio preamplifier, transistor Q1. Q1 matches the low-impedance output of the balanced modulator (product detector) more closely than is possible with a vacuum tube. As a result, a very low hum level is maintained, and the audio voltage is raised to a value more usable by the tube-type second audio preamplifier. Further amplification takes place in the second audio preamplifier and audio output stages to bring the audio signal up to a level sufficient to drive an 8-ohm speaker. An audio gain control adjusts the sound to a comfortable listening level.

RF-301 MILITARY SSB TRANSCEIVER

Commercial and military single-sideband transmitters, receivers, and transceivers are similar to amateur equipment in basic

Fig. 12-34. RF-301 transceiver.

design and functions. However, equipment designed for these applications, particularly the military, is generally more rugged in construction and may contain provision for frequency stability not necessary in the amateur service. The RF-301 transceiver, manufactured by RF Communications, Inc., Rochester, N. Y., is an excellent example of a high-quality instrument designed for full military or commercial application. Complete circuit details of this unit are not available for publication at this time. However, the following brief description will be of interest to the advanced amateur or student who has not had much contact with well-designed commercial SSB communications equipment.

The RF-301 (Fig. 12-34) is designed for full compatibility with all high-frequency equipment, SSB and AM, used by the U. S. defense agencies. The operating modes include SSB (upper and lower sideband), AM, CW, and FSK (with an external adapter).

318

Because of its splashproof construction, it can be mounted in an open boat or vehicle. The transceiver is designed to withstand severe vibration and shock. It can be used under conditions of extremely high humidity and is resistant to fungus. The unit can be used in either tropical or arctic regions, in vehicles, boats, transportable shelters, or in fixed-station applications. Included in the chassis is a "silent" cooling fan to produce a continuous flow of air through the power-supply and power-amplifier sections. The air inlet is in the center of the bottom surface of the enclosure, and the air outlet is at the rear. For operation in very dusty areas, a shockmount which has a special dust filter must be used. The filter may be changed from the front of the installation. When the transceiver is placed on the shockmount, the fan is immediately over the filter.

The unit contains a 115/230-volt, 50- to 60-cycle power supply built into the cabinet. In addition, a small module can be added within the cabinet, which makes it possible to use the transceiver on DC as well as AC power. Modules are available for either 12- or 24-volt operation. This means that if the RF-301 is normally used in a jeep or boat on 24-volt DC power, it is possible to connect the transceiver to AC power at night when a generator may be available or when the boat is at pier.

The only tubes used in the RF-301 are in the power amplifier, its driver, and the receiver RF input stage. Tubes are used in these particular circuits in both high-power stages because in stages where the cross-modulation effects must be very low, tubes are still much superior to transistors. All other circuits are completely transistorized, both to reduce power requirements and to improve reliability. The synthesizer, RF amplifiers, exciter, power supplies, etc., are all solid-state designs.

The transceiver can be tuned to any frequency between 2.0 and 15.0 megacycles. The heart of the frequency-selection system is a fully transistorized, highly stable synthesizer. By setting the front-panel controls, it can operate at any 1-kc channel increment over its entire frequency range. Standard stability is 1 part in 10^6, which is suited for normal voice SSB, AM, and CW communications. With an optional integral high-stability crystal-oven reference, the stability of the RF-301 can be increased to 5 parts in 10^8. In addition to synthesizer frequency control, by pulling out on the 1-kc selector knob the synthesizer is "unlocked," and this knob can be used as a VFO with a 10-kc tuning range. In this way, continuous tuning is provided with a resolution of 100 cycles or less.

Most amateurs are familiar with VFO frequency selection, but few have had any contact with a frequency-synthesizer system.

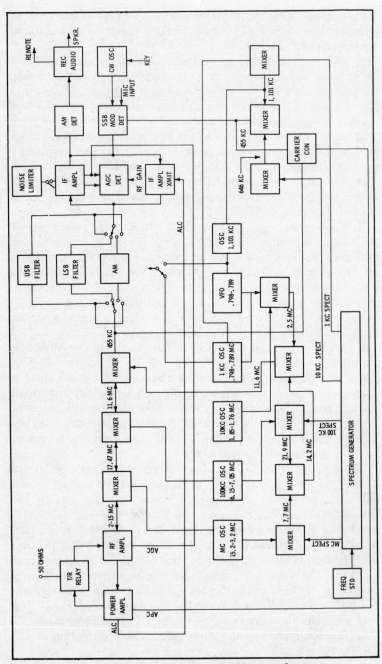

Fig. 12-35. Block diagram, RF-301 transceiver.

320

Most commercial equipment designed for government, police, military, and similar applications operates on a single channel or a group of channels, rather than over an entire band as is customary in amateur equipment. In many cases, a number of stations will be operating on the same channel and if all of the transmitters and receivers are required to maintain a high degree of accuracy in the emitted signal frequency and receiver tuning, no retuning during communication will be necessary. This enables the equipment to be operated by relatively inexperienced personnel. The main advantage of a synthesizer frequency-control system, as compared with a VFO or other variable frequency-control unit, is that of extreme frequency stability. In most systems, the synthesizer signals are supplied in steps of 1 mc, 100 kc, 10 kc, and 1 kc. These frequencies, or their multiples, are then fed to a bank of mixers, where any series of frequency channels within the design limits of the equipment can be produced in 1-kc steps. The techniques involved are based on the principles of mixer action previously described. However, these techniques are highly refined, and, for very accurate frequency control, the primary oscillators may be automatically and constantly compared to a frequency standard. The RF-301 block diagram (Fig. 12-35) will give the advanced amateur or engineering student some idea as to the functions of the synthesizer. The term "synthesizer" is used because the actual operating frequencies are "synthetic," in the sense that no oscillator is producing signals at the fundamental, multiples, or submultiples of the operating frequency.

Two Collins mechanical filters are used (USB and LSB) in both transmit and receive for sideband selection. This type of filter system is used almost universally in military single-sideband

Fig. 12-36. SB-6FA transceiver.

321

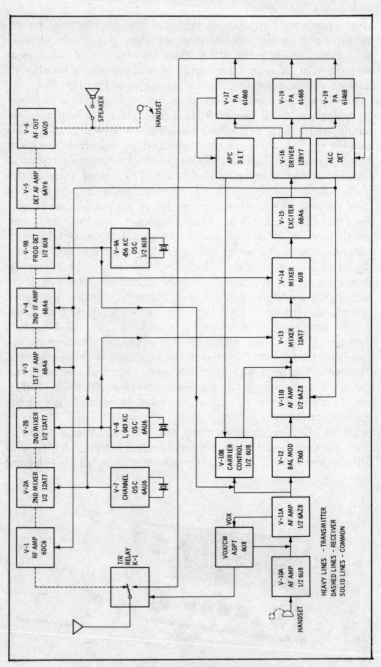

Fig. 12-37. Block diagram SB-6FA transceiver.

equipment to provide an extremely high degree of receiver selectivity and unused sideband suppression.

The power output of the RF-301 is 100 watts PEP on single-sideband and 100 watts average on CW and FSK (with a separate adapter). On compatible AM, the carrier power is 25 watts.

The RF-301 receiver sensitivity is rated at 1 microvolt with excellent cross-modulation characteristics. The selectivity on SSB

Fig. 12-38. The SB-6FA and matching RF-101 linear amplifier.

and CW is 300 to 3500 cycles at 6 db down (mechanical filter). On AM, the selectivity is a nominal 8 kc. The audio output is 2 watts to the built-in speaker. The antenna input impedance is 52 ohms, nominal. The image rejection is −65 db and the IF rejection is −70 db. The AGC characteristic is fast attack and slow release.

SB-6FA SSB TRANSCEIVER

The SB-6FA base-station single-sideband transceiver (Fig. 12-36), also manufactured by RF Communications, Inc., is designed for commercial or semi-military applications. This equipment provides six crystal-controlled channels between 1.6 and 16.0 mc. Oscillator stability is one part per million. The power output is 125 watts PEP and average and may be operated at full power-output rating, single-tone, key-down continuously at temperatures of +65 degrees centigrade. The unit is designed especially for CW, teletype, and facsimile as well as for voice operation. It contains a built-in telephone patch. VOX and CW capability are available with the use of a plug-in module. Either upper- or lower-sideband emission may be specified, or selectable sideband is available with a plug-in module. No separate external boxes are required for any of these functions. Front-panel controls are kept to a minimum, for easy operation by untrained personnel. Rear plugs are provided for the antenna coupler and handset.

Maintenance of the unit is extremely simple. All tubes and internal adjustments are reached through the hinged cover on top of the cabinet. The bottom of the cabinet is removable. Almost all components are accessible for service and maintenance without removing the chassis from the cabinet. Cable harness wiring is used, and many components are mounted on subassembly boards.

The SB-6FA receiver sensitivity is rated at 0.5 microvolt on SSB and 1.5 microvolts for AM reception. Separate Collins mechanical filters are used in transmit and receive. In AM, the receiver IF bandwidth is increased from 2.1 kc to 6 kc, and an envelope detector replaces the product detector.

As shown in the block diagram (Fig. 12-37), the balanced modulator in the SB-6FA transmitter uses the 7360 beam-deflection tube in an arrangement similar to that described in Chapter 3. The photograph (Fig. 12-38) shows the SB-6FA transceiver and matching RF-101 linear amplifier in use at a typical commercial installation.

Chapter 13

Tests and
Measurements

During the operation of any radio transmitter, there are a number of characteristics of the emitted signal which must be known at all times. The most important is the carrier frequency. If the transmitter is operated in the commercial or military service, the carrier frequency will generally be specified by the licensing authority and must be maintained within the very close tolerances stated in the rules and regulations for the particular service. When the transmitter is operated in the amateur service, the exact operating frequencies are not specified, but the emitted signal must be confined within the limits of certain bands. In both instances the FCC regulations require, as part of the station equipment, some means of accurately measuring the frequency of the emitted signal. Furthermore, separate equipment must be used for frequency measurements and for control of the transmitter frequency.

The second important characteristic which must be known is the output power level. Most transmitters are licensed for operation at a specified power output level. The FCC rules specify that the power input to the final amplifier of an amateur transmitter shall not exceed 1,000 watts. This value is determined by multiplying the plate voltage and plate current of the amplifier, as read on standard DC indicating instruments. In the case of SSB and other suppressed-carrier transmissions, the rules further specify that the plate voltmeter and milliammeter used for determining the DC input power have a time constant not in excess of 0.25 second, and that the linearity of the transmitter be adjusted to prevent the generation of excessive sidebands. The input power shall not exceed 1,000 watts *on peaks*, as indicated by the plate meter readings. With grounded-grid or other types of power amplifiers in which the driving power appears in the output circuit, the DC input power to the final RF amplifier must be reduced by the amount of the applied driving power. There are also further restrictions in power input near the legal power limit unless accurate measuring instruments are used during operation. An accurate means of measuring the power input is imperative. The FCC regulations, with regard to maximum legal power in the amateur service, are frequently enforced by both operator and station license suspensions, as well as other penalties.

The third characteristic of the emitted signal which must be known is the undesired power output. This is the RF power which is not confined to the frequencies within the specified channel limits, and which does not contribute to the transmission of intelligence. These "spurious" signal components not only may reduce the intelligibility of the transmitted signal, but may also interfere with other communication channels. Radiation of spurious signal components not only is a violation of the FCC rules; it is an indication of slipshod operating practices, poor engineering design, or both. The amateur operator should place pride in the radiation of a clean signal above all other considerations.

FREQUENCY MEASUREMENT
METHODS AND TECHNIQUES

The two most common methods of frequency measurement are the frequency counter and converter, and the calibrated receiver and secondary frequency standard. The frequency counter and converter method is most generally used in the engineering laboratory, where extreme precision is required. Another use is in the manufacture of crystals, where the frequencies must be held to very close tolerances. Frequency counters are considered more or less standard equipment in any modern electronics engineering laboratory. With instruments such as the Hewlett-Packard 524B, a frequency resolution as low as 0.1 cycle per second is possible. Highly accurate frequency standards—beyond the financial resources of the average amateur, and rarely found in the field—are included in the equipment of practically every engineering and research laboratory. Since most such equipment is very expensive and varies in design and application, it will not be discussed here. Interested readers can obtain specifications sheets and other data by writing to the laboratory equipment manufacturers who advertise in the electronics engineering journals.

The second method of frequency measurement, using the calibrated receiver and secondary frequency standard, is less accurate than the frequency counter method. Many of the better-quality receivers contain internal frequency standards, generally called "frequency calibrators," which can be calibrated to a standard of known accuracy. These internal frequency standards usually consist of a 100-kc crystal oscillator designed for a relatively strong harmonic output, which is internally coupled to the input circuits of the receiver. A small trimmer is provided in the oscillator so that the crystal frequency may be varied slightly for calibration against a known standard. If a receiver such as the Collins 75A4 or 51J is used, the 100-kc oscillator may be calibrated against the U. S. Bureau of Standards radio station WWV or WWVH. By using the receiver BFO, the kilocycle dial can be calibrated at the adjacent integral 100-kc points above and below the frequency at which the measurement is to be made. The accuracy of the frequency measurements made with either of these receivers will be on the order of ±250 cycles, and the

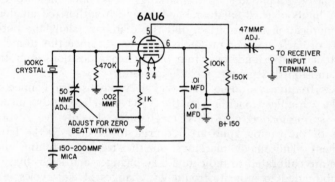

Fig. 13-1. Schematic of a 100-kc calibrator.

greatest accuracy will be in the vicinity of the 100-kc check points. Before the oscillator is calibrated against WWV, the receiver and crystal calibrator should be allowed to warm up for at least one hour before the oscillator harmonic is adjusted to zero beat with WWV. If frequency measurements are to be made over a long period, the crystal-oscillator harmonic should be checked against radio station WWV at least every 30 or 45 minutes.

If a 100-kc crystal calibrator is not part of the receiver design, a suitable secondary-frequency standard may be constructed, as shown in Fig. 13-1. The 100-kc crystal may be obtained from any manufacturer of quartz crystals. Where maximum frequency stability over relatively long periods is required, crystal-frequency standards mounted in thermostatically controlled ovens are also available. The oscillator output circuit should be designed to resonate at or near the frequency to be measured.

327

HAMMARLUND HX-500

The exact method of measuring the transmitter carrier, using the calibrated receiver of the same station, will vary somewhat with different equipment. The Hammarlund HX-500 design includes a Calibrate Level control, which can be adjusted so that the amount of signal fed into the receiver from the transmitter is sufficient for monitoring, as observed on the receiver "S" meter and heard in the loudspeaker. A very limited amount of RF power is "leaked" from the final-amplifier tank circuit to the receiver input through the antenna relay wiring.

The HX-500 transmitter contains a slide-rule type of dial which is marked off to indicate every 10-kc change in frequency on each of the eight direct-reading bands. In addition to the 10-kc markings, every band contains two heavy dotted and two heavy diamond-shaped markings. The dots indicate the outer limits of each amateur band in which authorized amateur communication is permitted, and the diamonds show the outer limits of each amateur radiotelephone band. Since the 10-meter amateur band extends over four band-change positions, only the first and fourth segments include markings.

The frequency tuning and dial lock knobs are connected to the variable capacitor (on the VFO sub-chassis) by means of a spring-loaded gear-drive mechanism. Twenty-five revolutions of the tuning knob are required to cover a 500-kc band segment. The major markings on the frequency-tuning dial scale are calibrated to indicate 1.0-kc changes and each division is subdivided to indicate frequency changes of 200 cycles.

As shipped from the factory, the "O" marking on the knob skirt is mechanically aligned to the high-frequency end of all bands. Since most amateurs operate within a limited portion of a particular band, the knob markings should be indexed for the highest accuracy possible in the area of operation. To correct for this knob runout, the dial lock permits the knob to be turned while the dial pointer remains stationary. The transmitter signal should be zero beat against the 100-kc calibrator check point nearest the desired operating frequency, and the main dial then locked with the lock knob. The tuning knob is then rotated until the "O" line coincides with the fiducial, and the lock knob turned to release the main dial. The transmitter frequency, as read from the dials, can be determined in a relatively simple manner. As an example, assume the transmitter frequency is 3962.4 kc. The tuning knob is turned until the pointer indicates the nearest 10-kc point below the desired frequency. In this example the nearest 10-kc point below 3962.4 kc is 3960 kc, and the tuning knob "O" should coincide with the fiducial at 3960 kc. The tuning knob is now rotated to add two major divisions of the skirt calibration (2 kilocycles) and two subdivisions (400 cycles). The 3960-kc reading on the main dial plus 2.4 kc on the knob skirt equals 3962.4 kc. This frequency indication will be sufficiently accurate within a reasonable range of frequencies on each side of the calibration point. However, when the transmitter is operating on frequencies removed from the calibration point and particularly near the band edges, its frequency should be checked against the harmonic of the 100-kc calibration standard. The transmitter tuning dial should then be recalibrated if necessary.

COLLINS 32S-3

The Collins 32S-3 transmitter is calibrated in a somewhat different manner. As shown in Fig. 13-2, the band and its 200-kc segment are selected by the band switch (7). The tuning dial (3) is then adjusted for the desired frequency within the 200-kc

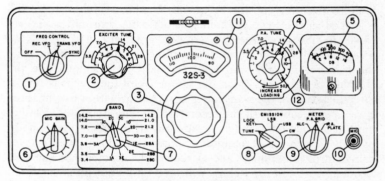

Fig. 13-2. Front panel of 32S-3 transmitter.

band segment. As an example, suppose we wish to place the transmitter operating frequency on 14.195 mc. The band switch is placed on 14.0 mc and the tuning dial is rotated to 195 kc. The frequency, as read from the dial, will be 14.0 mc plus 195 kc, or 14.195 mc. To read the frequency, add the dial reading to the band-switch setting. As another example, if the band switch is set to "3.8" and the dial is set to "5.0," then the frequency is 3.805 mc. or 3,805 kc.

When the 32S-3 is operated in connection with its companion 75S-3 receiver, the receiver must be calibrated first. To check the internal 100-kc crystal-oscillator frequency standard, tune

329

the receiver dial to zero beat with WWV at 15.0 mc while the station is not transmitting a tone. Turn the Off-Standby-Operate-Calibrate switch to the Calibrate position. Adjust 100-kc "adjust" trimmer C61 for a zero beat between the crystal-oscillator harmonic and the WWV signal. The receiver VFO dial calibration can be checked by tuning the 100-kc calibrator to zero beat near "100" on the dial scale. When the signal is at zero beat, the movable hairline is then moved directly over the "100" mark on the dial scale. The dial scale is then rotated to the "0" and "200" marks and adjusted to zero beat with the harmonic of the 100-kc oscillator. Zero beat should occur at both 0 and 200 ±1kc on the dial scale. The 1kc end-point spread must not be checked until the dial has been calibrated at "100." If there is no end-point spread and zero beat does not coincide at 0 and 200 ±1kc an electrical adjustment of the VFO circuit may be necessary, as outlined in the manufacturer's service manual. However, if the receiver is new or in otherwise good operating condition, the adjustment is not likely to be required.

Once the receiver dial has been accurately calibrated, the Off-Standby-Operate-Calibrate switch of the 75S-3 is placed in the Standby position, and the Frequency Control switch of the 32S-3 is placed in the Sync position. Set both the transmitter and receiver to the same sideband (upper or lower), and adjust the receiver dial to the desired operating frequency. Slowly tune the transmitter VFO dial until the beat note sounds like the chirping of a canary. When the frequency of the chirps is two or three per second, the transmitter is zero beat within two or three cycles per second with the receiver. This fine tuning adjustment must be carried out slowly and carefully. If the microphone in use is very sensitive and omnidirectional, turn down the receiver gain control to eliminate any extraneous beat notes near the zero frequency. The desired chirp will then be higher pitched. When the transmitter is tuned to the exact frequency of the receiver and the two frequencies are at zero frequency and phase difference, there will be no audible output from the receiver. Set the hairline of the transmitter VFO dial to agree with that of the receiver. Switch the transmitter Frequency Control knob to Transmitter VFO, and the receiver and transmitter are ready for operation on the same frequency.

SIGNAL-LEVEL AND POWER-OUTPUT MEASUREMENTS

When measuring the power output from a single-sideband transmitter, it is generally taken for granted that the various circuits and tubes are operating normally and that the transmitter has been adjusted for proper linearity and a minimum of distortion products. In a well-designed and properly adjusted transmitter, the undesired-signal power output will usually be at least 35 to 40 db below the desired output. Stated another way, the undesired-signal power output should be not over 1% of the desired output.

Most of the commercial SSB transmitters being manufactured today are rated in terms of "peak envelope power" (PEP) output. Output-power measurements are routine for the development or test engineer in the laboratory, and in commercial installations in the field. They are not so easily carried out by the average radio amateur, however—chiefly because most amateur stations lack suitable test equipment. In most cases, the amateur must be content with determining the DC input power and calculating the output power based on the theoretical efficiency of his linear RF power amplifier. Despite a minimum of test equipment, however, it is possible to determine the PEP level at the output terminals of a single-sideband transmitter with a reasonable degree of accuracy.

Power output and distortion measurements in SSB transmitters are usually made with two-tone audio test signals. It is suggested that you review the discussion of two-tone single-sideband waveforms in Chapter 7, and also refer to Figs. 7-6 and 7-7 during the description which follows.

A typical setup for power measurements from a two-tone single-sideband test signal is shown in Fig. 13-3. Dummy load R_L should be of the proper value to terminate the output im-

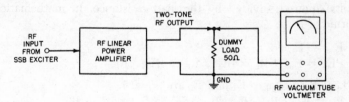

Fig. 13-3. Setup for power measurements, using a dummy antenna and an RF VTVM.

pedance of the transmitter and should have a resistance tolerance of not more than ±0.5 ohm. It should also present a minimum reactance to the signal source and must be capable of dissipating the output power without excessive heating. Most modern SSB transmitters are designed for an output impedance of 50 ohms. Since commercial loads are manufactured in various sizes and terminations, it is suggested that the interested reader write the manufacturer in order to determine the load best suited for his own application. Unless the proper load and terminations (fittings) are used, particularly at the higher frequencies, the power level readings will be subject to considerable error.

The power may be determined by measuring either the RF voltage developed across the dummy load or the RF current which flows through it. The Hewlett-Packard 410B vacuum tube voltmeter is widely used in laboratory RF voltage measurements. It has a useful frequency range from 20 cps to 700 mc and seven voltage ranges from 0.1 to 300 volts. The input impedance is 10 megohms, 1.5-mmf shunt capacitance. Various voltmeter accessories such as voltage dividers, connectors, shunts, and multipliers extend the useful range of the 410B for other measurement purposes. The 410B is a negative peak-reading meter calibrated in terms of *rms*. When the VTVM is used with the proper high-impedance AC probe for RF measurements, the reactive characteristics of the 50-ohm transmitter termination will not be disturbed—provided, of course, that the probe is connected to the RF circuit with a minimum of additional shunt capacitance or series inductance. The voltmeter readings should be taken as accurately as possible, since any error will be squared when the power is computed. If accurate readings are obtained from the meter on a two-tone test signal, it should be possible to calculate the PEP power to an accuracy of 5% or better.

The VTVM will indicate the rms sum of the two RF voltages produced by the two-tone audio test signal (see Fig. 7-7). Since, in the two-tone test signal, E_1 is equal to E_2 in amplitude, the peak envelope power will be equal to the VTVM reading in volts squared, divided by the load resistance. In mathematical form:

$$E_m = (E_1 + E_2)$$
$$PEP = E_m^2 / R_L = 4E_1^2 / R_L \text{ or } 4E_2^2 / R_L,$$

where RF voltages E_1 and E_2 are equal
$$P_{av} = E_1^2 / R_L + E_2^2 / R_L = 2E_1^2 / R_L \text{ or } 2E_2^2 / R_L$$

Summarizing: (1) $PEP = E_m^2 / R_L$
(2) $P_{av} = 0.5 \text{ PEP}$
(3) $P_{av} \text{ tone 1 or } P_{av} \text{ tone 2} = 0.25 \text{ PEP}$

where,
E_m is the VTVM indication in volts (rms),
R_L is the dummy-load resistance in ohms,
PEP is the peak envelope power in watts,
P_{av} is the average power in watts.

The Collins Radio Company also manufactures a dummy load for alignment, adjustment, or loading of their 100-watt single-sideband transmitters such as the 32S-3 and KWM-2. It may also be used for adjustments of the 30L-1 linear amplifier if operated for only short periods. The DL-1 dummy load is housed in a wraparound ventilated cabinet $5^{11}/_{16}'' \times 3^{1}/_{2}'' \times 7^{5}/_{16}''$. The cabinet is finished to match the Collins "S" line SSB transmitter and receiver cabinets. The DL-1 contains fittings at the rear for the antenna and transmitter connections, and either the dummy load or the antenna may be connected to the transmitter by means of a toggle switch on the front panel. The DL-1 has been designed to provide a good impedance match to the 52-ohm transmission lines.

Fig. 13-4. Collins 312B-4 wattmeter, speaker, and control console.

Another device often used for both output-power measurements and tuning adjustments is the directional wattmeter, which can be used while the transmitter is feeding power to the antenna. When used with SSB transmitters, the directional wattmeter is generally modified with additional capacitance to increase the time constant of the voltmeter circuit. In this manner, the meter can be made to indicate aproximately 0.8 of the

333

peak envelope power and will follow the speech-waveform peaks more closely.

The directional wattmeters manufactured by Collins are available in several different combinations of circuitry and cabinet styles. The 302C-3 consists of a directional coupler unit, which is connected in series with the transmission line, between the transmitter output and the antenna; and the indicating microammeter and selector switch which are housed in a separate small cabinet. The 302C-3 is calibrated for "forward" and "reflected" power levels of 200 and 2,000 watts. The 312B-4 speaker console (shown in Fig. 13-4) houses a speaker, an RF

Fig. 13-5. Collins 312B-5 wattmeter, speaker, and control console.

directional wattmeter with 200- and 2,000-watt scales, and switches for station control functions. The unit also includes a phone patch unit. The 312B-5 (shown in Fig. 13-5) also contains the oscillator assembly, in addition to the speaker, directional wattmeter, phone patch, and control switches. The 312B-5 is designed for use with the KWM-2 transceiver and enables the latter to transmit and receive on separate frequencies.

Detailed circuit descriptions of the directional wattmeters are not included here, since the units are generally designed to be used with specific types of single-sideband transmitters. It is suggested that you write the manufacturer, to determine the instrument best suited for your particular application.

334

LINEARITY MEASUREMENTS IN
POWER AMPLIFIERS

The term "linearity," as applied to linear RF power amplifiers, is the "figure of merit," or degree of accuracy, with which the power level of the RF envelope waveform can be increased without introducing distortion. The envelope waveform which appears in the output circuit of an amplifier should be an exact replica, except for power level, of the waveform applied to the input circuit. The design factors which determine the linear-amplifier characteristics were discussed in a preceding chapter. Therefore the discussion which follows assumes that the amplifier input and output circuits are properly designed and that the various plate, grid, and screen voltages have been adjusted to the manufacturer's specifications for the particular tube or tubes in use. The test equipment required will consist of an oscilloscope, two envelope detectors, and a dummy load. The oscilloscope should contain vertical and horizontal amplifiers of identical fre-

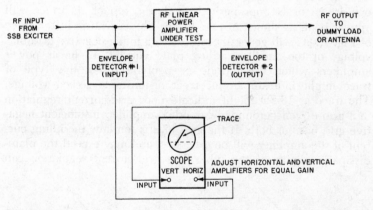

Fig. 13-6. Block diagram of oscilloscope and envelope detectors set up for linearity measurements.

quency response and phase-shift characteristics. The frequency response of the two amplifiers should be flat to at least twenty times the frequency difference between the two test tones. An oscilloscope suitable for RF-amplifier linearity measurements is the Hewlett-Packard HP-130B.

The block diagram in Fig. 13-6 shows the connections of the oscilloscope and the two envelope detectors to the input and output circuits of the power amplifier. The amplifier should be terminated in a suitable dummy load. The schematic in

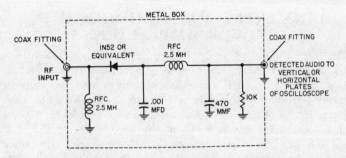

Fig. 13-7. Schematic of the envelope detector.

Fig. 13-7 shows the circuit of the envelope detector. The two units shown in the block diagram are identical in all respects.

With a two-tone test signal applied to the transmitter speech amplifier and the horizontal and vertical amplifiers of the oscilloscope adjusted for equal gain, the oscilloscope screen pattern should be a straight line at a 45° angle with respect to the base line, as shown in Fig. 13-8A. If the linear amplifier is being overdriven or is improperly loaded, the top of the trace will appear bent, as shown in Fig. 13-8B. The curvature in the trace of Fig. 13-8C will generally indicate too much negative grid-bias voltage or too small an idling plate current. In linear power amplifiers which use tetrode or pentode tubes, this type of trace might indicate an incorrect or unstable screen voltage. The trace at 13-8D might indicate poor grid-current regulation in a grid-driven (grounded-cathode) amplifier, insufficient negative grid bias, or both. If the grid bias is too low, the idling current of the amplifier will be excessive, and may exceed the plate-dissipation limits of the tube. The grid-current regulation can

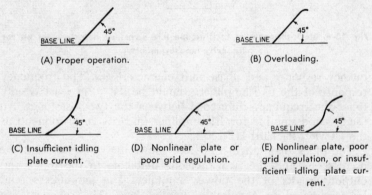

Fig. 13-8. Linearity traces.

be improved by reducing the value of the swamping resistor across the tuned grid circuit. In most cases where the grid circuit is heavily swamped, the grid driving power must be increased considerably. The trace at 13-8E probably indicates a combination of the conditions at C and D. So it will be necessary to make slight changes in the grid bias, grid circuit swamping, and driving power, until the trace approaches that of A as closely as possible.

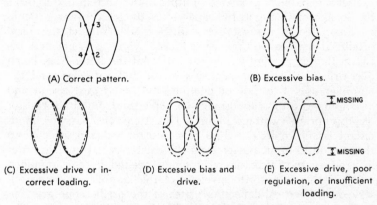

(A) Correct pattern.

(B) Excessive bias.

(C) Excessive drive or incorrect loading.

(D) Excessive bias and drive.

(E) Excessive drive, poor regulation, or insufficient loading.

Fig. 13-9. Two-tone oscilloscope patterns.

Amateur-radio literature has generally stressed the use of two-tone RF envelope patterns as a guide to linear power-amplifier adjustment. The envelope method is relatively simple since no envelope detectors are required. The oscilloscope patterns shown in Fig. 13-9 are typical of those encountered during adjustment of a single-sideband transmitter.

It should be apparent that the RF envelope pattern shown in Figs. 13-9A, and 7-6A are the same. A vector analysis of a two-tone SSB waveform is illustrated in Fig. 7-7. Before any adjustments of the linear power amplifier are made using the envelope method, the waveform at the exciter output terminals should be observed. If the waveform at the *properly terminated* output of the exciter appears as shown in Fig. 13-9A, you can proceed to adjust the linear amplifier. If the waveform differs from that in A the cause of the discrepancy must be determined and corrected before proceeding further. It is best to terminate the exciter in a standard dummy load and to observe the two-tone envelope waveform across the resistance load. The same two-tone envelope waveform should be observed at the input (grid or cathode) circuit of the linear power amplifier and across the dummy load. If not, the amplifier input is affecting the waveform of the driving signal and will introduce distortion into the output signal. The most probable cause of envelope distortion in the input circuit is excessive grid current due to insufficient grid bias or insufficient swamping of the tuned grid circuit, and is most likely to occur in linear power amplifiers operated in the class-AB_2 or -B modes. A common cause of envelope distortion in all classes of linear amplifiers is the application of excessive drive voltage or power from the single-sideband exciter. If the exciter is capable of greater RF output than that required to drive the linear amplifier to its full capabilities, the reserve power should be dissipated in a resistance load. Several manufacturers have produced a so-called "power reducer," which is connected between the exciter and amplifier to prevent the latter from being over-driven. When the exciter is in the 100-watt class and the amplifier uses a tetrode or pentode, the tuned grid circuit and swamping resistor can usually be replaced by a fixed resistor of appropriate wattage rating. This type of "passive" input circuit is shown in Fig. 10-9. The resistor value is selected so that the full output power from the exciter is required in order to produce the maximum grid swing needed by the amplifier.

When the output RF envelope of the amplifier is being observed, the vertical-deflection plates of the oscilloscope are generally connected directly across the dummy load resistor. The horizontal-deflection sweep rate should be adjusted so that ten or twelve envelope patterns appear on the screen. The horizontal centering and gain controls are then adjusted so that only a single pattern appears at the center, as shown in Fig. 13-9A.

In the ideal pattern, shown at Fig. 13-9A, the portion of the trace between points 1 and 2 and between 3 and 4 will appear as a straight line. The crossover of the two lines should form a well-defined **X** as shown. The top of the pattern should form a gently rounded peak and the whole pattern should be symmetrical above and below the reference line drawn through the crossover points.

The pattern shown at Fig. 13-9B indicates excessive negative bias on the amplifier grid. The grid bias should be reduced until the crossover point is sharply defined as the **X** of pattern at A. The pattern shown at Fig. 13-9C indicates excessive drive or incorrect loading of the linear-amplifier output circuit. The pattern at Fig. 13-9D is the result of too much amplifier grid bias and also excessive drive or incorrect loading, or both. The peak flattening shown at Fig. 13-9E illustrates extreme envelope distortion due to either excessive drive, insufficient loading of the linear-amplifier input, or poor regulation in the driver stage. A rapid test, to determine whether the flattening is being caused by insufficient loading or by some characteristic of the input signal, can be made by slightly detuning the plate tank circuit in the final amplifier while observing the pattern. If the flattening disappears, the loading of the amplifier circuit must be increased. If the flattening remains when the tank circuit is detuned, however, the trouble is in the amplifier input circuit or exciter output stage.

All practical circuits have some degree of intermodulation distortion, which produces spurious RF products whose frequencies appear above and below those of the two test tones. The most objectionable spurious signals are the odd-order products; these fall in or near the desired transmission band and, once generated, cannot be eliminated by either the transmitter or receiver. The spectrum analyzer pattern in Fig. 13-10 shows the grouping of the third-, fifth-, seventh-, and ninth-order products around the two test tones.

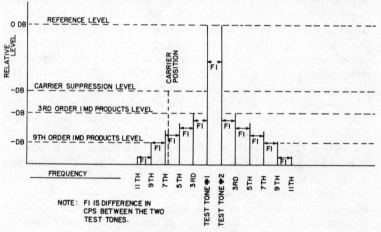

Fig. 13-10. Spectrum-analyzer pattern.

The most effective and hence the universal laboratory method of measuring spurious signals within the passband of either a SSB transmitter or receiver is with the spectrum analyzer. This instrument displays a complete picture of the spectrum in the vicinity of the desired passband; thus the effects of any adjustment in the transmitter circuits are immediately apparent.

The degree of intermodulation in the passband can be determined to some extent by using a highly selective communications receiver. However, this method requires a great amount of patience and skill. The third-order products are generally the largest, as shown in Fig. 13-10; and the higher-order products become progressively smaller. If the two test tones are at least

339

2,000 cycles apart, the third-order spurious products should produce a reading on the carrier-level meter of the receiver. Readings are then taken at the frequencies of the fifth- and seventh-order products. If the carrier-suppression level is known, the "S"-meter reading obtained at the frequencies of the distortion products may be compared with the carrier-level indication. In this manner, an approximate idea of the intermodulation distortion level can be obtained.

Elimination of intermodulation products in an existing transmitter can become a serious problem, since such elimination is largely a matter of design. If the amateur is using a commercial exciter to drive a homemade linear RF power amplifier, as many often do, the trouble is most likely to be in the power-amplifier stage. The intermodulation distortion level of the average commercial SSB exciter will be at least 35db below the level of the desired signal. When the level of the transmitted distortion products increases in a homemade grounded-grid amplifier, a common cause is an impedance mismatch between the exciter and the cathode of the power-amplifier tube. In grounded-grid linear-amplifier circuits, the input impedance at the cathode of such tubes as the 4CX-1000A and 4-1000A will be around 100 ohms—provided the amplifier is *properly designed and loaded*. The average 100-watt SSB transmitter, when used as an exciter, will have an output impedance of about 50 ohms. The amateur customarily will feed the exciter signal to the amplifier cathode through a short length of 50-ohm coaxial cable. It is obvious that a 2-to-1 impedance mismatch will exist and that standing waves will appear on the coaxial line. The cathode impedance of the grounded-grid amplifier, while nominally about 100 ohms, will vary considerably with changes in the plate-circuit loading. In addition, the input impedance of the amplifier will change as the driving-signal amplitude does. Unless the impedance match between the exciter output and power-amplifier input is reasonably close, the impedance variations will be reflected into the driver plate circuit and appear as phase modulation of the SSB signal. In the Collins 30L-1 linear amplifier, this problem is solved by using a separate pi-network circuit, at the filaments of the 811A's, for each frequency band. The length of the interconnecting coaxial cable is selected so that when it is added to the lumped constants of the proper pi-network, the effective transmission line is equal electrically to one-half wavelength. The pi-networks are switched, when the bands are changed, so that the electrical length of the interconnecting line will remain one-half wavelength, or multiples of one-half wavelength, at all operating frequencies.

340

INDEX

341

Automatic level control (ALC), 160

Automatic load control, 221, 222

CONTENTS OF FOLDOUT SECTION